Best wishes!
Charles Stenson
Psalm 92:12-14

ALEXANDER

THE SERVANT BOY WHO BECAME A COLONIAL VIRGINIA FRONTIERSMAN

CHARLES STINSON

ISBN 0-7414-4362-7

Cover illustration courtesy of the National Park Service, Harpers Ferry Center Commissioned Art Collection.

Published by:

INFINITY
PUBLISHING.COM

1094 New DeHaven Street, Suite 100
West Conshohocken, PA 19428-2713
Info@buybooksontheweb.com
www.buybooksontheweb.com
Toll-free (877) BUY BOOK
Local Phone (610) 941-9999
Fax (610) 941-9959

Printed in the United States of America

Printed on Recycled Paper

Published November 2007

DEDICATION

This book is dedicated to my wife, Irene, who has been my "Elizabeth" for more than forty-eight years.

ACKNOWLEDGMENTS

Without the encouragement and support of my family, this volume would not exist. My wife Irene has anxiously awaited the completion of portions of the book. As they were finished, she read them and offered comments. My daughter Becky was among the first to read the finished manuscript. My two sons, Mike and Tim, have closely monitored my efforts from the beginning, serving as both my supporters and critics. Their help has been invaluable and without it this volume would be inferior to what it is now. Although they have been kind to me when offering corrections, they have reminded me at times that it was a good thing I wasn't one of their students! I have utilized most of their suggestions and feel they have enhanced this book but the final decisions on the content have been mine. I take responsibility for not heeding any advice they have given.

In addition to the above, there have been other family members and friends aware of my work who have encouraged and helped me. Space will not allow me to acknowledge all of them by name but I feel compelled to mention one. Frances Louise Stinson (1922-2002), of Dallas, Texas spent the last one-third of her life doing research on our family. Her accomplishments were phenomenal considering she traveled little during those years and never owned a computer. She rejoiced over pictures that I mailed her of sites from Virginia and documents that were related to Alexander Stinson and others. Her health would not allow her to travel to Virginia for the dedication service of the monument that was installed for Alexander in 2000, but she was pleased to be able to witness the realization of her dream via videotape. Shortly before her death, she responded to my plea to put her family records into a single volume (that volume is listed in my bibliography). She sent copies to selected libraries, historical societies, and friends, and sent me a copy with permission to reproduce it as needed. Many family researchers now own a copy of her work. The thoroughness with which she conducted her research and the unselfish spirit with which she shared her findings should encourage each of us to do the same.

TABLE OF CONTENTS

PART ONE: Journey to America

PART TWO: Welcome to Williamsburg

PART THREE: Moving West

INTRODUCTION

Extraordinary people remain in our memories long after the more common ones are forgotten. We often remember minute details about them, such as where we met them and who introduced us to them. I was approaching retirement age before I was introduced to Alexander Stinson, Senior, my ancestor seven generations removed. It was through the initiative of family researchers from other states that the long overdue introduction was finally made. As a Virginia resident, I was in an advantageous position to investigate queries from Stinson researchers as far away as California and Texas about our common ancestor. The quest by family members to know him better has accounted for countless hours of research, both in America and overseas. Details of his life have emerged from the study of court documents, church records, and other writings, some of which are nearly three centuries old. As the chronicles of his life began to unfold, I was captivated by his story and felt it was worthy of sharing. I hope that you will agree.

Alexander Stinson first appears in Colonial Virginia court records in 1717 as a servant boy indentured to Susanna Allen, who operated an ordinary in Williamsburg. When I first discovered this information in the York County Court record books, I went immediately to the Rockefeller Library in Williamsburg seeking information on Miss Allen and her ordinary. An unnamed librarian, to whom I am indebted and now apologize for my failure to identify, quickly found the information for me. I vividly remember his apparent surprise as he said, "Why, that's the Alexander Craig House." In amazement, I asked, "Do you mean it still exists?" It does. It is located only four lots from the Capitol building on the north side of Duke of Gloucester Street. The temperature that July day was approaching one hundred degrees as I hurried from the library to the Alexander Craig House. I will not attempt to explain how I felt as I stood looking at the house. My feelings were not from the results of the heat, but from the thrill of my discovery.

In the intervening years, I have shared information with many of my Stinson kin who continue to be actively involved in research. I have also been the recipient of some of their finds, for which I am grateful. Many questions remain unanswered about our ancestor, and these answers may never be found. My purpose in writing this book is twofold. First is the desire to record and share some of the information that I have discovered in such a way that others may experience the same sense of delight that I had when researching his life. Secondly, I wanted to present it in a format that is readable and enjoyable. Thus I have chosen to create a fictionalized version of his remarkable life that is inspired by and based upon both the documents that attest to his life and others that inform us about the era in which he lived.

Let me also address two unanswered questions about Alexander that have been debated for years. The first concerns his origin. At the time of this writing, I do not know if he was born in the Colony or came from the British Isles. Some researchers believe each way. I hired a researcher in Scotland to search for evidence there, and although he found nothing conclusive, he did find several Alexander Stinsons who could have been our ancestor. For those who would like to do further research, they seem to be clustered in lower Scotland and the border country of Northern England. I chose to begin his story there instead of America for one reason. Either he, or his ancestor, endured the rigors of crossing the Atlantic in a situation similar to the one described in this book. He was pursuing his dream of freedom and a new life so that those of us who descended from him could be born free men and women. The second issue that I would like to address is whom he married. Again, I do not know. For years, many of our family researchers have believed and taught that Alexander married an Elizabeth or "Betsy" Cary because of his strong alliance with the Cary family. Others have believed that he was married to someone in the family of Joseph Hooper because some of his children were mentioned in Hooper's 1750 will. A thorough investigation of all available information on these two prestigious Colonial families has led me to disagree with both of these arguments. It is my prayer that future research will reveal the answers to his origin, his wife's name, and many of the other unanswered questions that have plagued us. If family members accept this book as being the final word on the Stinson clan and its American progenitor, then I have failed in my purpose for writing it.

I would also fail if I neglected to make one more important observation. It is my sincere conviction that Alexander Stinson was the epitome of an ordinary man, the kind that made America great. Some researchers have tried to make him into something he was not, from kidnapped royalty to privileged status by marriage. I believe neither, but he is still my hero. One of my first discoveries about Alexander was that he was illiterate. Numerous documents exist that he signed with "his mark," or an "X." Standing in sharp contrast to this are some of the other names on those documents. They were people whom he conducted routine business with and were among the best known and most educated in the colony. Names like Henry Cary, the builder, Colonel William Mayo, the surveyor, and Benjamin Harrison, of Berkeley Plantation are all well known by students of

Colonial Virginia history. They were also well known by Alexander as shown by copies of documents included in the Appendix of this book. Another astounding detail about his life was his accomplishments. His journey from an indentured "servant boy" to a well-known and respected landowner, possessing over two thousand acres in what is now Buckingham and Cumberland counties, is well documented. To me, this only adds to the intrigue of this man who apparently lived to be nearly ninety years old.

Journey with me back into the early eighteenth century and let me introduce you to Alexander.

Charles Stinson
Forest, Virginia
2007

Part One: Journey to America

The Long Awaited Letter

Alexander and his friends were playing chase in the village street when the boy being pursued stopped suddenly and stared at the hastily approaching stranger. Without a word being spoken, the other three boys took up positions close to their friend and waited as the man came closer.

"Can you lads tell me where Joanna Stinson lives," he asked, "I have a letter for her." Alexander stepped forward and said, "That's my Mum, I'll take you to her," and started off while he was still speaking. Hurrying the short distance to the house, he jerked the door open, and called out, "Mum, there's a man here with a letter for you!"

Joanna came rushing to the door followed by Alexander's grandparents. "It's from America," the man said, "and I'll be wanting a shilling for bringing it here." After receiving his pay, he handed her the letter and left. The family watched anxiously as Joanna opened it and when she saw the familiar handwriting, she said, "It's from John, this may be the letter we've been waiting for." She then began to read aloud.

My dear Joanna,

At last the time has come for you and Alexander to join me in America. I have received my land and have on it a small house that will serve until we can do better. I have contracted passage for both of you from Bristol to Yorktown with Captain Isaac on his ship, the Bristol Merchant. I have paid passage for one and will have money to pay the other passage when you arrive. Use your money to prepare food for the voyage. Make enough hard biscuits to nurture you both during the long journey since the ship food is not good. You will need to be ready to depart Bristol by the middle of August and I will meet you when you arrive at Yorktown. I live not far from the harbor and will check there daily when the time of your arrival draws near. If I am not there when you arrive, remain on the ship until I come fetch you. Papa can help you prepare for your trip to Bristol. Too much baggage will be a great hindrance to you but plan to wear as many warm clothes as you can. Tell Mama and Papa I pray for the day when we can all be together again. I can hardly wait to see you. May the Almighty watch over you as you journey.

Your loving husband,

John

Alexander was jumping with joy until he looked at the faces of Papa and Mama and saw they were weeping. Quieted by their display of emotion, he stared at his mother, searching for an answer. On her face was a trace of a smile, indicating she was feeling the same joy that her son was feeling, but the troubled look in her eyes showed the pain she was feeling for the old couple. Slowly, he began to understand. Mama and Papa believed that when he and his mother left for America to join his father, they would never see each other again. Turning to his grandmother, he said, "Don't you cry, Mama. One day I'll come back for you and Papa and you can come live in our house in Virginia." The portly woman did not speak but hugged her only grandson tightly for a long time as her husband quietly left the room.

The weeks that followed were filled with activity and excitement as the family prepared for the mid-August departure. The two women spent much of their time preparing the food and clothes that Joanna and Alexander would take with them. Papa was busy making arrangements to get them to Bristol in plenty of time for the voyage. When he and Mama were alone, they would talk about their sorrow and try to comfort each other. One day when Alexander had gone with his mother to one of the local merchants, the woman sat down at the table and began to weep.

"I wish our John had never gone to America."

"Please don't say that Mama. You know he will have a better life there."

"But I miss him so much. It's been five years, and I miss him now more than ever. What are we going to do when they are gone? I don't think I can stand it."

"Maybe in a few years we will be able to go."

The woman quit crying and sat quietly staring at the floor for a long time. Finally she said, "No Papa. We'll never see any of them again."

When the day finally arrived for them to leave, Papa had the arrangements complete. He would carry them by wagon to the harbor, where they would spend their first night. From there they would be taken by boat to Bristol, a journey of several days. There, they would board their ship for America. Arising early that morning, Mama had been busy cooking at the hearth. When the others arose, a hearty breakfast was already waiting for them. Giving Alexander a hug, she said, "I've fixed your favorite breakfast so you will eat a lot. It may be a long time before you get another good meal."

As they sat down to eat, Papa gave thanks for the food and Mama served their plates. There was little conversation as they picked at their food, pretending they were eating. Suddenly, Mama began to sob and stood up to leave the room. Jumping up from the table, Joanna took her mother-in-law in her arms and the two women stood weeping for several minutes. Papa quietly pushed his plate away and said to the boy, "Try to eat your breakfast, son, you'll need it later." Alexander nodded at his grandfather but made no attempt to eat. He had a big lump in his throat and knew he couldn't swallow the food.

In a few minutes, his grandmother stepped back and said, "This is so silly, me carrying on like this," and wiping her eyes with her apron, she said, "now let's all sit down and eat. I just became sad when I realized how long it might be before we are all together again for a meal. Let's enjoy this one together. Of course I'm sad because you are leaving us but I'm also happy for you and for John. It's the right thing for you to do." She smiled at Alexander and leaned down and kissed him on the cheek. Returning to her chair, she said, "You eat your breakfast that I fixed for you." The remainder of the mealtime passed without incident as everyone made a half-hearted effort at eating.

As soon as it was daylight, they loaded their meager possessions on the wagon. Alexander was surprised to see so many of the neighbors there at such an early hour. They had all come to tell them goodbye and wish them safe traveling. He was even more surprised to see all of his friends there to tell him goodbye. Many of them had already shared their dream with him that one day they too would go to America. Hugging and kissing him one last time before he climbed into the wagon, Mama began crying again and was still crying as they rode out of sight. For the first time, Alexander wished he wasn't going to America.

As the boat sailed slowly toward Bristol, Alexander and his mother began to relax and talk with the two other passengers on board. One, a Mr. Estes, was a merchant who was making a business trip to Bristol. The other, a Mr. John Allen, was going to visit his sister and her family who lived there. Both men would be coming back with Captain Ballard on his return trip. The only other person on board was Ballard's son, John, who helped his father sail the boat. It was a warm day and the water was relatively calm with just enough breeze to let them make good progress. Alexander had never been on a boat before and he was fascinated by everything. If the trip to America was going to be like this, he knew he was going to enjoy it.

As he sat staring off the stern at the wake made by the boat, the scene from a few hours earlier gradually came back to his mind. His grandfather was standing on the dock and waving as the boat moved out into the open water and then quickly began moving away, following the shoreline. Papa never moved and was still watching and occasionally waving until he disappeared from sight. Tears welled up in Alexander's eyes as he thought about the old man riding back alone on his long journey home. He knew his grandma would be anxiously waiting and watching for him. She would want to know everything about the trip. He could picture them sitting together at the table and wondered if they would cry again. Lost in his thoughts, he was embarrassed when he noticed one of the passengers staring at him as the tears rolled down his cheeks. He turned away and looked through blurred vision at the whitecaps of the waves breaking in the distance. The wind had increased and Alexander could feel the spray from the waves as they crashed against the side of the boat. His mother looked worried, but nobody else seemed to be concerned by the way the boat was being tossed about. During the next few days, she would become accustomed to the motion as they journeyed along the coast toward their destination.

The sun, which had shone brilliantly the entire afternoon, was disappearing on the western horizon when they finally entered the calmer waters of the Bristol harbor. As they slowly made their way inland, Joanna was hoping they would not have to spend another night on the small boat. Soon they were able to see the ships tied at the wharves. Hopefully, they would find that the *Bristol Merchant* was among them. As the boat approached the public wharf where they would disembark, they spotted the ship, tied up just a short distance away. Papa and Mama would be

5

pleased to know how smoothly things had gone for them and how easily they had completed this part of their journey. After the boat was secured and the wharf master paid, the men offered to help Joanna and Alexander carry their belongings to the ship. As they walked the short distance, a tremendous sense of peace swept over Joanna. They would soon be safe aboard the ship with a secure place to spend the night and hopefully in a few days be on their way to America.

A fat sailor sat at the top of the narrow bridge leading from the wharf to the ship, eating a piece of fish. He hardly glanced at them when they stopped at the bottom of the bridge. "Is Captain Isaac here?" asked Joanna.
"No," said the sailor, stopping eating only long enough to take a big drink from a tankard sitting beside him.
"Do you know when he will be back?"
"Next week," said the sailor, as he continued eating.
"My son and I are passengers to Yorktown and need to find our quarters," said Joanna, a hint of concern in her voice.
"Nobody comes aboard until the ship is loaded and ready to sail," said the sailor, never looking at the woman or the others standing with her. "That will be at least a fortnight."
Joanna gasped as the implication of the statement began to sink in. Neither was the force of it lost on the men who stood with her. Only Alexander seemed undisturbed by the news as he looked from one adult to another for an explanation.

Captain Ballard was the first to speak, "You will be welcome to stay aboard with John and me until we sail. We will be here for several days." The other two men quickly agreed that it was the best solution since the houses along the waterfront that had beds to let were not a proper place for a woman and a child, and the city was unsafe at night. After returning the baggage to Ballard's boat, Estes and Allen hurried away, anxious to get to their destinations before dark.

As the other four began preparing to spend another night onboard the ship, Captain Ballard insisted that Joanna and Alexander sleep in the small cabin. He and John would take turns sleeping on the deck while the other one stood watch. As they lay down to sleep, Joanna began to feel overwhelmed with the new problem that had suddenly been thrust upon her. Tossing about in the darkness, she began considering her options. Her first thought was to return home with Captain Ballard and wait closer to the departure date before returning to Bristol. If she did, she would have the additional expense of traveling from Bristol to home and back again plus the emotional pain of leaving Mama and Papa another time. Since she could not get word to Papa to meet them, she would also have to hire someone to take them from the waterfront back to the village. To further complicate it, she was unsure of the departure date of the ship to America and could not learn anything for certain until Captain Isaac returned next week. By then, it would be too late to return home.

If she stayed in Bristol, she must find suitable quarters and meals and that would also be expensive. If she ate the food she had prepared for the journey, they had no way to get more before they left and may suffer for it later on the journey. Either way, she seemed destined to spend all the money she had before she ever left England. At least, she had some money to meet this emergency and was thankful that John had suggested a plan that had allowed her to have it. As the morning light broke softly over Bristol harbor, she came to a decision. Somehow, they would stay in Bristol until the ship sailed for America.

They had just finished their scanty breakfast and were making plans about searching for a place to stay when Mr. Allen came hurrying back to the boat. He was very excited and anxious to speak to Joanna.

"When I arrived at my sister's home last night, I shared your plight with them and they have offered to help. They will furnish you and the boy a bed and meals for ten pence a day. I hurried back to tell you before you obligated yourself to something less suitable. They are fine people and willing to help you."

"Oh, thank you," said Joanna. "That is wonderful news!"

"A blessing from God is what it is," said Mr. Ballard. "There's no place near the water fit for you and the boy to stay. John will help you move your stuff."

Excited about the good news, everyone began helping Joanna and Alexander gather the baggage for the short walk to their temporary new home.

Chapter 2

Delayed in Bristol

Alexander stood close to his mother as John Allen rapped on the door of his sister's house.

"Anne, this is Joanna Stinson and her son Alexander," said Allen as his sister opened the door. "This is my sister, Anne Carter," he continued, "and these are her children, Abigail and James."

"I'm happy to meet both of you," said Anne, "please come inside. When John told my husband and me about your dilemma, we wanted to do something to help you."

"Your kindness is more than we could have ever hoped for," said Joanna. "I want you to know how grateful we are to you and Mr. Carter."

"My husband is at work now," laughed the woman, "but when he returns this evening he is going to insist that you call him William, and please call me Anne."

"If that's what you prefer, I will."

"How old are you Alexander?" asked Anne Carter.

"I'm ten, but I'll be eleven in December."

"Abigail is twelve and James is nine, so the three of you should get along fine."

The two siblings soon became fast friends with their new guest, playing together at every opportunity. To everyone's amazement, they even seemed to enjoy the time they spent together with their chores.

Joanna and Anne talked non-stop as they worked together with the housework. They were each amazed at how well and how quickly the two families had blended so that now it was if they had been life-long friends. Working together, they finished their daily tasks quickly, which allowed time for them to go for a walk about the city. Each of their walks included a trip to the docks to check the progress of the loading of the *Bristol Merchant*. The streets leading to the docks were filled with people. Horses and mules dragged goods to and from the ships on sledges, the cobblestones that paved the streets providing a smooth surface for them to slide upon. Overhanging houses lined both sides of the narrow streets. The houses had no sewer systems, but an open channel in the center of the street provided a sewer drain straight down to the water. Even though city law forbade it, pigs freely roamed the street and used the channel for a feeding trough. Joanna found the contrast between the city and her tiny village far greater than she had ever imagined.

As they walked about Bristol the first day, Anne said, "If you ever see a noisy crowd gathering, stay away from them. It usually means there is going to be a public hanging or whipping. Some find it entertaining but it's not something I want to see. Neither do I want my children to see it." Pointing to a large building in the distance, she said, "That building is Bridewell prison, it is one of several prisons in the city."
"Who is imprisoned there?" asked Joanna.
"Men, women, boys, and girls are all thrown in there together."
"Why?"
"Often for minor things like trespassing. I am told that they are ill fed and live in filth."
Joanna stared at the prison and shuddered.
"There are often outbreaks of diseases in the prisons that spread into the city," continued Anne, "We will not walk close to any of them."
The children had become very quiet as they stared at the building. "Do they ever hang the people that go to that prison?" asked Alexander.
"Sometimes," said Anne, "but most are released if they don't die from illness. Others are sent to the colonies as indentured servants."

Each evening as darkness settled over the city it became a

place of extreme danger. Criminals would attack almost anyone they found outside at night. The well-to-do, if they had to go out in the dark, would hire men to carry torches and a bludgeon of some sort to protect them, but the poor took their chances. The Carters, like most other families, went to bed at dark, wanting neither to pay the expense of good candles or bear the smoky, dim light of the cheap ones. It was easier to go to bed and hope you didn't have to go out until morning. Lying awake in her bed, Joanna would listen to the sounds of the night. Voices, both near and afar, were often incomprehensible, but others were all too easily understood as they cursed and screamed in the darkness. She seldom worried about the danger that lurked outside. Her greatest worry was about what she and Alexander would do if their journey was delayed much longer.

The days passed by quickly. Each day, as they checked the progress of the loading of the ship, they hoped they would be told it was time for the passengers to board. August gave way to September and the *Bristol Merchant* was still not ready to sail. As they returned home from the docks one afternoon, Joanna began to share her feelings of anxiety with Anne.

"I am worried about how long we are having to stay in Bristol. I wasn't prepared for such a long stay here and I'm afraid I will run out of money."

"You have nothing to fear. If you do, you can continue to stay with us."

"You have already done far more than was necessary and I don't want to become a burden on you and your family."

"Stop talking like that, we consider you as family and would never allow you to suffer."

The long-awaited day finally arrived. Passengers would be allowed to board the ship tomorrow and it would sail the following day. As the two families gathered the evening before for supper, it was a bittersweet experience. Alexander and Joanna had accomplished their goal of staying in Bristol until sailing time only because of the generosity of the Carters. What had begun as an act of benevolence by the Carters had resulted in an enduring bond between the two families. Now, they were facing the reality that after tomorrow, they would no longer be able to share the joy of their new friendship. For Alexander and Joanna, the acute pain they felt was reminiscent of leaving Papa and Mama. Tomorrow would be another day of tears and they were dreading it.

They sat longer than usual at the supper table. When the two women rose to clean up the dishes, the three children moved near the hearth and sat talking until it was time for bed. "After the children are in bed," said Anne, "William and I would like for you to join us for another cup of tea."
"Thank you," said Joanna. At first, she was puzzled because they had never done that before. Thinking about it as she prepared the boy for bed, she concluded that they were doing it as one final act of kindness. She was glad. It would give her another opportunity to express her appreciation.

When Joanna returned to the dimly lit room, the Carters were already sitting at the table. The flickering flames from the fireplace gave enough light for them to see and added welcomed warmth to the chilly evening.
"William and I believe that it was the providence of God that brought you and Alexander to us in your time of need," said Anne Carter, as she poured the tea. "These weeks have meant so much to both of us and our children. It is a time we will never forget and always cherish."
"I don't know what would have happened to me and Alexander if it had not been for you and your family," said Joanna. "I know I will never be able to repay you for what you have done, but I want you to know how grateful we are for everything."
Joanna became emotional as she tried to express her feelings of gratitude to this couple who had stepped forward to provide a home for her and her son when they had no place

to go. An awkward silence followed as she wiped away the tears running down her face.

William was the first to break the silence. Reaching across the table, he placed a small bag in front of Joanna.

"We want you to have this," he said.

"What is it for?" she asked, after opening it and seeing the coins inside.

"It is a portion of the money that you paid us to stay here," answered Anne.

"Why are you returning it?"

"We've determined that we charged you too much so we're returning a fair part to help you on your journey."

When Joanna began to protest, William spoke again, "We cannot allow ourselves to profit from your misfortune. We insist that you take it. One day, we may come to your door in Virginia seeking your help."

"I pray God would allow me to see you again in Virginia, not from misfortune, but to enjoy your friendship again. I can never repay you for all you have done."

As she clutched the money, she began to weep again. That night, as she lay down to sleep, she felt a peace that she had not known for many weeks. No longer did she have to worry about running out of money. Their needs had been amply supplied and she had funds left for America. Tomorrow, they would board the ship to begin the long awaited journey across the sea. John was waiting there for them. Soon, they would begin their new life together. She slept peacefully.

Anne and the children waved as Joanna and Alexander boarded the ship and promised to be back early the next day to see them leave. One of the crewmen directed them toward their quarters below deck, but made no offer to help them with their baggage. Struggling through the narrow opening and down the ladder, they made their way to the next level, a large open room that was already beginning to fill with passengers. Those who had arrived early had chosen their places and directed Joanna and the boy to do likewise. There was only the wooden deck where they would all sleep and store their meager belongings. The spot they claimed would be their home for the duration of the trip. Passengers continued to board the ship, crowding into the empty spaces until they were all taken. The fat sailor whom they had seen before, appeared about midday and ordered everyone to move closer together because there were still more passengers to board. Finally, late in the afternoon, the last one arrived and took his space in the cramped compartment.

The passengers were soon confronted with another problem that most of them had never anticipated. If they left their space to walk about the deck or even to go relieve themselves, who would watch their belongings? An elderly Dutchman with a large white beard had claimed a space beside the Stinsons. He was the first to suggest to Joanna that they agree to watch each other's possessions when one had to be away. At first, she had a difficult time understanding what he meant in his broken English. As soon as she understood, she quickly saw the wisdom of his suggestion and agreed to it since he seemed to be a trustworthy person. This man had probably sailed before and knew the necessity of such an agreement. Others who had overheard the conversation immediately began looking for someone to make the same covenant with.

Alexander was anxious to go up and see what was happening above deck, but Joanna was afraid for him to go alone. As they climbed from the stuffy room to the main deck, they were greeted by a strong breeze blowing from the ocean and a beautiful sunset like the one they had seen the night they arrived. As they walked slowly about the ship, Joanna said, "Just think. Your father can see that sun right now in America just like we can, but he is so far away that it will take us many weeks to get there."
"I wonder what he's doing right now?" asked the boy. Joanna continued watching the sunset and talking about America, but Alexander's attention was being drawn to what was happening on the street.

Alexander was standing by the ship's rail watching the sun set when his mother walked up to him.

"Alexander, we should go below now."

"I wanted to watch the sun go down. Can't I stay a little longer?"

Joanna looked over her shoulder at the other passengers walking on the deck.

"I suppose there is no harm in you staying a little longer. But stay right here, and as soon as the sun is out of sight, come below to find me."

As his mother walked away, Alexander moved to where he could see both the sun and the activity on the street by the docks. There was more activity along the waterfront now than there was in the daytime, but of a different sort. Instead of the workingmen and beasts, there were hordes of sailors and tawdry women who apparently lived in the squalid waterfront district. They were going in and out of the public houses and the other buildings along the street or huddled in groups talking loudly. The filthy words which spewed forth from their mouths harmonized perfectly with the dirty surroundings at the waterfront.

The gunnels of the ship were low enough to allow him to see over easily, but quickly increased in height toward either end of the boat. He stood where he could observe what was taking place, but with a few steps backward, he would be out of sight of anyone passing by on the dock. He could observe without being observed. He was embarrassed by some of the things he saw and heard and was constantly looking over his shoulder to make sure Joanna didn't suddenly appear. He knew she would not approve.

He was unaware that two of the street women were approaching until they were very close to him. Blocked from his view by the high side of the ship, he had been startled by their voices. Frightened by their presence and not wanting them to see him he stepped back until they passed.

When they reached the center of the ship, they stopped, but continued talking. Out of sight, but standing only a few feet away, Alexander was afraid to move. They obviously knew the *Bristol Merchant* sailors well and were discussing their plans to spend the night with some of them, knowing it was their last night on shore. In the days to come, Alexander would wish many times that he had never heard their next conversation. One of the passengers walking about the deck was a young mother with a little girl about five years old. The two women were watching them as they left the deck and went below.

"That little lass will probably never see America."

"Why?"

"The sailors tell me. They say the little ones are usually not strong enough to survive the journey."

Alexander slipped quietly away unobserved and climbed down the steps to the stuffy room. A single lamp hung from the ceiling and cast eerie shadows over the figures lying crowded on the deck. Alexander squeezed into the narrow space beside his mother and lay there thinking about the conversation he had heard. Across the room, he could see the little girl snuggled close to her mother.

Lying on the hard wooden deck in the crowded conditions set the stage for a long, uncomfortable night. A variety of other sounds were mixed with snores, moans, and complaints about the quarters. People were constantly getting up and down throughout the night. Some would leave and return shortly to their spaces. It appeared that most were disturbed by all the activity, but a few slept on seemingly unaware that there was anyone else around. Down in that hold, it was impossible to tell when daylight came, but when some left and didn't return, others assumed it was time to get up.

The elderly Dutchman was gone when Alexander awoke. Joanna was sitting up, resting her back against the side of the ship, and watching the activity taking place around her. "Today's the day, Mum," said Alexander, smiling at his

16

mother. "How long do you think it will take us to get to Virginia?"

"Too long, but it depends mostly on the weather."

"When do we get to eat?"

"When our neighbor gets back to watch our things. He has gone to eat now and we'll go when he returns."

Alexander stood up and stretched, looking around in the semi-darkness. Across the ship, he saw the little girl sleeping soundly beside her mother. He wished he had not heard the conversation of the two women last night and wondered if it were true. He wanted to tell his mother about it, but did not want her to know what he had done.

Chapter 3

Journey of Suffering and Death

Alexander gave his mother a puzzled look when they were given the little bowl of thin soup, a small biscuit, and a cup of water for breakfast. Eating without comment, they hurried off to the upper deck. On deck, they were surprised to see how many people had already gathered on the dock beside the *Bristol Merchant*. Several older couples were there to see younger family members off. They reminded Alexander of his grandparents. As they had promised, the Carters were there. The captain announced that the ship would not be sailing for two more hours. They were waiting to go out with the tide.

The passengers who wished to join their friends on the dock were given permission to visit until it was time to leave. Alexander and his mother were delighted to have another opportunity to spend time with their friends.

"I wish you could see our quarters," said Joanna. "We have just enough space to lay our bodies on the hard deck."

"Where do you keep your belongings?" asked Anne.

"At our head and feet. There is no where else."

"What did you have for breakfast?" asked Abigail.

"Dirty water and a biscuit," said Alexander, as he looked at his mother and grinned.

"Really?" asked James.

"It was supposed to be soup," laughed Joanna, "but it wasn't very tasty."

While the women talked, the children amused themselves by watching the seamen make the last-minute preparations to sail.

"I would like to climb up high like that man," said Alexander.

"I bet you'd be afraid," said James. "If you fell in the water you'd drown!"

With everyone back on board, they watched as the bridge was taken away and the last mooring removed. The ship sat motionless for a few moments as if it were reluctant to leave. Slowly, it began to inch away from the dock. Although he could not feel the motion, Alexander knew they were moving as the distance between the ship and dock began to increase. He could see his two young friends running along the dock waving frantically as the ship drifted away. He waved back.

Alexander wouldn't look at his mother because he didn't want her to see his tears. He was having difficulty seeing his friends because of the increased distance and his blurred vision, but he continued waving. After a few more minutes, Joanna said, "I don't think they can see you anymore." Alexander lowered his arm and turned to look at his mother. She also had tears streaming down her face.

With quivering lip he said, "That made me think about Papa, the last time we saw him. I wonder if we'll ever see any of them again."

Joanna hugged her son close to her and said, "Of course we will," trying to conceal her doubts.

As the ship sailed toward the sea, Joanna wanted to stay above deck and enjoy the view and the beautiful weather, but felt obligated to go below. She needed to watch their belongings and allow their friend, the Dutchman, to come on deck. He volunteered to stay below so they could visit with their friends because he had none there to see him off. She felt uneasy about leaving Alexander on deck, but he promised her he would be careful and there were others to look out for him. Mr. Jansen smiled when she returned and insisted he go on deck.

"You go up and I'll stay here. It's beautiful up there."

He agreed but said, "I come back soon and you go back with boy."

True to his word, he returned shortly.

Returning to the deck, Joanna rejoined her son. "You should

have seen the big ship we passed," said the boy. "It was real close to ours and much bigger. Somebody said it was returning from America." Joanna listened intently as the boy continued. "There were lots of people on the deck. We waved at them and they waved back."

"I wish I could have seen it," said his mother, "maybe we'll see another one." Standing beside her son, she watched the changing shoreline as they swiftly glided by. Tomorrow, they would be entering the open sea and out of sight of land. She wondered if she would ever see her homeland again. A feeling of sadness and foreboding swept over her.

As the band of weary passengers settled down for the night in their crowded quarters, they talked. Most were excited that their journey had finally begun after such a long delay, but some were worried. The greatest concern was over the lack of communications. They had been told very little about what to expect on the trip. Others expressed concern over the meals, but some felt they would improve once they were under way. One passenger reminded them that it was the season for fierce storms and expressed his fear that they may encounter one. After much discussion, they slept.

The up-and-down motion of the ship and the sound of the waves pounding against the wooden hull awakened them early the next morning. While they slept, the ship had sailed from the sheltered harbor into the open sea. Soon, people began to be seasick, adding to the already dismal conditions in the cramped, smelly, quarters. Pleasant memories of yesterday were fading quickly and the reality of what lay ahead was beginning to come into focus.

As some began to move about on the ship, they found that walking was much more difficult than the previous day because of the pitch and yaw of the ship. Those venturing out first in search of breakfast returned with the news that there would be no breakfast that day. The angry passengers sent a delegation to register a complaint with the Captain and inform him of their need for food. Returning from their mission they told the group of the irate Captain's response. "He said we would be fed once every day, but there would only be a warm meal once every three days, weather permitting."

Some of the passengers became panicky at the news because they had not prepared any food for the voyage, believing it would be provided. Others who had left home with food had consumed it during their journey to Bristol or during the long wait that ensued. Those who had small amounts of food had brought it only to supplement what they would receive in daily rations. Joanna remembered the urging of her husband to prepare food for their journey and the many hours she and Mama had worked to make the nourishing biscuits that she had stored away, untouched, in her baggage. She now realized that they were more precious than any other possession she had.

The misery of the passengers compounded as the days slowly turned into weeks. Not only were many experiencing hunger from want of food, but also the rations they received were very few, poorly prepared, and unclean. As they were receiving their daily portion one day, one of the men complained loudly to the sailor serving the soup. "I can't eat this slop. It's not fit for a pig to eat!"
"That's your choice mate, take it or leave it. The pigs didn't want it!"
The water also was dark and foul tasting, worsening each day. Many people were suffering from dysentery, fever, chills, boils, and sores in their mouths. The stench in the quarters was sickening. Lice were abundant, especially on those too sick to scrape them from their bodies. When it appeared that things could be no worse, a violent storm struck in the middle of the night.

For several days the fierce storm raged. Unable to stand on the rolling ship, the passengers were confined to their filthy

21

quarters with nothing to eat or drink, and nowhere to relieve themselves except where they lay. Most were convinced they would sink to the bottom of the sea, thus ending their miserable state of existence. The pitiful cries and prayers of the people were unending. Day and night they could be heard above the howling wind, the torrents of rain, and the crashing waves. On the third night, the storm began to diminish. Daylight brought calm seas and the sun. They had survived.

The fat sailor appeared with two others and ordered everyone on deck. When protests were made that some were too sick to walk, he ordered them to be carried above by the more able-bodied ones who must then return to clean the quarters. Lying on the deck, the sick and starving people soaked up the healing power of the sunshine and breathed deeply the clean, fresh, air, but for some, it had come too late.

The little five-year-old girl lay motionless on her mothers lap. Nobody, not even her mother, seemed to be aware of how sick she was until she was brought into the sunlight. Her pale skin made her look like a corpse. Only an occasional, shallow breath gave evidence that she was still alive. Her mother, who was also seriously ill, rocked her gently back and forth in her arms.
"Please don't die," she pleaded. "Please don't leave me."
Suddenly, the mother stopped rocking and stared intently at the little girl. She was waiting for her to draw another breath. It never came.

Alexander and his mother sat watching a short distance away. Already disturbed by what he had seen, the boy was unprepared for the ear-piercing scream that came from the frail woman holding her dead daughter in her arms. After the scream, she slumped forward over the girl sobbing, her gaunt body jerking fitfully. Joanna and several other women surrounded the woman, placing their arms about her. They talked to her, trying to comfort her, but she would not be comforted. The Captain, coming to investigate the scream, immediately set in motion the plan to bury the child at sea. When the mother learned the fate of her child's body, she became hysterical. "Please, sir," she begged the Captain, "wait until we come to land so I can bury my little girl."

"We must bury her now."

"Please! It can't be that much longer! I can't stand for her to be thrown in the sea!"

The Captain motioned for his men to prepare for the burial. When the woman saw that her pleading was useless, she appealed to the passengers.

"Please don't let him throw my little girl in this dreadful ocean. Help me! Don't let him do it! Help me!"

In her weakened condition, she soon lapsed into a semi-conscious state.

When the men returned to the deck from the cleaning detail, Joanna said to Alexander, "Go below and stay until after the burial service."

"I wish I could stay up here in the sunshine."

"I'll come get you as soon as it's over."

As he was returning to their quarters, he saw the fat sailor leaving. Nobody else had returned to the compartment and he understood why. Even though the floors had been cleaned, the stench was still nauseating. Sitting alone in that dreary place, he tried to imagine what was happening above deck. He trembled as he thought about it and remembered the conversation between the two women on the dock at Bristol the night before they sailed. "The little ones are usually not strong enough to survive the journey."

Joanna came for Alexander after the burial and they rejoined the other passengers in the sunshine and fresh air. The little girl's mother was lying motionless on the deck. Only her lips moved as she muttered incoherently. She never appeared to be aware of the brief ceremony that had taken place only a short distance away. Attended by only the strongest, they had watched silently as the body of the little child was released into the cold, dark waters. In a few days, the mother would follow her child.

The passengers were allowed to remain on deck throughout the day, even while they ate their meal. The ship's biscuits were even less appetizing in the bright sunlight. They were now filled with tiny red worms that had woven their webs throughout. At least they had some fresh rainwater that had been caught during the storm. Delaying their return to the filthy quarters as long as they could, they were finally forced below by colder temperatures. As Joanna busily rearranged their things to prepare the bedding for the night, she gasped. Their food was gone! Her legs buckled under her and she sat to keep from falling.

Frightened by her actions, Alexander asked, "Mum, are you sick?"

She was silent for a moment, and then said "No, I'm all right, I just needed to sit down."

Her first thought was not to tell him. Realizing she could not hide it from him, she said, "Somebody has stolen our food." Overheard by some of the other passengers, the news quickly spread through the compartment. Knowing they would be suspected, the men who had cleaned the quarters came voluntarily to her. "We did not take your food and we did not see anyone bothering anything."

"Was anyone down here when you left?"

"Some of the sailors remained below after we finished."

"I saw the fat sailor leaving when I came down," said Alexander.

As her shock gave way to anger, Joanna began to regain her strength and set out to find Captain Isaac. She angrily told him what had happened. "I believe that some of your crew has stolen my food."

He became furious and yelled, "If it's a thief you're wanting to find, then go back below and look among your companions. You'll find none among my crew. Don't bother me again about a few old moldy biscuits." Turning to walk away, her legs would hardly hold her up. Stumbling along the deck in the darkness, she felt defeated and very afraid.

Lying awake in the darkness, Joanna was now oblivious to the sounds and smells that she had found so repulsive a few hours ago. She was consumed by the thoughts of their loss. Fingering the small bag of money she had sewn into her inner clothing, she remembered that she had never told Alexander she had it. Although it now seemed worthless compared to the stolen food, she decided she would tell him tomorrow. The nourishing biscuits, even though they had eaten them sparingly, had made the difference in their survival. The difference between sickness and health. Their loss may make the difference between life and death.

Alexander also lay awake. Aware of the torment being endured by his mother, he could not sleep either. Because of his young age, he did not fully understand the seriousness of their situation, but he knew he wanted to change it. He had never seen his mother in such turmoil and it frightened him. She would find no peace until the food was recovered. He must find the one who stole their food and get it back. He was convinced the fat sailor was the thief. Tomorrow, he would find out for sure.

The next morning, Joanna was sick. When she attempted to stand, her legs were too weak to support her. Her vision was not clear and the motion of the boat aggravated the dizziness she was experiencing, causing her to be nauseated. She believed it was because of what she had endured the day before. The little girl's death and burial had been the most traumatic thing she had ever witnessed. Followed by the stolen food, the encounter with captain, and a sleepless night, she was sure that was why she did not feel well. Although she was unable to go on deck, she allowed Alexander to go because the weather was tolerable again that day. This was the opportunity he was hoping for.

The crew's quarters were on a different part of the ship and were off limits to passengers. They were now in the fifth week of their journey and Alexander could recognize all the crewmembers and tell when they were all on deck. He waited until he knew there were none in the quarters. When he was sure nobody was looking, he made his way there. Confident that he had slipped in unobserved, he began to look for the space occupied by the fat sailor. Each sailor's bed was built up from the deck with a sea chest fastened securely to the end. On one of the beds lay a large shirt. Alexander was sure this was the right bed so he began trying to get the sea chest open.

"Can I help you find something, mate?" someone asked. Surprised by the voice behind him, the boy turned to look into the face of the fat sailor who stood towering over him with a smirk on his face. Alexander was more frightened than he had ever been in his life. Bravely gathering his strength he said, "Yes, you can find the food you stole from me and my Mum and give it back to me now."
"Oh, so you think I stole from you? I suppose you've been telling everybody I'm a thief."
"I haven't told anybody yet," said Alexander, "but if you don't give it back to me now, I'm going to tell the Captain."
The sailor's big hand shot forward, grabbing Alexander by the front of his coat, picking him up from the floor. Nearby, was a gun port in the side of the ship. Dragging Alexander to the window, he opened it. Picking the small boy up, he thrust his head through the opening so he could see the ocean below. "You'll not be telling anybody my lad," said the sailor, "unless you tell it to Davy Jones."
"What are you doing?" shouted another voice from behind them. Turning around, the sailor dropped Alexander to his feet and released his grip. "I'm showing the boy how the ocean looks from up here."
Alexander recognized the man as one of the ship's officers. "You know that gun port is not supposed to be open," said the officer, "close it! Don't ever bring another passenger in

here! You know they're not supposed to be in the crew's quarters!" Turning to Alexander he said, "Get out of here boy, and don't you come back!" Scurrying away as fast as he could, Alexander could still hear the man's angry voice behind him, but he never looked back as he hurried below deck.

Joanna, who had been dozing, awoke when her son eased down beside her. Sensing something was not right about the way he was acting, but not able to see him well in the dim light, she asked him, "Is anything wrong?" Trying to remain calm and control his voice, he said, "No, Mum. I'm all right." Reaching her hand out to touch her son, she soon fell asleep again. The boy sat trembling for a long time thinking of the narrow escape he had and wondering if the fat sailor would try again to kill him. Alexander did not venture back to the deck that day, but stayed close to his mother.

Chapter 4

A Sad Arrival

Alexander awoke with a start. He'd dreamed that the fat sailor had thrown him from the ship. The moment he hit the water he jumped and woke up. When he jumped, he disturbed his mother and she moved and moaned, but did not awaken. As he lay there with his heart racing, he became increasingly more concerned about his mother and wondered if she had become sicker. He wanted to wake her up, but decided it was best not to disturb her. Usually, it was hot and stuffy in the crowded room, but for the first time, he felt cold tonight. He could tell it was raining again and the ship was being tossed around by the wind, but not like before. He was glad it was raining-it would mean more good water to drink.

He was still awake at dawn when people began to stir but his mother continued sleeping. Daylight came slowly because of the darkened skies. When it was light enough to see, he looked across the room at the woman whose little girl had died. Her lips were no longer moving and she was very still. Sitting up so he could see better, he watched her attentively. He was sure she was dead. Joanna usually woke early but this morning she was still sleeping soundly even with the increased activity around her.

Hearing voices at the entrance, he looked in that direction and was gripped by fear as the fat sailor and two others entered. Looking around the room, the fat one walked straight toward the woman, bent down and touched her and said, "She's dead, check the others." The other two sailors walked up and down the rows of people looking at each one to be sure they were still alive. It was the first time they had come for that purpose, but the next morning they would be back. It would become a ritual that would be repeated every morning until the end of the voyage. When they determined

28

there were no others, they walked to the dead woman, picked her up, and started for the door.

Everyone was awake now and all eyes were focused on the fat sailor as he began speaking. "There's foul weather outside and ice on the deck. All of you stay below until further orders."

"What about the lady's funeral?" asked one of the passengers.

"There will be no funerals in foul weather. The crew will bury her. You can pray for her soul just as well down here." With that remark, he picked up the woman's possessions and left, never once looking at Alexander.

If the sailor's remarks and actions were offensive to the passengers, they would have responded with horror at the scene unfolding on the upper deck. Out of sight of the passengers, and with a guard posted to insure they all stayed below, several of the crewmembers gathered around the dead woman's body. Under the watchful eyes of the Captain, they searched her body for hidden money and other valuables which were given to the Captain. Her clothing and any possessions discarded by the Captain were thrown into a sea chest to be divided among the crew at the end of the voyage. Her naked body was cast into the sea.

Below, several of the men were busy gathering material and rigging a canopy near the door to catch the cold, fresh, rain water. Soon, they had gathered enough to begin bringing it to the other passengers. They continued until everyone had a drink. As more was made available, they all drank their fill. Joanna was obviously weaker now and had a fever. Alexander kept himself busy wetting a small cloth with the rainwater and keeping it on his mother's forehead. When she roused, he would also give her small sips to drink. He was sure she would regain her strength if she had some food to eat. Once again, anger welled up in him as he thought of the stolen food. Mr. Jansen, almost as if he knew the boy's thoughts, leaned close to him and said, "If I had any food I

would give it to you. I don't think anybody has any left."
Alexander nodded his head but said nothing.

The wind and rain continued through the day and night. The cold, damp air added to the misery of the passengers, who were using all their resources trying to stay warm. Already wearing many layers of clothing, they wrapped themselves in any extra clothes and blankets they could find. Those not shaking from fever and chills were now shaking from the cold. Few among them appeared to be enjoying any degree of comfort or health. Early the next morning, the three sailors appeared again and began their search for dead passengers. In the far end of the room, they discovered one. He was a man from Derbyshire who was traveling alone. Because he was completely covered with a thin blanket, the other passengers had not been aware that he was dead. The scene from the previous day was repeated as his body and possessions were carried away.

Joanna continued to grow weaker and her fever raged. Occasionally, Alexander could get her to wake up enough to take a tiny sip of water. He continued to bathe her brow with the cool water. Sometimes she seemed agitated, and several times she called his name. When he answered her, she tried to tell him something about money and immediately went back to sleep. Alexander was puzzled. He wondered if she was remembering their time in Bristol when she was so concerned about running out of money.

About mid-day, the storm ended and the sea slowly returned to normal. Dark clouds continued to block out the sun and the ice remained on the deck. The passengers were still confined to their quarters, but for the first time in days received an allotment of the thin soup. It tasted as if it had been made from very old, salted meat. They devoured the wretched tasting stuff for its warmth, hoping also to receive some nourishment from it.

Just before dark, Alexander was greatly encouraged when his mother opened her eyes and spoke to him. "John is waiting for me," she said.

"Yes, Mum," said the boy, "he's waiting for both of us at Yorktown. We should be there soon."

"Today," she said, and closed her eyes again. He hoped perhaps she was improving and by tomorrow would be much better. He tried to get her to drink some water but she would not.

Awakened abruptly from a sound sleep, the boy lay there in the dark trying to determine what woke him. Then, it happened again. His mother's body began to shake violently and then fell limp and still. Reaching out in the darkened room, he touched her face and realized her fever was gone. He felt her hand and it was cold. Shaking her and calling her name brought no response. Repositioning himself with his back to the wall, he struggled to get her cradled in his arms and held her very tightly. Once more, her body shook, but not as violently as before. Perhaps she was just cold, he thought, and was now beginning to get warm. Shortly after that, he began to notice the difference in her breathing. Gradually, it became weaker and then stopped.

He wanted to scream out for someone to help, but he knew there was no help. For hours, he sat there in the darkness weeping and holding his mother's body tightly in his arms. His mind raced from one thought to another. He wondered how he could prevent them from burying his mother in the sea. They should be very close to Virginia. He knew that when the morning came, the sailors would come again to check. He must convince them that she was asleep. He would never let them drag her away from him. Every muscle in his small body ached and his arms and legs were becoming numb, but still he would not move.

He trembled with fear when he heard the voices of the three sailors at the door. As they began their rounds, one of the sailors stopped in front of them. He stared at the woman, still wrapped in the blanket and cradled in the boys arms. Perhaps it was the fear he saw in the boy's eyes or his tear stained face that attracted his attention. He reached down and lifted the blanket and looked at the woman's face. Turning to the others, he said, "Over here." As the other two approached, Alexander screamed at them, "She's sleeping, leave her alone!" As the two men tried to lift her body, the boy would not release her. Together, they pulled her from his grasp.

As they started toward the door, Alexander jumped to his feet and rushed after them, only to be intercepted by the fat sailor who roughly pushed him away. Losing his balance, Alexander stumbled over one of the passengers and went sprawling onto the floor. Turning to leave, the sailor didn't see the boy get up and come running toward him. Hurling his small body towards the big man with all his might, he plowed into the middle of his back, sending him stumbling forward, smashing his face into the edge of the doorway.

With blood flowing from his nose and mouth, the sailor turned on the fallen child. Grabbing him by the arm, he slung him across the ship with such force that he went tumbling along the floor. Regaining his feet, Alexander started toward the door again when a strong hand gripped his arm. It was Mr. Jansen. "Don't do it son. It's no use." Collapsing onto the blanket, the boy placed his head on his knees and began to cry uncontrollably. Soon, his cries were reduced to a pitiful whimper. Exhausted, the weakened child fell asleep.

Awakened by the murmur of voices, Alexander was immediately aware of the pain in his body. For a moment he was puzzled by it and then he remembered. A sickening feeling swept over him as he thought about his mother and he began to cry again. Lying very still and pretending he was still asleep, he listened to the conversations taking place around him. The passengers were all wondering how far they were from Virginia. If the captain or any of the crewmembers knew the answer, they were not sharing it with them. They agreed that if they did not arrive soon, none of them might live to get there.

Alexander began to think about his father, waiting for them in Yorktown. He was probably very anxious now because the boat was long overdue. It had been more than five years since his father left for America. He had worked hard, serving four years as an indentured servant. When he regained his freedom, he worked another year to save enough to bring his family to be with him. His father believed that in America, his family could have a good life together. Now, this could never be--Joanna was dead.

The next few days were like a dream to Alexander. The rain and cold continued, making it impossible to get warm. Patches of ice on the deck prevented the passengers from leaving their quarters. Huddled in the hold of the ship with the other passengers, he drifted in and out of sleep. When he awoke, he was in a daze and usually didn't know if it was day or night. The remaining food was now inedible and the abundance of rainwater provided the only refreshment. At last, the sun appeared. When the ice melted, they were allowed back on deck. Those who were able to come above were enjoying the sun and fresh air when someone shouted, "Land ahead!"

It was unbelievable that such a transformation could take place so quickly. Passengers who appeared to be near death were suddenly standing, shouting, praying, and offering thanks and praises to God. It would still be several hours before they arrived at their destination, but they seemed assured that they could endure their misery for a while longer. They had hope.

The captain appeared and silenced the crowd. "Nobody will be allowed to leave the ship until I give them permission.

Don't get in the way of my men while they are securing the ship. If you have paid for your transportation, you will be allowed to leave first. If someone is meeting you to pay your fare, you will be the next to leave. If you can't pay, you will remain on the ship until someone is willing to purchase you as an indentured servant. There will be buyers meeting the ship. Bring your belongings above deck, stay above deck, and stay out of the way!"

As the ship was made fast to the dock, a small group of people gathered to greet them. Alexander was searching frantically for his father, but did not see him. Although he had not seen his father for five years, the boy thought he remembered what he looked like. Even if his father had changed, he knew how old he would be. There was nobody in the crowd that could have been him. He remembered that his father had written that if he were not there when they arrived, they were to wait until he came for them. Seated beside the moveable bridge, the captain settled accounts with each person before they were allowed to leave. Alexander anxiously waited, dividing his time between watching the activity on the boat and searching the dock for his father. As the day passed, fewer people remained on the ship.

The activity on the street along the waterfront reminded him of Bristol except Yorktown was a much smaller town. The boy continued to study each person he saw approaching, hoping one of them would be his father. As he scanned the streets, he noticed a tall, gray-haired, clergyman walking towards the ship. Moving quickly across the dock and up the bridge, he engaged in a lengthy and sometimes heated conversation with the captain. Finally, he gave some money to the captain and bent down and signed a paper. When he straightened up, he turned around and walked toward Alexander.

"Hello Alexander," he said, "my name is Reverend James Sclater. I am the rector of Charles Parish and a friend of your father. He had planned to meet you and your mother, but couldn't be here, so I came instead. The Captain told me about your mother and I am very sorry."

"Where is my dad?" the boy asked. "Is anything wrong with him?"

Glancing at the baggage sitting beside the boy, the minister said, "If these are all yours, I'll help you carry them to the carriage and we can talk later. I know you will be glad to get off this ship." Alexander was troubled because the man had not given him a direct answer, but he did not ask any more questions. Reverend Sclater grabbed the largest portion of the baggage and started toward the dock with the boy following him. Just before they reached the bridge, they came face to face with the fat sailor. Alexander stopped and the two of them stared angrily at each other. Instantly, he found himself entertaining a hatred that he had never felt before in his life. The thought racing through his mind was one that he wanted to verbalize, but was afraid to. Looking squarely into the sailor's eyes, he thought, "one day I am going to kill you!" Reaching the dock, and realizing the boy was not with him, the minister stopped and called back to him, "Alexander, is anything wrong?"

Turning toward Reverend Sclater, he said "No sir," and ran quickly to join him.

Alexander had never ridden in a carriage before, and this one seemed especially nice. As they ascended the hill, he looked back at the picturesque waterfront with the stately ship sitting moored to the dock. Anyone looking at it would have difficulty believing the torment that had been endured by the souls that had sailed upon her. As they crested the hill, Alexander turned to look at the beautiful homes built along the city streets. They were not crowded together like the homes in his village or Bristol. When they came to a road on the other side of the town, they turned left and were soon traveling through the open country.

"Where are we going?" asked the boy.

"To my home," said the minister. "I have a wife and

children there. We have six children and three of them still live at home. You will get to meet them."

Alexander wanted to ask him again about his father, but the man kept talking.

"I can only imagine how difficult it must have been for you to lose your mother during the trip. I lost one of my children when she was only nine years old. Her name was Mary, the same name as her mother. God gave my wife and me another little baby girl the next year, and we named her Mary also. She is ten now, her sister Martha is twelve, and their brother James is fifteen. They are looking forward to meeting you."

"What made your little girl die?"

"I don't know. People die from lots of things and we never know why. Sometimes the doctor calls it fever. Sometimes ague. Sometimes they say distemper. She was sick with a fever for several days and just weakened away. My wife nearly grieved herself to death."

The minister continued to make conversation with the boy. When they came to a fork in the road, he turned onto the left fork.

"Is this the road you live on?" asked the boy.

"No, we have one more turn to make, but it isn't very far. The glebe land is on the Poquoson River."

"That's a strange name."

"That's an Indian name."

"Have you ever seen an Indian?"

Reverend Sclater laughed and said, "Many times, and you will too."

Turning left again onto a smaller road, they drove toward a beautiful two-story house nestled among large trees. The white frame house stood in sharp contrast to the dark brown wooden shingles that covered the roof. Many outbuildings, cultivated fields, and orchards surrounded the house.

"Is this where you live?" asked the boy.

"Yes, this is home." As he stopped in front of the house, a

servant came out to take care of the horse. Stepping down from the carriage, the minister turned to the boy and said, "Let's get your things and go inside and meet the family."

"When will my daddy be here?"

"Let's get you freshened up a little and find you something to eat, then we can talk about your daddy."

The boy was becoming more concerned over the man's evasiveness about his father, but the thought of food distracted him for the moment. Suddenly, the door opened and the three children rushed outside to greet their father and meet their guest. After the introductions, the minister said to the children, "You run along for a while and you can visit with Alexander later." Once inside, he met Mrs. Sclater, a gracious lady who had food prepared for him. Like a starving animal, he devoured everything set before him. He was aware of his rudeness, but helpless to change it, a fact he would later apologize for. He thought the food was the best he had ever tasted.

After the meal, Reverend Sclater said, "One of the servants has prepared a bath for you. We also have some clean clothes for you. They'll get your other clothes washed and have them returned tomorrow. After you get through with your bath, we'll talk." Following the servant into a back room, he found a large tub of warm water prepared. For the next hour he soaked and scrubbed himself as the servant continually added more hot water to his bath and helped him pick lice off his body and from his head. He had forgotten how good it felt to be clean.

Part Two: Welcome to Williamsburg

Chapter 5

Yorktown Friend and Advocate

Alexander felt much better as he joined Reverend Sclater and his wife who were seated in the front room near the fireplace. Sitting down in front of the fire, he stared into the dancing flames for several minutes before turning to the minister and asking, "When will my daddy be coming for me?"

Looking very solemn, the man replied, "Alexander, I hate to tell you this, but I have some more bad news for you. Your daddy isn't coming for you. He has gone to be with your mother."

The boy stared at the minister in disbelief. Forewarned by his father's absence and the rector's previous unwillingness to discuss it, the boy was still not prepared for the news that his father was dead. Turning his gaze slowly back to the flickering flames, he sat silently for a long time with tears running down his face and dripping from his chin. The minister and his wife sat quietly observing the boy, but making no comments. Without taking his gaze from the burning fire, he finally spoke. "What happened to him?"

Shifting uncomfortably in his chair, the minister said, "Someone killed him."

Turning quickly toward the man and wiping his tears with the back of his hand, you could hear the anger in his voice as he said, "Who?"

"We don't know," said the minister, "but Sheriff Tyler is trying to find out." Choosing his words carefully, Reverend Sclater began telling the story that he had rehearsed in his mind many times. A story he thought he would be telling to a dead man's wife, not to his eleven-year-old son. Alexander sat attentively, listening to every detail, but never asking a question until the man finished. "Your father had become our friend, just as I told you on the boat. He was a parish member here for the four years he was indentured. He attended the Sunday services faithfully each week until he moved to his new land. He then attended services in Yorktown."

Pausing for a moment to gather his thoughts, he continued. "Your daddy worked hard to prepare a home for you and your mother and save enough money to pay your passage. He accomplished this at great personal sacrifice. He was looking forward to you being here and rode to the waterfront every day to see if you had arrived. He became very anxious as the weeks passed and your ship did not come. They do not have a minister in Yorktown at the present time so he had nobody there to talk to. Several times lately when he came to town, he continued down here. He would stay for supper and discuss his concerns with me. I was concerned about you too, but I was also worried about him."

The boy listened intently, waiting for the man to resume the story. "Each time he came to town, he brought with him the money he had saved to pay for your passage. Almost everyone in town knew why he came there each day. Some people also knew that he carried the money with him. On one of his visits here, I discussed with him the danger of carrying the money and my fear that he may be robbed. Even though he was armed, he often returned home after dark and could easily be ambushed. Your daddy knew it was dangerous, but felt he had no other choice. After our discussion, he decided to leave the money with me and it would be here and available when he needed it."

The minister paused for a long time, staring at the floor. Finally, looking back at the boy, he took a deep breath and said, "That was the last visit John made to our home. Several days later, he was killed while returning home from town. He was found early the next morning by a neighbor who immediately notified the Sheriff and me. He had been

40

shot from his horse just a short distance from his home. Whoever shot him tried to make it look like Indians had killed him but nobody believed it. He was buried on his land, just a short distance from the house."

They sat in silence for a few minutes staring at the fire. Turning again to the minister, Alexander asked, "How can I find out who did it?"

"That's the Sheriff's job. I am confident he will find out. Many of the indentured servants were criminals before they were sent here. Some of them have become runaways and resumed their life of crime. Seaport towns like Yorktown also attract many other undesirable people. There are always a lot of sailors who spend their free time ashore. The Sheriff believes he will find the guilty one among some of these people."

"What happened to my daddy's house?"

"The house had been searched but nothing seemed to have been stolen. I suppose they were looking for the money. Everything is still there. I was expecting you and your mother any day and thought you would want to go there to live."

"How did you know when the ship came today?"

"One of the men in Yorktown agreed to let me know as soon as your ship arrived so I could come get you."

"What happened to my daddy's money?"

"The single fare that your father had paid was claimed for your mother because she had lived to complete more than half the journey. I argued with the captain about it, but it was useless. He would not release you until I paid your fare."

"Can I still live in the house?"

"No," said the minister, "children can't own property and there are other laws in the colony concerning their care."

For a long while, Alexander was silent and then asked, "Can I live here with you?" Shifting uncomfortably in his chair again, the man said, "I don't think that will be possible. It isn't because we don't want you, but the laws I mentioned

41

determine where you will live. Our Governor has decided that orphaned children must be indentured to a craftsman so they can learn a trade. They would not allow you to be assigned to me."

The three of them sat silently for time, staring at the flames. Looking at the minister again, the boy asked, "Why does God hate me so much?" Mrs. Sclater gasped and placed her hand to her mouth. Standing up quickly, she excused herself and left the room. Seemingly undisturbed by the question, the pastor said, "God doesn't hate you. He loves you. Why do you ask such a question?"
"Because of the bad things He let happen to me. My mama and daddy are dead because of evil people and He didn't do anything to stop it. Now I have to live with somebody I don't know and work for them. If He doesn't hate me why did He let this happen?"
"Alexander, I don't have any answers that will satisfy you right now," said the minister. "I do know that God loves you very much and does care what happens to you. You must ask Him to help you and believe that He will. God takes bad things and uses them for good. I hope that you will believe me." Alexander would not look at him but sat staring into the fire. He liked Reverend Sclater, but right now he could not believe him.

Mrs. Sclater returned to the room and announced that it was bedtime. Standing up to leave, the boy turned to the minister and asked, "Will you show me the house where my daddy lived?"
"Certainly. We will plan to go one day soon."
"Thank you. I would like to see it."
Turning to follow Mrs. Sclater, he glanced back at the man and said, "Good night."

For the next few days, the minister was busy with parish duties and preparing for the Sunday worship service. Alexander spent most of his time with the three Sclater children learning what life was like on the Glebe. It was a fascinating place. "Would you like to go crabbing?" asked James, one morning after breakfast.

"We want to go!" screamed both of the girls.

"Mother's not going to let you go," said the older brother.

"She will too. She's let us go before," they protested.

"Only if you stay on the shore. You may not go on the dock," said Mrs. Sclater who had been listening from the other room.

"And only if you catch enough for supper," said their father who seemed to be amused by the entire conversation.

"What's crabbing?" asked Alexander.

"You'll find out when one pinches you!" said Mary and the entire family began to laugh.

The four children gathered their equipment and trudged along the rutted roadway that led to the river. James had tried to coax his father into carrying them in the carriage or have one of the servants take them in the wagon, but failed. "You have nothing better to do than walk," he said. "You can be there almost as quick as we can hitch up a horse. Now if you catch so many you can't carry them, maybe we can send a team for them." James didn't seem to appreciate his father's humor.

The tide was in and the crabs were plentiful. In just a few minutes, James caught the first one.

"Pick him up, Alexander," said Martha.

"He won't hurt you," laughed Mary.

Alexander picked up a small stick to examine the strange looking creature. The girls laughed hysterically as the quick moving crab almost pinched his finger. Within an hour, the children had caught a basket of crabs.

"Daddy will be pleased with our catch today," said James.

"Does he really eat these things?" asked Alexander.

"He loves them," said Martha.

"You'll like them too," chimed in Mary.

That night, they had boiled crabs for supper. Alexander was uncertain about eating them until they showed him how to pick the meat from the shells. After the first bite, he needed no further persuasion.

Alexander looked forward to meal times every day. Some of the food was like his grandmother cooked and equally as good. He thought of his grandparents often but especially at mealtime. When he thought about them, he became very sad. He knew they would be anxious to hear from America, but he could not bear to think about them learning what had happened to his parents. He was afraid the news would kill them. He wished he could return home, but felt ill when he thought of crossing the ocean again.

One evening he talked to Reverend Sclater about his grandparents and asked what he should do. "You must write them. It is only fair that they know the truth. If they never hear, they may believe that none of you are alive. They need to know that you are alive and well. As soon as we learn what you will be doing, I will help you write them."
The boy hung his head for a moment and said, "I can't write. My daddy was going to teach me."
"I'll write for you, but you must still learn to write. It is very important and you know your parents wanted you to learn."

On Sunday morning, they all dressed in their best clothes and went to church. Alexander was surprised to see what a large crowd had gathered. Most of the people were dressed in very fine clothes, finer than any he had ever seen in his village. Some walked to the church, but most came in carriages. It was an impressive gathering, and different from any that Alexander had ever attended. Reverend Sclater did not read his sermon in a monotone voice, but looked directly at the people as he spoke. Occasionally he would read from the scriptures, but just as often he quoted them from memory. The people seemed to be very attentive to his words although he spoke plainly to them about their sin and the need to seek God's forgiveness.

Sunday dinner was a meal that Alexander would never forget. Grandma's grandest meal would not have compared to the large amount of delicious food they enjoyed after church. Alexander wondered if this was something that was observed every week, but did not ask. He was glad that his father had been able to share some meals at this table, but when he thought of his mother, starving to death in the filthy ship, he felt guilty that he had survived and was enjoying such good food. After the meal, Reverend Sclater turned to the boy and said, "Let's go sit by the fire and talk."

Alexander remembered the last conversation they had in that room. The room brought back memories of the painful news he had received. He wasn't anxious to have another conversation there, and wondered what it would be about this time. Noting the concerned look on the boy's face, the pastor said, "I hope what I tell you today will not be bad news, but good. I'll be going to Williamsburg tomorrow to a meeting and hopefully will learn what will happen to you. The rectors, the churchwardens, and some of the vestrymen from the area parishes will be meeting with Governor Spottswood. He will tell us his plan about how we are to handle orphans in our charge. I want you to go with me. On the way, we will stop by your fathers house and spend some time there."
"Will I be coming back with you?"
"I don't know. It will depend on whether they have someone available for you. If they do, then you will go with them. If not, you will come back with me until they find someone. We will carry your things just to be prepared."

Alexander was silent for a long while and then spoke again. "If I have to stay, will I ever see you and your family again?"
"Certainly you will. We go to Williamsburg often. My daughter and her family live there. When we visit her, we could visit you. Most likely you will stay in the town, but

45

if you are sent somewhere else, I promise you I will still come to see you. I feel a great responsibility for your care."

Growing silent again, the boy seemed in deep thought. In a moment, he looked at the minister and said, "I have some things that belonged to my mother. One of them is a new dress she had made to wear for my daddy. I don't want anything to happen to her things. Can you and Mrs. Sclater keep them for me?"

The pastor blinked away the tears from his eyes and said, "Of course. We'll be glad to keep them until you have a place where they will be safe." After an awkward silence, Reverend Sclater stood and said to the boy, "Why don't we take a walk. I ate too much dinner and I believe I know somebody else who did." The boy obediently stood and followed the man from the room.

Early the next morning, they left for Williamsburg. When they arrived at the Yorktown road, the minister asked, "Would you like to ride over to the town and see if the ship is still there?"

"Yes sir," said the boy.

Stopping at the top of the bluff, they could look down at the waterfront. He could imagine his daddy sitting there each day on his horse, looking to see if they had arrived. The *Bristol Merchant* was still there. She was being loaded with hogsheads of tobacco and had settled deep in the water. They watched as strong slaves rolled one of the two thousand pound barrels onto the ship and lowered it into the hold with ropes. Tobacco would occupy the passenger space on the return trip to England.

Leaving town, they rode along the banks of the York River for several miles. The boy shivered from the winter air. Passing large plantations, Reverend Sclater told him who lived on each of them. He showed him the large tobacco fields, now standing empty except for the stubby stalks left from the harvest. Noisy flocks of geese and ducks were

46

everywhere, both on the water and in the air. Some very strange looking birds were standing like statues in the shallows and occasionally, one would be seen flying overhead.

Soon, the road turned inland, leaving the river behind. Winding between very large trees, it sometimes curved away from a swampy area to higher ground. Occasionally, smaller roads could be seen leading off into the woods. When they came to one such road, the minister turned onto it. Barely out of sight of the main road, they entered a clearing where a small house stood. On one side of the house was a fenced garden area and behind it, a little barn. On the other side of the house, was a new grave. The clergyman did not speak as he stopped the carriage in front of the house and stepped down to the ground. Hopping down from the other side, Alexander walked slowly toward the grave while the minister tied the horse. Watching the boy for only a moment, the man stepped up on the porch of the house, unlocked the door, and went inside.

The minister looked around to be sure nothing had been disturbed since his last visit and then sat down to wait for the boy. As he waited, he thought of how the property would have to be disposed of. It would probably involve the parish vestry and the York County Court. Sadly, the child standing outside by his father's grave would not benefit from the sale of any of it. The one meant to live in this house was now here, but could not stay. The one who was the legal heir to everything would own none of it. He was now a penniless orphan in a strange land. He did not even know where he would sleep tonight.

When Alexander came inside, he had been crying. The knees of his pants were wet and dirty where he had been kneeling beside his father's grave. He walked around looking at the house and furnishings. Nothing looked familiar to him. He sat down across the table from Reverend

Sclater and said, "I wish my mum could have been buried beside him," and began to cry again.

The minister's heart was breaking for the young lad and he could not prevent tears from forming in his own eyes.

Slowly getting to his feet, Alexander said, "I'm ready to go," and turned toward the door. Reaching the road, they continued their journey westward.

"What is Williamsburg like?" asked the boy.

"I like Williamsburg, and I believe you will like it too. It is a large city with level streets and many shops and homes. The Governor's house and the Capitol building are there because it is the capital of the Virginia Colony. The College of William and Mary is also there."

"Is it close to the water like Yorktown?"

"No. Actually, it is about midway between the York River and the James River. Because of that, the early settlers called it Middle Plantation. The name was changed to Williamsburg about a dozen years ago when the capital of the colony was moved from Jamestown."

"Why was it moved?"

"There was a big fire and Jamestown was destroyed. A lot of people had already moved from Jamestown to Williamsburg before the fire because it was more hospitable. There were less mosquitoes and better soil for crops."

"I hate mosquitoes."

The minister laughed. "You don't have to worry about them for a few more months. Next month, we will celebrate Christmas. The people of Williamsburg celebrate it in a grand way. They decorate their homes beautifully and have big parties and lots of fine food."

"It couldn't be finer than the food Mrs. Sclater cooked Sunday. That's the best food I ever tasted."

"I'll tell her you said that. She'll be pleased that you enjoyed it," said the minister, smiling as he spoke.

"My daddy was indentured for four years and he worked on a plantation. He learned to do a lot of things. What did you mean that I would be indentured to a craftsman?"

"You would be like an apprentice so you could learn a trade. The Governor wants everyone in the colony to learn a trade."

"Where will I live?"

"Whoever indentures you has a responsibility to take care of you. They must provide you proper food, housing, clothes, and medical care. They should teach you to read and write. They must also treat you fairly. If they don't, there are laws to protect you and you can take them to court. You must also be fair in your work for them and treat them with respect."

"Will I have to serve four years too?"

The minister was quiet for a moment before speaking. "No, son. You will probably have to serve until you are twenty one years old."

Alexander was silent for the remainder of the trip. He didn't even comment when Reverend Sclater pointed out the Jamestown road to him, he only glanced at it and then continued staring straight ahead.

Soon afterwards, the houses of Williamsburg came into view but Alexander still expressed no interest until they turned onto Duke of Gloucester Street. The sights and sounds soon captured his attention and he was trying desperately to see what was on both sides of the street as they passed quickly by. Stopping outside a large brick building, the minister said, "You can come in with me, but will have to wait in the hall while I attend the meeting."

Chapter 6

Indentured

Alexander placed his belongings on the bench in the large hall where Reverend Sclater had left him. When he sat down beside them, he noticed the dirt on the knees of his pants and began trying to brush it off. Suddenly, a soldier jerked the door open at the end of the hall. He remained at rigid attention while holding the door open for the group trailing along behind him. A man in a robe with a large white wig on his head came hurrying in and approaching Alexander, shouted, "Stand up!" The boy jumped to his feet and watched as the man passed and hurried away down the long hall. As soon as he was gone, the boy sat back down.

The next man through the door was not hurrying and was more splendidly dressed than the first. Alexander watched with curiosity as he approached, followed by a group of elaborately dressed men. Stopping in front of the boy, the first man stared at him for a moment and said, "Weren't you told to stand?"
"Yes sir."
"Then why didn't you stand?"
"I did. And then I sat back down."
The man shook his head in bewilderment, and continued down the hall. The irritated looking group of men with their flowing robes, fancy buttons, and big powdery wigs followed him. Each of them glared at the boy as they passed by.

The last man in the group was a short, pudgy man, who seemed to be having a hard time keeping up with the others. Shuffling up to the boy he yelled, "Stand up!" Again, Alexander stood up.
"Don't you have any respect for the Governor?" yelled the man, pushing his face as close to the boy's face as he could.

His foul-smelling breath was repulsive.

"I didn't know he was the Governor," replied the boy.

"The next time you are told to stand, remain standing until you are told to sit," screamed the man.

"Yes sir," said the boy. By then, the group was far down the hall and the short-legged man shuffled away as fast as he could, trying to catch up. As soon as he was out of sight, Alexander collapsed on the bench in a fit of uncontrollable laughter.

Others continued to come through the hall and enter the meeting room. Alexander would try to regain his composure when he heard someone coming. He did not want anyone to see him sitting alone laughing; they may think he was mad. Several hours passed as he waited for Reverend Sclater to return. He amused himself by walking up and down the hall and looking out of the windows, but he never ventured far from his belongings. Occasionally, he would think about the pudgy little short-legged man who was trying to act important. Each time he thought of him waddling quickly down the hall he would burst into laughter again.

When the men began leaving the meeting room, Alexander returned to his bench. As soon as he saw the Governor and his party coming, he stood until they had all left the building. None of them looked at him as they passed. Reverend Sclater was among the last to appear. He was talking with three men as they came down the hall. Alexander recognized them as men he had seen at Charles Parish and wondered if they were vestrymen. When the minister stopped in front of him, the other men nodded to the boy, but kept walking.

"We do have an assignment for you," said the minister. "The Governor has brought a number of people here as his personal servants who are skilled in various trades. Most of them need apprentices. One of them is a barber named John Timberlake. You will be indentured to him."

"Does that mean I have to stay here today?"

"Yes. I will take you to the shop to meet Mr. Timberlake and make sure you are properly settled before I leave."

Unhurriedly, the boy reached down and picked up his belongings. He had hoped he would be able to return home with Reverend Sclater. He was not interested in meeting Mr. Timberlake and had no desire to be a barber.

"We have some other things to do first," said the minister. "We are going to visit my daughter, Sarah, and have dinner with her."

"Where does she live?"

"Only a short distance from here, but we'll take the carriage. I'll take you to Mr. Timberlake's shop later."

As they rode the short distance to the house, the minister said proudly, "You'll get to meet my grandchildren. My little granddaughter's name is Mary and she's two years old. She's also named after my wife. She has a little baby brother named Doyle. I don't know if my daughter's husband will be home or not. His name is Henry Cary and he's a busy man. He's building the new Palace for the Governor."

Stopping in front of a modest home, they tied the horse and walked to the door. Opening the door, the minister called out, "Sarah?"

A pretty young woman came rushing excitedly to the door. "Father!" she cried, as she threw her arms around the man. "I didn't know you were coming to town."

"I had to attend a meeting at the Capitol. I would like to spend the night if it's convenient."

"You know it is!"

Noticing the boy for the first time, she said, "And does this young man also need a place to stay?"

"No, but he sure could use something to eat. Can't you see how hungry he looks?"

Sarah laughed and said, "I know who's hungry. The same one that's hungry every time he shows up at my door!"

Extending her hand to the boy, she said, "I'm Sarah. I don't think I've ever met you." Shaking her hand, the boy

52

mumbled, "I'm Alexander Stinson."

They had barely closed the door when it opened again and a man walked in. Extending his hand to the minister, he said, "Hello Mr. Sclater. What brings you to Williamsburg?"
"Hello Henry. I had to come for another meeting. This time it was with the Governor."
"Wonderful!" said the man, laughing. "I wondered who had been keeping him busy all day. He hasn't been down at the palace bothering me." Turning to the boy, he exchanged introductions and said, "Let's see if we can find something to eat." Taking his wife by the hand, he led the group towards the dining room.

After they had eaten, Reverend Sclater and Alexander returned to the carriage. The minister paused for a moment and looked up the street. "It's only a short distance to walk, but I think I'll take the carriage." Once they were seated, he said, "Let me show you some of the town while we still have the opportunity. You may have to go to work as soon as you get to the shop." For part of the next hour, they rode slowly up and down the streets of Williamsburg with the minister pointing out the main buildings to him.

Stopping in front of the barbershop, they went inside. The man in the first room was busy showing a wig to a customer, but excused himself for a moment to acknowledge the clergyman.
"Are you Mr. Timberlake?" the minister asked.
"No sir, I'm David Cunningham. Mr. Timberlake is in the next room. I don't know who told you about him, but I'm glad you've come to see him. He really needs some divine help!" said the man, loudly.
Knowing they were being overheard, Reverend Sclater laughed as he started toward the other room with Alexander following closely behind. When the minister reached the doorway, he stopped short and the boy almost bumped into him.

"So it's a Reverend that David's talking to," came a strongly accented voice from within the room. "Well, since you're here, I'm hoping you'll be talking to him a bit too. Mind you now, I need to tell you a few things before you do."

Standing on tiptoe, Alexander stretched to peek around the pastor to find the source of the voice. A handsome, medium-built man stood looking toward the door with a smile on his face.

When Alexander's gaze moved away from the man who was speaking, he knew why Reverend Sclater had stopped so suddenly. Reclining in a chair, unclothed to his waist, was another man. In his left hand, he grasped a blood-covered stick. A little stream of blood oozed slowly down his arm from a small cut just below his elbow. Most of the blood gathered on a white cloth wrapped around the stick. Occasionally, a drop would fall from the cloth into a small pan sitting on the floor. The man was being bled, a practice thought to relieve many human ills.

Still smiling, the man said, "I'm John Timberlake, if you be looking for me."

Never moving from the door, the minister said, "I am Reverend James Sclater, Rector of Charles Parish. I have just attended a meeting with the Governor and the area rectors and vestrymen. I assume you are aware of the Governor's plan for all of the craftsmen in the colony to have indentured servants. I have a boy in my charge that is to be put in your care. I'll wait until you are through so we can talk." Alexander watched as the man nodded his head and the smile disappeared from his face.

Stepping back into the room, they waited. Near the rear window was a long table with many kinds of hair on it. Some of the hair lay stretched between the teeth of a large comb. Some seemed to be sorted by color and length and lay in bundles on the bench. On a tall pedestal was a rounded block, roughly shaped like a head. On the block was a large wig. Another chair, similar to the one in the other room, sat near the end wall. Beside it on a table, sat a basin of water and an assortment of razors and shears. While Alexander was studying the room, the man who had been looking at the wig left.

David Cunningham walked over to where they were standing. Looking at Alexander, he said, "So you are going to be our little shaver?" Seeing the puzzled look on the boy's face, he laughed. "That's what we call an apprentice boy. One of your jobs will be to shave men's heads."
Looking more puzzled, the boy said, "Why do I need to do that?"
"So their wigs will fit them. If they get too much hair on their heads, their wigs don't fit. They have to keep it shaved off."
Reverend Sclater seemed greatly amused at the conversation.
"What else will I be doing?" asked the boy.
Enjoying the dialogue, Mr. Cunningham said, "Hopefully, you will learn to do everything we do, but that will take time. There are a lot of things that you can do to help us now."
"Will I have to make people bleed?" asked the boy, as he glanced toward the other room. The man roared with laughter. "Not any time soon; but it really isn't as bad as it seems."
"I don't think I would like that," said Alexander, shaking his head from side to side.

While they were talking, the man whom they had seen in the back came walking into the room. Now fully dressed, he left the shop and quickly disappeared down the street. John Timberlake, who had been listening to the conversation, came through the door with a broad grin on his face. "Don't you be worried boy, it will probably be at least a fortnight before we let you bleed anyone. We'll have to teach you to use a fleam first."
"What's a fleam?"
"A blood knife." Still smiling broadly, he held one out towards the boy. Alexander looked at it, but showed no

interest in touching it. Turning his attention to the minister, he said, "Well Reverend, let's talk." Starting towards the door, he looked back at the boy and said, "You stay with Mr. Cunningham until we get back."

Walking towards the street, he turned to the minister and said, "We can sit and talk across the street at the ordinary and have a cup of tea, if you'd like."
"That will be fine."
Since it was late afternoon, there were no other customers in the tavern. As they took a table by the window, Susanna Allen entered from a back room.
"Hello Reverend Sclater. Aren't you worried that your parish folk will learn whom you are keeping company with?"
"Now mind your mouth, Sue Allen," said Timberlake. "He has already heard enough of that kind of talk from your David. You just bring us both a good cup of tea."
"Tea!" said the woman, tossing her head back and laughing loudly. "Aren't you afraid the shock will be too great for your stomach?"
"Reverend Sclater, I must apologize for the conduct of my friends. I'm afraid their jesting may convince you I'm a dreadful person and ruin my chance of ever getting an apprentice."
To the contrary, the minister was enjoying the bantering immensely. It was a refreshing experience for him because he seldom had the opportunity to interact with people like these. Thinking of the rigidly conducted meeting he had attended earlier that day, he was amused by the contrast.

Miss Allen brought their tea and they began their conversation in earnest. "Have you ever had an indentured servant before?" asked the minister.
"No, but David has. He had a lad who worked as an apprentice in our shop."
"The colony has some very strict laws concerning their care. Are you aware of them?"
"I am. But even if there were no laws, I would do right by

the boy. I hope you don't take our teasing seriously. I have my faults and may not be as religious as I should be, but I'm not a bad person."

Reverend Sclater smiled and said, "I believe you. The boy will be eleven years old the ninth of December. That's just a few days away. I can attest to that because his father told me. I suggest we write the indenture for ten years, which will make him of age when it is completed. If you agree, I will prepare a copy for you, one for the boy, and I will record it in the parish record."

Timberlake thought about it for a moment and said, "I'm agreeable to that but I would like to know more about the boy. What can you tell me about him?" For the next hour, the two men drank tea and talked.

Driving back to his daughter's home, the minister reflected on the events of the day. It seemed so long since he and the boy left home that morning. The heart-breaking stop at John's house and grave, the long, boring meeting with the bigwigs, and the light-hearted bantering of the common folks were things he would remember and tell his wife. The most painful memory he had was leaving Alexander behind. Reverend Sclater had been driven to tears again by the look on the lad's face as he watched the carriage drive away.

Chapter 7

Learning To Be A Servant

Alexander lay awake listening to the voices drifting up to his room from Duke of Gloucester Street. Some were from the distant taverns and the coffeehouse while others were from people walking past. Occasionally, a carriage would pass and he would listen to see how long he could hear the sound of the horses' feet before they faded in the distance. Once, he jumped up to look at a particularly noisy one, but the coldness quickly drove him back to the warmth of his bed. The small mattress, lying on the floor in the corner of the room, was comfortable, but not nearly as nice as the real bed he slept in at the Sclaters' house. He was all alone in the upstairs room over the shop. Mr. Timberlake was the only other person living in the house and he was at the ordinary. When he returned later that night, Alexander was asleep.

They were up early the next morning. The fire had been banked the night before by adding more wood to the hot coals and then covering it with ashes. By scraping the ashes away and adding dry wood, the fire was soon burning brightly, but it would take a while to get the house warm again. Mr. Timberlake prepared breakfast while Alexander brought in more wood and fresh water from the well in the back yard. People would soon be coming into the shop so everything must be ready. Their first customer, much to the boy's surprise, was a man complaining with a toothache.

"My tooth kept me awake all night," said the man. "I think it's this one right here," he said, pointing to one inside his swollen jaw. "Lay down on the bench and let me take a look," said Timberlake. "I think you're right. All we can do is pull it and see if it is the one." As he gathered his tools together, he sent Alexander to bring a candle and instructed him how to hold it for him. "Now you get a good grip on the sides of the bench," he said to the man, "and don't you move." Having to stay close with the candle, the boy had no choice but to watch the entire process.

Locking the pincers over the suspected tooth, Timberlake began working it back and forth. Blood began running down the pincers and onto his hand. The man was groaning and making horrible grunting sounds as he held on tightly to the side of the tall, angled, bench. Beads of perspiration were on the foreheads of both men. "Hold the light up, boy!" yelled the barber. Giving the tooth one more twist and a pull, it came free. "Get that pan," yelled Timberlake to the boy. Alexander picked up the blood pan from the floor and handed it to him. "Don't give it to me, hold it for him!" The boy poked the pan in front of the man and he spat a large bloody blob into it. Alexander began to feel sick.

"We need a bucket of water in here," said Timberlake. Alexander grabbed the bucket and flew from the room and out the back door. The cold air was refreshing as he walked toward the well. Opening the well top, he untied the rope, and lowered the well bucket. When he heard it hit the water, he jiggled the rope around until he felt it sink. He then began to draw the heavy bucket up, pulling the rope hand-over-hand through the pulley. He didn't stop until the bucket was above the edge of the well top. Holding the rope tightly with one hand, he pulled the bucket to him with the other, getting splashed in the process. He slowly lowered it until he could grasp the handle with both hands and empty it into the water-bucket from the house.

By the time he got back inside, he was feeling better, even though his shirt, trousers, and shoes were wet from the splashing water. As he walked into the room with the water, Timberlake was placing a small roll of cloth into the man's mouth. "Bite down on this," he said, "and leave it there for about an hour." Turning to Alexander, he said, "Pour me some water in this basin, so I can wash my hands. You need to wash the instruments and pan before the blood dries."

David Cunningham arrived just as the other man was leaving. He hung his coat on the peg and turning to Timberlake, asked, "What was Mr. Bolling doing here so early?"
"He heard we had a new man," said John, "and he came over to see if he would pull a tooth for him. The boy did a good job. I think he likes that kind of work. We may be able to turn all the tooth work over to him as soon as his arm muscles get bigger."
Alexander grinned, but said nothing. He couldn't believe how quickly this man could change. A few minutes earlier, he was yelling orders at him and now he was teasing him like he did yesterday.

An older couple arrived behind Mr. Cunningham and was introduced to the boy as Jacob and Anna Sanders. They also worked in the shop, but not every day. When the barbers had orders for new wigs, they helped make them. For the remainder of the day, Alexander used his free time to watch them work. They explained how the wigs were made and showed him what they were made from. The most valuable wigs were made from human hair left its natural color. Cheaper wigs were made from cow tails, horsehair, silk thread, and even linen. The most difficult part seemed to be attaching the hair to the net cap that fit on the head. Alexander was sure he could never learn how to do that.

The boy's busy schedule helped the time pass surprisingly fast. The two barbers usually kept him busy in the shop. Depending on what they were doing, they would teach him new things about the work or assign him projects he could complete on his own. When the barbers were away and the Sanders were there, they would also give him jobs to do. The job he liked best was running errands. These short trips provided him an opportunity to visit other shops in town and meet the people who worked there.

He disliked the evenings the most. After supper, he was usually alone. He had never stayed alone before in his entire life. Timberlake normally went to the taverns immediately after they ate and didn't return until late. The flickering fire burning in the fireplace brought back many painful memories to the boy. He would keep the fire burning until bedtime and then bank it before climbing the narrow, curving, steps to the cold, dark, room above. Lying there in the dark, he would remember his family and cry. It was then he began to dream the dream. He sometimes wondered if his daddy had dreamed the same dream. One day, he would be free. He would become a landowner. He would have a family again. As he dreamed his dream, his tears would stop. Soon, the weary little boy would fall asleep.

All the shops were closed on Sunday. The laws of the colony required that all people attend worship service. Masters were required to see that their slaves and servants attended. Part of the churchwarden's responsibility was to bring charges against anyone who missed services for two months. John Timberlake grumbled the entire time as they were preparing for church. "A man should have the right to choose if he goes to church or not," he said. "The Governor has no right to tell a man when and how he should worship the Almighty." Alexander listened politely, but never replied. Timberlake didn't look like he felt well and continued to splash cold water on his face as he talked. "The one morning I could sleep late and rest from a hard week's work, I have to get up and go to church." Secretly, Alexander was looking forward to going, but he would never let Timberlake know it.

The church building was similar to Charles Parish where he worshipped the previous week except it had a balcony. He expected to sit with Mr. Timberlake, but just before they entered the building, he said to the boy, "You must sit upstairs with the slaves and servants. I'll meet you outside after the service." The impact of that statement began to sink in as Alexander was walking up the steps. Stepping cautiously out into the balcony area he stopped and looked around. Everyone stared at him. He wanted to turn and run.

The black slaves were all sitting together in one area. In another place, the white servants were sitting. Walking slowly toward the white servants, he chose the seat furthest away from the group and eased his small body down into it. He sat there staring straight ahead. It wasn't until the service started that he began to look around the crowded church. The Governor was there as well as many of his attendants. The boy smiled when he recognized the short, pudgy, man he had seen shuffling down the hall earlier in the week. These and other notable people occupied the choicest seats on the lower level. The common people took the remaining ones.

The service was very different from the one he had attended last week. The readings and sermon were especially boring. His mind wandered back to the previous Sunday and the fiery message delivered by the Reverend Sclater. He then began thinking about the delicious meal he had after church in their home and wished he were back with them. He wondered if he would ever have the opportunity to go back and visit the children. He had enjoyed the few days spent with them, especially the crabbing. Two snickering boys sitting nearby interrupted his thoughts.

Turning his attention to them, he discovered the source of their amusement. One of the bigwigs below was fast asleep. His chin was almost touching his chest. When his wife became aware of it, she gave him a sharp poke in the ribs with her elbow. Jerking his head up and opening his eyes, he would sit upright for a few minutes and the scene would be repeated. The nearby adults seemed to be equally amused at what was happening, but afraid to laugh. They tried to look scornfully at the children when they showed any response but had a difficult time not smiling themselves. When they weren't looking, Alexander and the two boys would exchange grins. Before the service was over, he had decided he liked sitting in the balcony.

Several weeks passed and people were busy preparing for Christmas. The town was being transformed by Christmas decorations that were increasing in numbers daily. Horses and carriages crowded the streets each day, bringing more people to shop and enjoy the festive atmosphere. Shops were soon depleted of their wares. They would not be restocked until after the Christmas season had ended because most of the craftsmen were no longer working. Many of the servants and slaves also were given time off for the season. Unfortunately, those who were involved in household work and cooking found their work increasing.

A wealth of wonderful odors poured forth from the kitchens of Williamsburg. The smell of roasting meat, mince pies, fruitcakes, and plum puddings filled the air. The sounds of laughter and music drifted from the taverns and coffeehouse throughout the day and into the night. The large, brightly lit homes were often filled with fancily dressed visitors, many of whom came great distances to be entertained there. Even the smaller homes seemed to have a continuous flow of visitors coming and going.

One morning after breakfast, John Timberlake announced to the boy, "We are going to close the shop until after the Christmas season. I will be gone a lot but probably will be home each night. If I don't, I'll be back some time during the day. You can go out when you want to. All you need to do is keep the wood box filled, the fire burning, and fresh water drawn. Be sure to bank the fire if you leave." Alexander was excited about his new freedom. It would be more fun than running errands because he would not have to hurry back to the shop.

Alexander filled the wood box and drew a fresh bucket of

water. He could hardly wait for Mr. Timberlake to leave. It was late morning before the barber donned his coat and headed for the door. The boy watched him as he crossed the street and disappeared into Susanna Allen's ordinary. Placing several more logs on the fire, he carefully shoveled ashes over them until the flames died down. Grabbing his coat, he slipped out the back door and around the house.

Large crowds of people were already on the streets. Crossing quickly to the other side, he walked leisurely towards the college. Many of the shops were closed and those that were open were unusually crowded. When he came to an open shop, he would stand outside and look in, but was scared to go inside. He had no money to spend and was afraid he would be chased away by the shopkeepers. Walking the full length of the street, he turned and went down the other side, taking in all the sounds and smells that filled the air. When he reached the barbershop, he went in to check the fire and get a drink of water.

Returning to the street, he continued his journey. Every building was adorned with Christmas wreaths and other decorations. Evergreens, holly, mistletoe, magnolia leaves, berries, cones, and even fruit decorated doors, gates, fences and posts. Groups of laughing people thronged the streets. Even those individuals hurrying along on some unknown mission frequently stopped to exchange greetings with those they met. The Capitol gate and doors were decorated but there were no people in sight. Turning up the street where the Carys lived, he decided to stop and say hello to them. When he knocked on the door, one of the servants answered. "Mistuh and Miz Cary's gone to Warwick," she said. "They won't be back 'til after Christmas."
"Warwick?" asked the boy.
"That's where Mistuh Cary's folks live," she said. "That's his real home. He just stays here when he's working here."

Turning towards Nicholson Street, he walked towards the

Governor's mansion. The noise from the crowds died away. He walked slowly, but his mind was racing as he looked at the beautifully decorated homes. When he reached the palace, he stopped and stared at the huge, unfinished, building. He had stopped here once before and watched the men working. That day, it was filled with workers. Today, there were none. He stood there staring at the empty building for a long time. Turning around, he started walking dejectedly toward the shop. He had never felt more alone in his life.

He sat down before the smoldering fire and stared at the swirls of smoke rising from the ashes and disappearing up the chimney. He had always loved Christmas, but this year was different. He felt a sadness that he had never known before. It would not go away nor allow him to experience the joy that others seemed to feel. He could hear the sound of people outside. Happy people. People enjoying Christmas. He thought about last Christmas in the village with Grandma, Grandpa and his mother. He wondered what his grandparents were doing. They probably were sad this Christmas too. He missed them. He missed his mother. Tears began to run down his cheek and drip on the floor.

A carriage stopped outside and he heard voices. Jumping up and looking out the window, he couldn't believe what he saw. Reverend and Mrs. Sclater were there! Wiping his eyes with the back of his hand, the boy ran to the door and jerking it open, rushed outside. The pastor was helping his wife from the carriage when he ran up. "Alexander," she cried, "how good it is to see you." Reaching out to the boy, she hugged him tightly.
When she released her grip, he turned to the minister and said, "What are you doing here?"
Putting his arm around the boy's shoulder, he said, "We came to see you and bring you some gifts. The children wanted to come but there was not enough room for all of us."
Turning back to the carriage, he picked up a basket covered

with a cloth.

Following the boy inside the shop, the minister sat the basket on the table and removed his coat. "Is it always this cold in here?" he asked.

"No sir," said Alexander, "the fire is banked because I've been out. I'll get it going." Hurrying to the fireplace, he scraped away the ashes and the wood burst into flames. Placing more wood on the fire, he returned to the couple who were still standing and said, "Would you like to sit down?"

"Not until we give you your gifts," said Mrs. Sclater, as she uncovered the basket and began unloading all kinds of good things to eat.

"Is that all mine?" asked the boy.

"Yes," she said, "but I'm sure you will want to share some with Mr. Timberlake." Alexander smiled as he looked at the food and said, "You must have remembered that I love sweets."

"I thought you loved all food," teased the minister.

"I loved everything I've ever eaten at your house and your daughter's. I went to see them today, but they have gone away."

"Yes," said Mrs. Sclater, "they've gone to her husband's home for Christmas. We plan to go there for a visit next week. We want to see Henry's family and also spend some time with our grandchildren."

"Are all of you going?"

"Oh yes. All three of the children are anxious to go."

Alexander shook his head and said, "Mr. Cary's family must have a big house if all of you can stay there."

The couple laughed. "They have enough room," said Mrs. Sclater.

Reverend and Mrs. Sclater sat with the boy for almost an hour listening to him tell about what he had learned in the barbershop. The woman grimaced as he vividly described how he watched Mr. Bolling have his tooth pulled. They both laughed as he told them about the man sleeping in church.

"That seems to be a problem in every parish," said Reverend Sclater.

As they prepared to leave, the pastor said, "I wrote your grandparents a letter and it has already shipped. When I receive a reply I will let you know."

Immediately, Alexander felt very sad again when he thought about his grandparents receiving the letter containing the bad news. He was quiet for a moment and then said, "Thank you."

Grabbing his coat, he followed the couple out to the carriage and received another hug from Mrs. Sclater.

Before they drove off, Alexander asked, "Did the Sheriff ever find out who killed my daddy?"

Growing very solemn, the man said, "He thinks he knows, but hasn't been able to find them. I'll come tell you when I know." The boy waved to them as they drove away then turned and ran inside to the food.

Elizabeth

Alexander stood at the barbershop window staring out at the people who were beginning to stir on Duke of Gloucester Street. He could feel the warmth of the fireplace on his back. A loud popping sound came from the fire. He turned and looked to be sure no sparks were on the floor. Looking back to the street, he saw the silversmith passing by. When the man saw Alexander in the window he smiled, and waved at the boy. Continuing across the street to his shop, he unlocked the door, and went inside. In a few minutes, smoke began coming from the chimney. It had been a cold winter, especially the long three months since Christmas. Even though it was April, it was still very cold, but soon it would be warm enough for them not to need a fire for heat, only for cooking. Spring was in the air.

The door of Susanna Allen's ordinary opened. David Cunningham stepped out and began walking briskly towards the barbershop. Mr. Cunningham owned a house in Williamsburg but usually stayed overnight at the ordinary. He had two young children, Jane and David, but Alexander rarely saw them. He also owned a one hundred acre plantation in York County, but Alexander didn't know where it was. He didn't know anything about his wife or why he stayed at the ordinary. There was a lot he didn't know about the man. Once he asked John Timberlake if Mr. Cunningham was related to Miss Allen. Timberlake chuckled and said, "You ask too many questions, lad."

When Mr. Cunningham started up the steps, Alexander opened the door for him.
"Thank you," he said, smiling at the boy. "You look like you're ready for work, I hope John is. Where is he?"

Miss Allen into the carriage taking great liberty where he placed his hands. Kissing her on the cheek, he bid her farewell and turned toward the house. He never once looked at Alexander.

As they approached the Williamsburg Road, Susanna Allen spoke for the first time. "Pick the gun up carefully and hold it like you did before." Once he was settled again in his seat, she said, "We have plenty of time to get home before dark. Let's see how well you remember the way. I want you to direct me back." Directing her to turn right, he sat in rapt attention with his eyes on the road for fear of missing some landmark that would guide them home or help him on some future trip.

A fine, cold, rain began to fall as they approached Williamsburg. Alexander felt proud that he had led them back without making a mistake. He was shivering again. This time, he knew it wasn't from excitement, but from the cold rain that pelted him. His thin clothes offered little protection from such weather. He would be glad to be inside again where it was warm and have something to eat before settling down to dream his dream. He could shut out the sights and sounds of the world around him and the bitter memories of the past with his dream. One day he would have a better life. Until that day, his dream would keep him alive.

They arrived in town shortly before dark and most of the shops were already closed. When they stopped in front of the ordinary, Cooper stepped from behind the building and took the reins of the horse. David Cunningham emerged from the ordinary door to help Miss Allen from the carriage.
Turning to Cooper, she said, "The cider needs to be put in the cellar before you move the carriage."
"Yes, Miss Allen," he responded.
Looking at the boy, she said, "Give the gun to Mr. Cunningham--he will take it inside. Go around to the

kitchen and tell Dinah I said to give you some supper before you go home."

"Thank you Miss Allen," said the boy, as he handed the gun to the man standing silently in the street.

Dinah, the Negro cook, looked around as the boy cautiously opened the kitchen door. Standing in the doorway, almost as if he was prepared to run, he said, "Miss Allen said for you to give me some supper before I go home."

Staring at him for a long moment, she said, "Sit down over dare on dat stool."

Glancing at the stool sitting at the end of a small table, Alexander moved slowly toward it and sat down. A huge fireplace covered almost one entire wall of the small kitchen. A large black pot hung over the burning coals of a wood fire. A wide, shallow, pan with a lid on it, sat in a bed of ashes near the hot coals. In one corner of the room, there was a narrow stairway, almost identical to the one in the barbershop. The room was warm. It felt good.

The woman dipped into the large pot with a long-handled ladle and poured its contents into a wooden bowl. She sat it before the boy and handed him a spoon. Without speaking, she turned around and went back to the fireplace. Removing the lid from the shallow pan, she took a knife and lifted a thick piece of bread onto a small wooden plate. Setting it before the boy, she stared at him in amazement because he wasn't eating. He had been busy watching her.

"Eat," she said to the boy, "it's good." Dipping the spoon into the bowl, he carefully tasted the hot stew.

"It is good," he said, returning the spoon quickly to the bowl.

"Eat yo' bread wif it," she said. Alexander took a bite of the bread with the next spoonful of stew. It tasted different from any he had ever eaten. It was delicious.

"What kind of bread is this?"

"Good bread," she said, smiling. "Want some mo'?"

Alexander ate the bowl of stew and two pieces of the bread. Picking up the empty bread plate, Dinah returned with a slice of pie. "Don't you tell Miz Allen I gave you no pie or you won't nevah get no mo'."

Alexander grinned and said, "I won't tell." His stomach was full, his clothes were now dry and he was very warm. He was a contented little boy who had found himself a new friend. The door opened, and a young girl entered the kitchen. She was carrying a large bowl filled with dirty dishes. Alexander had never seen her before. When she saw him, she stopped abruptly and stared at him for a moment before sitting the container down and closing the door.

Looking at the girl, Dinah smiled and said, "This here is Miz Elizabeth. She done come to live wif us."

Alexander nodded to the girl, who was looking at him again and said, "Hi."

Never taking her eyes off of him, she asked, "Who are you?" Alexander felt defenseless against the gazing eyes and simple question of the pretty little girl. He hardly recognized his own voice when he muttered, "My name is Alexander. I live across the street." Dinah was greatly amused by the actions of the two children. Smiling broadly, she said, "He lives in da barber shop wif Mistuh Timberlake."

Alexander sat on the wooden stool watching the other two clean up the kitchen. All of a sudden he remembered that he had not been home and wondered if Mr. Timberlake even knew where he was. Jumping up quickly, he startled the cook.

"I have to go tell Mr. Timberlake I'm home," he explained. "Thank you for supper."

The girl was looking at him again, but said nothing as he passed close to her. When he reached the door he turned to both of them and said, "Bye." Dinah was smiling broadly when she said, "Bye." The girl said nothing.

Walking across the yard in the cold night air, he realized he had forgotten his coat. Turning around, he was almost at the kitchen door when it flew open. Elizabeth was standing there holding his coat in her hand. "You forgot this," she said.

"Thank you," said the boy. Taking the coat from her hand, he hurried back across the yard towards the street. When he reached the fence, he turned and looked back. The girl was still watching him.

John Timberlake was standing just inside the door with his coat on when the boy entered. "Welcome back," he said, "how was your trip?"

"Good, but I got wet and cold coming home."

"You're not wet now,"

"Miss Allen gave me supper. I've been in the kitchen eating and got dry and warm beside that big fireplace."

"Oh no. If you've been eating Dinah's cooking, you'll never be satisfied with mine again. You wait 'til I see Sue Allen."

Alexander laughed and said, "It was good. Have you ever tasted any of that bread she makes?"

Timberlake roared with laughter. "That does it. You'll never be happy eating here again. You'll be hanging around that kitchen like a starving dog."

"Why do you have your coat on. Are you cold?"

"Yes, my boy went away and didn't take care of the fire and I'm freezing."

Alexander looked at the blazing fire and then back at the man who was laughing again. "I'm getting ready to go out," he said. "I knew you would be here soon so I was waiting for you before I left. I'll see you in the morning."

Alexander sat for a long time staring at the fire and thinking about everything that had happened that day. Finally, he banked the fire and climbed the curved steps to the cold bedroom. He was tired and the bed felt good. He thought about what he had seen on his trip and how he had remembered the way back. He thought about Dinah, and the delicious meal he had enjoyed in her warm kitchen. He thought about the pretty little girl, Elizabeth. He could still see her standing in the door watching him. She would now become part of his dream.

Chapter 9

Ordinary Life

Alexander was returning from the blacksmith shop with a pair of shears that he had taken for sharpening. When he passed the ordinary, he saw Elizabeth coming from the kitchen and waved to her. Slipping quickly through the gate, he ran across the yard to meet her. "What are you doing?" he asked.

"I can't talk to you now," she said, glancing uneasily towards the house, "I have some work to finish inside."

Elizabeth had become his best friend in the few weeks she had lived at the ordinary. He continually looked for opportunities to be with her. He especially enjoyed sitting with her in church on Sunday. The other boys teased him, but he didn't care. When he could, he spent Sunday afternoons visiting with her, Dinah, and Cooper at the ordinary. Sometimes, Dinah would secretly make cookies for them to enjoy. Because of his new friends, Alexander was much happier now than when he first came to Williamsburg.

Returning to the shop with the shears, he gave them to Mr. Timberlake. The man walked to the window to examine them in the sunlight. He ran his finger along the edge of each blade and then operated them back and forth. Apparently pleased, he placed them on the shelf and returned to his customer, Mr. Davies. During the five months Alexander had been there, he had learned the names of nearly everyone in town. Most of the men and some of the women were regular customers at the barbershop. He enjoyed listening to their conversations, but still had little interest in becoming a barber. He would rather be outside running errands or doing chores. Seeing the water bucket was nearly empty, he picked it up and went outside to fill it.

When Alexander returned with the water, David Cunningham said, "How would you like to go with me to the Governor's house?"

Alexander stared at him but made no reply.

"It will be an opportunity for you to meet Governor Spotswood," said Timberlake.

"I've already met him," said the boy, "and he doesn't like me."

The two men exchanged skeptical glances and smiled. "Oh you've met the Governor have you," said Timberlake, "and may I ask when you met him?"

"The same day I met you. Reverend Sclater and the other ministers met with him and some of his fancy-dressed friends. He got mad and fussed at me for not standing up when he walked down the hall."

By now, both men were becoming keenly interested in his story. Sensing they wanted to hear more, he told them about his confrontation with the short, pudgy, man with the foul-smelling breath, and they began to laugh. "When he got through fussing at me for being disrespectful, the other men had left him. He tried to catch up with them and went down the hall like this," said the boy, imitating the hurried shuffle of the short-legged man.

The two men howled with laughter.

"Do you know who he was?" asked Timberlake.

"No," said Alexander, "I've never seen him in here, but I see him in church every Sunday. He always sits behind the Governor. I try to keep him from seeing me."

It was obvious that both men knew exactly whom he was talking about. Somehow, that seemed to make it even funnier to them.

"You have to go with me anyway," said Cunningham. "I need you to help me carry some things. The Governor probably won't remember you. If he does, I'll tell him what a fine lad you've become."

Still not convinced that it was a wise thing for him to do, the boy asked, "Why doesn't he come here like everyone else?"

"Because he's the Governor," said the barber with a chuckle.

Grudgingly, the boy went with him, carrying the tools while Cunningham carefully carried a new wig.

The trip was uneventful for the boy. If the Governor remembered him, he did not indicate it. His only interest seemed to be in the new wig. He appeared to be pleased with how it looked and fit. Alexander stood back and watched. He was far less interested in the fitting process then he was the dialogue between the two men. The Governor was very friendly to Mr. Cunningham and they seemed to know each other very well. As they walked back to the shop, he asked Mr. Cunningham, "How do you know the Governor so well?"

He smiled at the boy and said, "I was his barber before we came to Virginia. He brought me and John with him when he came here."

When they arrived back at the shop, John Timberlake said, "Reverend Sclater is in town. He came by to see you. He's gone down to see his daughter, but said he would be back soon." The boy hurried to the door and looked out. He saw the minister walking toward the shop and ran to meet him. After exchanging greetings in the middle of the street, they walked back to the shop.

"Pastor, I believe you've put a spell on my boy," said Timberlake. "He gets real excited when he sees you. He doesn't get that excited about pulling teeth or shaving heads. He didn't even get excited about visiting the Governor today. Maybe he wants to be a man of the cloth instead of a barber."

Alexander grinned, realizing that he was being teased again.

"Have a seat, Reverend," said Timberlake, "and let us fix you a cup of tea."

"Thank you, but my daughter is expecting me to eat dinner with her family before I start home. I had hoped Alexander could join us if you didn't object. You would also be welcome if you would like to come."

"I can't leave the shop right now, but I appreciate the

invitation. Please extend my thanks to Mr. and Mrs. Cary also; I regret missing a meal at their house. The boy may go and stay as long as you want him to. Just don't you go believing all he might tell you about me. Sometimes his imagination runs away with him!"

Smiling at the boy, the minister said, "I'll try to remember that."

Alexander had little to say during the meal but enjoyed listening to Henry Cary and his father-in-law discuss the things happening in Williamsburg. Mr. Cary seemed to know something about everything and had a ready answer for each question Reverend Sclater asked. Shortly after the meal, Mr. Cary stood and said, "I hate to leave such wonderful company, but I must get back to work. The Governor will probably be by after dinner to check on his house. He always has a lot of questions so I need to be there." Kissing his wife on the cheek, he turned to the minister and shook hands. "Give the family my love. We hope to come for a visit soon." Turning to the boy, he said, "Alexander, I understand you came by to see us at Christmas and we were gone. Don't wait until next Christmas to come back."

The boy smiled, and said, "Thank you."

Moving into the parlor after the meal, Reverend Sclater listened intently as the boy talked non-stop about what had happened to him since Christmas. When he finished, the minister began to question the boy about how he was being treated by Mr. Timberlake. His answers made him feel confident that things were going well.

"I hear he has a bad habit of swearing," said the minister. "Does he?"

The boy seemed uncomfortable responding to the question. Reluctantly, he said, "Yes, sir, but he never swears at me. I hear other people that swear as bad as him."

Although he didn't approve of the man's vice, he could tell by the boy's defense of Timberlake that he liked him and felt no malice towards him.

"I have some news for you," said the minister. "It's really the reason I came today. I promised you I would let you know when I heard any news about your father's killer. There were two men involved and they both are dead. Sheriff Tyler learned who they were and went to arrest them, but they had fled to North Carolina. He and his men followed them, but when they found them, one had already died from the fever and the other was dying. He confessed to the crime before he died."

The boy was quiet for several minutes before he spoke. "Do you know who they were?"

"I don't know their names. I only know they were criminals who had been sent to the colony as servants. They had run away and returned to a life of crime."

"I wish I could have killed them myself," said the boy, looking straight at the minister.

"Don't ever say such a thing again!" said Reverend Sclater, sitting upright in the chair and staring at the boy. "God says we are not to repay evil for evil--vengeance belongs to Him."

The boy lowered his head and stared silently at the floor.

Slowly relaxing in his chair again, the minister said, "I didn't mean to speak so harshly to you, but that's a serious thing to say. We must try to live good lives and leave the judgment of evil people to God. God says we should not kill. If you killed them, you would become just like them."

The boy looked directly at the minister and asked, "What about my Mum?"

"What do you mean?"

"Evil men made my Mum die. Will God kill them?"

This time it was the minister who lowered his head in silence for a moment before he responded. "I can't tell you what God will do," he said. "Our faith teaches that we trust Him. He will reward the good and punish the evil."

After a few minutes of awkward silence, the man spoke again. "I must be going, it's a long ride home. I wish you could go with me, Mrs. Sclater and the children would love to see you. They send you their greetings."

For the first time since they had finished the meal, Alexander smiled at the mention of his friends.

"Tell Mrs. Sclater that the food she brought me for Christmas was really good."

"Did you remember to share it with Mr. Timberlake?" asked the minister.

"I did," said the boy, "but he didn't eat much of it. He was gone a lot and ate at other places. I was glad--that left more for me to eat." They laughed as they stood to leave.

"Tell James and the girls I want to come back and go crabbing again," said Alexander.

"I'll tell them," said the minister.

As Alexander walked back to the shop, he felt satisfied that his father's death had been avenged. He was also happy to have spent time again with Reverend Sclater and the Carys. He wondered if Mr. Cary really meant it when he told him to come visit again. Although he was an important person in Williamsburg, he always treated Alexander with respect and had remembered his name. He was building some large buildings in Williamsburg. Whenever he had the opportunity, Alexander would slip away to one of the building sites and watch the men work. He wished he could learn to be a builder instead of a barber, but he never told anyone except Elizabeth.

It was the Saturday before Easter and Williamsburg was crowded because the Council was in session at the Capitol. They had adjourned early on Good Friday and the shops all closed for a church service. Today, they would be back in session and all the shops would be open. Arriving early, David Cunningham seemed surprised to find Timberlake and Alexander already in the shop.

"Did you hear about the riot last night?" asked Cunningham.

"What riot?" responded Timberlake.

"Didn't you go out last night?"

"No, I went to bed early. I thought things would be quiet

since it was Good Friday. What happened?"

"Some of the young dandies created an uproar at the ordinary last night."

"Who?"

"Mann Page, Ralph Wormley, John Grymes, Thomas Johnson, and Jimmy Burwell. They have to appear this morning before Mr. Blair."

"Ha! With the influence their families have, they'll not be fined a pence!"

Contrary to his prediction, each of the men who had been involved in the riot at the ordinary were fined, but only ten shillings apiece. This only served to aggravate the barber, who made no pretense of hiding his feelings to anyone who brought up the subject. Alexander didn't understand why he was so agitated about it until he learned that Timberlake himself was facing charges of being a common swearer and must appear in court at Yorktown. He was really angry with the churchwarden for bringing the charges.

On the day before his court date, the barber was in a sullen mood. He and David Cunningham had several private conversations. Sensing the way the man felt, Alexander was careful not to do anything that may upset him. He stayed available if needed, but otherwise out of the way. That night after the shop closed, the two sat down to eat.

"Jacob and Anna will work in the shop tomorrow while I go to Yorktown," said Timberlake. "Miss Allen will be going with me because she also has to be in court. David will oversee things here and at the ordinary. He will probably be over there most of the day, so I want you to go over there and help him if he needs you. I'm sure there will be some things you can do."

"Do you want me to do anything here before I leave?"

"Just be sure we have enough wood and water. David will tell you if he wants anything else done here."

Alexander wanted to ask him why Miss Allen had to go to court, but he was afraid. That night when he went to bed, he thought about the next day. He wished he could go with Mr. Timberlake to Yorktown and visit with the Sclaters, but knew he couldn't. He was excited about working at the ordinary tomorrow and being with Elizabeth and the others. He didn't mind working for Mr. Cunningham, who always treated him well. He wondered what Dinah would be cooking tomorrow. Maybe she would make some more of that good bread. Early the next morning, Mr. Timberlake and Miss Allen left for Yorktown. Alexander stayed at the shop until Mr. and Mrs. Sanders arrived and then left for the ordinary. When he walked in, David Cunningham was sitting at a table with several men drinking tea. Motioning for the boy to come to him, he said, "See if Dinah needs anything and then go to the stable and help Cooper. When you finish there, both of you come back here to help us with dinner."

Opening the kitchen door, Alexander stuck his head inside. Dinah was busy with the cooking and Elizabeth was helping her. "Do you need anything?" asked the boy.
"Not now," said the cook, "we won't need no mo' wood before tonight."
"What you cooking for dinner?"
"Never you mind, boy," said the woman with a big grin, "it'll be good!"
Closing the door, Alexander turned and walked towards the stable.

One of Cooper's jobs was to take care of all the animals. The ordinary owned horses, cows, chickens, and pigs. Horses that belonged to travelers also stayed there. The law required every ordinary operator to be bonded and have a license each year. They had to prove they were able to provide a good wholesome diet and clean lodging for travelers, and proper stabling and food for their horses before they received a license. Cooper was a quiet man who accomplished his work with little supervision. In addition to caring for the animals, he was responsible for providing wood for the ordinary and kitchen. His sleeping quarters were at the barn, but he ate all his meals in the kitchen. He was busy at his tasks when Alexander reached the barn.

"Mr. Cunningham sent me to help you," said the boy. He wants both of us to come help them with dinner when we finish here. What do you want me to do?"

"Feed da horses first an den clean da stalls. I'll show you what to do." Cooper showed him how much feed to measure for each horse and where to put it. He then cleaned one stall to show him how. "Be careful 'round 'em horses," he said, "don't get behind 'em, you might get kicked."

"How much does it cost to keep a horse here one night and feed him," asked the boy.

"Seven and a half pence."

"How much does it cost to stay in the ordinary and eat a meal?"

"Da same thing."

Alexander began to laugh. "You mean it costs the same thing for a horse to sleep in the barn and eat hay as it does for a man to sleep in a bed and eat Dinah's cooking?"

"Sho does. Don't seem right do it?" he said, laughing. "You better quit talkin' and git to work or Mistuh Cunningham gonna be out here aftuh both of us."

When they finished the work, they started towards the ordinary. "Do you know why Miss Allen had to go to court?" asked the boy. "Mr. Timberlake had to go for cussing so much in public."

Cooper smiled, "He sho can do dat now. But it don't seem right to fine him for it." He continued walking without replying to the boy's question. Just before they reached the kitchen, he stopped. "See dem new porches on da back? Mr. Henry Cary built dem for Miss Allen and she ain't paid him yet. Dat's why she had to go. But you dent hear dat from me, you understand? I don't need no mo' trubble."

"I understand," said the boy.

Stopping at the kitchen, they checked with Dinah to see if

she needed help. She had everything prepared and cooking. Elizabeth had finished cleaning up from breakfast, so Dinah sent her along with them to the ordinary to get ready for dinner. The three of them joined David Cunningham inside and they soon had everything prepared for the customers who would be coming shortly for their meals.

The trials had not gone well for John Timberlake or Susanna Allen. On their return trip to Williamsburg, they discussed the day's events. He had been convicted and heavily fined for his charge. The jury had heard the evidence that Mr. Cary presented against Miss Allen and were told to deliver their verdict to the next court.

"Sometimes, I think about selling the ordinary," said Susanna, "but I don't know what else I would do. I like the work but I'm not a good businessperson. I haven't paid Mr. Cary because I can't collect the money people owe me. It takes so much time, buying what I need and trying to collect money. If I could get somebody else to do that and let me run the ordinary, it would be much better."

"Why don't you sell it to me? You continue to live there and operator it and I'll take care of the business part. I've always wanted to own an ordinary."

"I know why you want to own it, you'd drink all the liquor and eat all the food and when everything was gone, I still wouldn't have any money. I'd be in worse shape than before!"

Timberlake laughed at her and said, "You're not believing a word I say, now are you?"

"And should I?"

"Yes, I'm, serious."

"And what would you do with your shop? And how would you work it out with David?"

"Let me think about it some more. I'll talk to David about it, he's smart about things like that."

The months passed quickly. Miss Allen was back in court again in July and convicted of operating a disorderly house and keeping company with a married man. The talks between her, John Timberlake, and David Cunningham became more intense, as plans developed for Timberlake to purchase the ordinary. Alexander was becoming more comfortable in his role as an apprentice, but still had little desire to become a barber. Secretly, he still wished he could work for Mr. Cary and learn to be a builder. He decided to discuss it with Reverend Sclater the next time he saw him. That opportunity did not come until Christmas.

Alexander's second Christmas in Williamsburg was much different from the first. The overwhelming loneliness he felt the first year was gone; his new friends had made the difference. He wondered if the Sclaters would return this year and they did. Not only did the parents come, but also all three children. Unlike last year, the Carys had not traveled to Warwick because Sarah Cary was expecting her third child. The Sclaters had all come for an overnight visit. When they arrived at the shop to bring Alexander his gifts, Mary was the first one through the door and announced, "Sarah and Henry said you can come eat dinner with us!" He was beginning to feel like part of the family.

It had been a wonderful day. Alexander had never seen so much food in one place at the same time, even at the ordinary. After the meal, everyone sat in groups talking. Sarah and her mother were still in the dining room. The minister and Mr. Cary were in the parlor, and the boys were moving from room to room. Mary and Martha could not keep their hands off the two babies, much to the delight of the servants, who were enjoying a well-deserved break.

Alexander was hoping he would find the opportunity to talk to Reverend Sclater alone. He wanted to tell him about the planned changes at the ordinary. He also wanted to ask him about the possibility of changing his apprenticeship and becoming a builder. He would love to work for Mr. Cary. The opportunity came when he saw Mr. Cary get up and go into the dining room. He heard him tell Sarah, "I have to go out for about an hour. I'll be back before dark." As soon as the man left, Alexander walked into the parlor where the pastor was sitting. James went into the dining room and sat down with his mother and sister.

Before the boy could speak, the minister said, "I'm glad we have a chance to talk. I have some more news for you."

"Have you heard from my Grandparents?"

"No. When I do I'll come straight and tell you. I have some other news for you."

Puzzled, the boy said, "What is it?"

"The fleet came in a few weeks ago," said the minister. "They always bring news to the colony as well as passengers and supplies. They brought news that the *Bristol Merchant*, the ship you came over on, never arrived in Bristol when it left Yorktown last year." Alexander sat looking at the minister. "Do you think they could have gone someplace else?"

"No. I think they sunk. They were overloaded with tobacco when they left Yorktown. Greed is a very deadly thing. Thank God, there were no passengers on board. Only tobacco and the crew."

Death of an Owner

Alexander sat quietly at the table knotting hair ends onto some strands of silk. They would be used later to make a wig. His small fingers were well suited for the task. As he worked, he listened to the conversation between John Timberlake and David Cunningham. After months of discussion, Timberlake was going to buy the ordinary from Susanna Allen. She would continue to live there and operate it, but he would be responsible for all the accounts. Nothing had been said about what effect this might have on the boy's indenture.

That evening, as they sat down to eat, Alexander asked, "What's going to happen to me when you buy the ordinary?" Timberlake looked surprised. "What do you mean?"
"How are you going to teach me to be a barber when you're not here?"
"I will still be able to spend most of the day here, I'll do the ordinary work at night. You will still be my apprentice. Nothing will change."
"Will you still live here?"
"Oh yes," said Timberlake laughing. "I'll still be home every night. The big difference is that I'll be working at night instead of playing cards and drinking."

The boy took little comfort in the assurance offered to him. Things were already changing. Mrs. Sanders was no longer able to work because of bad health and her husband was only there occasionally. David Cunningham had indentured two white servants, James Mennes and James Spence, to become barbers. They were both grown men that had recently come to the colony to live. Neither of the men lived at the shop and Alexander was glad because he did not like them. They showed him no respect because of his age and when the barbers were not there, they treated him like he was their servant.

The transaction for the ordinary was completed and John Timberlake became the owner in March. Contrary to what he had told the boy, he was at the ordinary many hours each day and generally until late at night. This required David Cunningham to spend more time in the shop than he normally did, but the change did not seem to create any contention between the two men. Alexander liked the new arrangement. He was also spending more time at the ordinary and running errands for both Timberlake, and Miss Allen.

One thing had not changed under the new arrangement. Alexander was usually asleep when Timberlake came home at night, just like before. The nights were particularly cold for October. Alexander stayed a long time by the fire one evening before he banked it and went to bed. He had been sleeping soundly when a voice awakened him. He sat up and looked around. A light was burning in the other room.
"Alexander!" called Timberlake from his bedroom.
"Yes sir?"
"Come here."
Alexander jumped up and ran to the other room. The man was doubled over in the bed, writhing in pain.
"Go get David, I'm sick."
"Where is he?"
"At the ordinary," said the man, in an anguished voice.

Slipping on his shoes and grabbing his coat, he ran to the ordinary. Stopping at the door, he realized he didn't know where to find Cunningham without disturbing everyone there. Running to the kitchen, he banged on the door, "Dinah, open the door, it's Alexander!"
He could hear movement inside and in just a moment the door opened and Dinah and Elizabeth were looking out at him.

"Do you know where to find Mr. Cunningham?" said the boy frantically. "Mr. Timberlake is real sick and needs him."

"I do," said Elizabeth, grabbing a shawl as she came out the door.

Alexander followed her as she slipped into the back door. Knocking gently on one of the doors, she called out, "Miss Allen?"

A voice from behind the door said, "Who is it?"

"Elizabeth," responded the girl. "Mr. Timberlake is sick and needs Mr. Cunningham." The door flew open and David Cunningham peered out. Looking at Alexander, he said, "What's wrong?"

"He's real sick and told me to come get you."

"Go back over there, I'll be there in a few minutes."

Elizabeth followed the boy as he ran back to the barbershop and up the steps.

"Go get me the pan," said Timberlake, as he held one hand over his mouth and the other across his stomach. Alexander ran downstairs, grabbed the blood pan, and bounded back up the steps, just in time. He was trying to steady the wobbly man when Cunningham walked in and took charge.

"Run down stairs and bring me some cold water and a rag."

When the boy returned, they began to wipe the man's brow with the cool rag.

"That's not going to help," said Timberlake, "I have this awful pain right here," pointing to his lower, stomach.

"Alexander, go tell Cooper to get the carriage ready and bring it here," said Cunningham, "I need to go get the doctor. Elizabeth, you stay here with me."

Rushing down the steps, he almost ran into Miss Allen coming in the door.

"They're upstairs," said the boy as he stepped back to let her enter.

Running to the stable, he beat on the door and called, "Cooper! Wake up, it's Alexander!" The words were hardly out of his mouth and Cooper was standing in the open door.

"Mr. Timberlake is sick. Mr. Cunningham wants you to bring the carriage to the barber shop so he can go for the doctor." Cooper disappeared into the darkness of the stable and Alexander turned and ran back across the yard. Every dog in town seemed to be barking at the commotion.

Racing back to the shop, Alexander found the situation unchanged. "Cooper will be here in a few minutes," he said. "Go watch for him and call me as soon as he gets here," said Cunningham. "He needs to get back to the stable. The three of you can stay with John until I get back."
Alexander called as soon as he saw Cooper come around the corner. Running down the steps, Cunningham said, "Get the fire going, it's cold in here. Put on a kettle of water, the Doctor may need some. When you finish, go back up and see if you can help Miss Allen until I get back." Pulling the door closed behind him, he disappeared into the darkness.

When he heard the carriage returning, Alexander opened the door for the two men.
"If Cooper comes back," said Cunningham, "tell him to leave the carriage here until you come get him."
As soon as the two men went up the steps, Elizabeth came down. "Do you think he's going to die?" she whispered.
"I don't think so, he hasn't been sick very long. The Doctor will probably give him some medicine to make him feel better." He was trying to appear brave, but inside, he was scared. What would happen to him if Timberlake died?

It was beginning to get light outside when Susanna Allen came down the steps. "Let's make some tea," she said to Alexander. As the boy began to gather things together, she said, "I'll do it if you show me where everything is."
"Is Mr. Timberlake feeling any better?" asked Elizabeth in a low voice.
The woman shook her head and said, "No."
"What's wrong with him?" asked the boy.
"I don't know," said Miss Allen.

92

"What did the Doctor say?" asked Elizabeth. "He didn't say anything. He just gave him some medicine to see if it would help him. It didn't."

When Miss Allen went back up the steps with a cup of tea for the Doctor, Cunningham came down. "Alexander," he said, "untie the horse and lead him back to the stable. Tell Cooper to unhitch him and put him back in the stall. The Doctor's going to stay for a while."
Walking the horse around the block took a long time. Alexander wished he could drive the carriage and hoped he could get Cooper to teach him. Cooper seemed very grave as the boy described to him Timberlake's condition. Shaking his head from side to side, he said, "Dat don't sound good. Dat's mighty bad." As the boy walked back to the shop, he pondered those words. He began to seriously think about the possibility that John Timberlake may not get well.

Crossing the street, he met Miss Allen and Elizabeth. "We have the morning work to do at the ordinary," said Miss Allen. "If David doesn't need you later, we could use some help."
"I'll ask him," said the boy. "Be sure you get your work done at the barbershop first," she said as she continued walking. Nobody was downstairs when he went in the shop. He walked gently up the stairs and stood near the bed. Timberlake lay on his right side with his legs drawn up under him. He gave an occasional low moan, followed by a short gasp. A damp rag covered his forehead and eyes. Cuts on both arms showed that he had been bled at least twice. Cunningham reached down and picked up the pan of blood from the floor and without saying a word, handed it to the boy. Alexander took it and silently disappeared down the steps.

News about the popular barber's illness spread quickly around town. People began stopping by the shop and asking in hushed voices about his condition. At first, Alexander

93

would go up and get Mr. Cunningham to talk with them, but after several trips he told the boy, "You talk to them. If they don't ask for me, don't come get me."

When Mennes and Spence came to work, Cunningham came down and talked to them. "Go home and get some rest. One of you plan to come back about three o'clock and the other about midnight. We'll need you here tonight if he's not better."

The Doctor left about mid-morning. He insisted he would walk home and said that he would be back later in the day. If they needed him before he returned, Alexander was to come get him. The boy ran quickly across the street to tell Miss Allen he could not help them and then returned to the shop. When nobody was there, he would stand at the top of the steps watching. When he heard someone enter, he would slip down the stairs and talk to them. When James Mennes returned that afternoon, the boy was exhausted. He went into his room and lay down on the mattress. Soon he was fast asleep.

When Alexander awoke, it was dark outside. Sitting up and rubbing his eyes, he tried to remember why he was sleeping on top of the bed in his clothes. Then he remembered. Getting up, he walked softly to the other room. The Doctor had returned and was sitting beside the bed watching his patient. David Cunningham sat in another chair nodding. John Timberlake continued to move himself around in bed as if trying to get comfortable. With each movement, he would groan. Without a sound, Alexander moved into the room. Stopping between the two men, he stood watching Timberlake.

Suddenly, the man opened his eyes and saw the boy standing there. "Now you show up," he said. "I was looking for you when they drew blood. We were going to let you do it. I wanted to be your first customer."

The boy smiled. He was glad to hear the man teasing him

94

again. "Can I do anything for you?"

"I reckon you can. When you see that Reverend friend of yours, ask him to put in a good word for me. I need all the help I can get," he said, smiling. The smile disappeared as he moved slightly and groaned with pain. Closing his eyes again, he said, "You're a good lad. You'll be all right."

Alexander stood for a long time between the two men, staring at John Timberlake. He appeared to be sleeping. Even when he wasn't moving, he was still moaning. The boy looked first at the doctor and then at Cunningham, and neither of them said anything. He turned and left the room. When he got to the bottom of the stairs, he saw that Mennes was still there. He took his coat from the peg, put it on, and went out into the night.

Turning toward the Capitol, he began walking briskly down the street. He had no particular place to go, he just needed to walk and think. He kept wondering what would happen to him if John Timberlake died. Each time he thought about it, he felt guilty for being more concerned about himself than he was for Mr. Timberlake. It must be a sin to think about himself at a time like this, but he couldn't stop it. He had thought that Timberlake might get well until he talked to him a little while ago. He was acting like he was joking about the Reverend, but it was almost as if he knew he was going to die. Alexander wished he could talk to Reverend Sclater.

All of a sudden, he realized he was in front of Henry Cary's house. He had walked there, almost as if drawn by some unknown force. Maybe Reverend Sclater was there, thought the boy. Standing outside, he could see Sarah Cary through the window. She was very large with child. Mr. Cary was home, but there were no other carriages at the house. Reverend Sclater wasn't there. Disappointed, he turned back toward the shop. When he came to the coffeehouse, he stopped again. Standing out of sight in the shadows, he watched the men inside drinking and gambling. When the Council was in session, it was always crowded with the

Burgesses, the Governor, and his friends. Between sessions, as it was now, the local men would often spend their evenings there. It was one of John Timberlake's favorite places.

He was almost back to the shop when he decided to go to the ordinary. Walking to the kitchen, he rapped on the door and called, "Dinah?"
Jerking the door open, the cook said, "Lawd, don't tell me something else's wrong!" Alexander couldn't help but laugh, as he said, "No, I just came by to see you and Elizabeth. Is she sleeping?"
"No, but she'd prob'ly like to be. Nobody got no sleep last night. She's inside helping Miz Allen."
Alexander went in and sat on the stool at the table. "You hongry?" asked the cook.
"No," said the boy.
"What'd you eat today?"
"Nothing."
Walking over to the table, she sat a large piece of gingerbread and some butter down and said, "Dat's all I got."

When Elizabeth came in, her dress was wet and dirty from washing dishes. "How's Mr. Timberlake?" she asked.
"The same," said the boy. "At least he was when I left."
"Where've you been?"
"Just walking."
"We could have used some help today."
"I couldn't come over," said the boy defensively. "I had to stay there so I could go get the doctor if we needed him. Mennes and Spence were both gone."
"I saw the doctor come back," said Elizabeth.
"Yeah. They're all over there now," said Alexander, and he began to tell them about the conversation he had with Mr. Timberlake and how sick he was. Dinah's eyes grew wide as she listened to the story.
"Oh my, my. Dat man ain't long for dis world."

"Why do you say that?"

"Just you wait an see."

"I have to go," said the boy. "Thank you for the gingerbread, it was good."

James Spence was sitting beside the fire when Alexander walked in. He turned to look, but didn't say anything as the boy hung his coat on the peg and went up the steps. The doctor was gone and David Cunningham was sitting where the doctor had been. Alexander seated himself in the other chair, but didn't speak. He did not want to disturb John Timberlake.

"Have you been to the ordinary?" asked Cunningham.

"I went to the kitchen."

"Did you eat anything?"

"A little, have you?"

The man shook his head from side to side.

"Want me to go get you something?"

"Not now." Timberlake made no response as they talked.

"I would like a cup of tea, but I'll go fix it. I need to move around a little. You sit here until I get back."

Alexander nodded, as the man stood up, stretched, and walked down the steps.

The boy slid his chair a little closer to the bed. Even in the dim light, he could see beads of sweat on the Timberlake's face. He wanted to touch his face to see if it was hot, but was afraid to bother him. The rag and the pan of water were still sitting by the bed. The cool rag might feel good on his feverish brow, but again, he was afraid to use it. He would wait until Mr. Cunningham came back and ask him. Sitting there alone, he thought about his mother. He remembered how sick she was and how he had mopped her brow with the cool rainwater. He also remembered how helpless he felt. Tears ran down his face. He knew that when his mother got this sick, she died.

When David Cunningham came back upstairs, Susanna

Allen was with him. He motioned for Alexander to come with him. When he stood up to leave, Miss Allen sat down in his chair. Following the barber back down the steps, he wondered what the man wanted. "She's going to sit with John for a few hours," said Cunningham, "so I can sleep a little."

"Sleep in my bed, I can stay awake until you get up."

"James will be here all night if we need him. One of you will have to go get the doctor if things get worse during the night. Miss Allen will wake me if she needs to."

Alexander backed up to the fire and stood warming himself.

"Things look pretty bad up there, don't they?" asked James Spence.

"He's real sick."

"Do you think he'll live 'til morning?"

"I think he might still get well."

"That's not what Cunningham said," the man scoffed.

Alexander glared at the man for a moment and then went back upstairs. He sat down in the empty chair without speaking to Miss Allen and gazed at the man lying in bed. Susanna Allen was having a difficult time staying awake. Alexander amused himself by watching her. Her eyelids would become heavy and her jaw would drop down. Just when he thought she was going to sleep, she would jerk her head up. When she saw him watching her, she would smile and shake her head. She reminded him of the man that went to sleep in church. He had no way of knowing how long Mr. Cunningham had been asleep, but it seemed like more than two hours. He wondered if Miss Allen would wake him up. He had dozed off himself when someone shook him and said, "You can have your bed back, I'm through with it."

He looked up to see David Cunningham smiling at him. Staggering off to the next room, the boy collapsed on the bed and went back to sleep.

Early the next morning when he awoke, he jumped up and went into the next room. David Cunningham was sitting on the side of the bed, bathing his friend's head with the cool rag.

"Is he any better?" asked the boy. The man looked at him and shook his head.

"Worse," he said in a low voice.

"Need anything?"

"James is making tea. Bring me a cup if it's ready."

The boy was only gone a few minutes. When he returned, Doctor Cocke followed him up the stairs. Handing the cup to Cunningham, he stepped back out of the way. As the doctor began to examine Timberlake, Alexander turned and went back down the steps. Susanna Allen was coming in the door, followed by James Mennes.

"The doctor is checking him now," said Alexander, looking at Miss Allen.

"How is he this morning?" asked the woman as she walked over to the table and poured herself a cup of tea.

"Mr. Cunningham says he's worse"

Just like the day before, people began to come and go, checking on John Timberlake. About ten o'clock, both men came down the steps and the doctor left. Cunningham sat down heavily on the steps, staring at the closed door. He was silent for a minute, and then looking at the others, he said, "He's gone."

Chapter 11

The Long Walk to Yorktown

Alexander and Elizabeth sat in the balcony looking at the crowd below. The church was packed with people attending John Timberlake's funeral. Commissary Blair was reading the familiar funeral service from the little black book. Finally, it ended and everyone stood. The minister walked slowly toward the door followed by six men carrying the coffin. As the congregation began to file out of the church, Alexander and Elizabeth moved towards the steps. They were among the last to reach the grave. The crowd had surrounded the gravesite until they could not see the minister. A fine rain was falling. It was hardly more than a mist, but it was enough to worsen an already dismal day.

When the benediction was pronounced, the mourners dispersed because of the weather. The two children stood apart from the crowd waiting for everyone to leave. Only a few people remained talking. Two who did remain were David Cunningham and Henry Cary. When Mr. Cary turned to leave he saw the children and walked towards them. Placing his hand on the boy's shoulder he said, "I was sorry to hear about John. I hope things will work out well for you."
"Thank you sir. Do you think Reverend Sclater knows about Mr. Timberlake?"
"I don't know," said Cary as he turned to leave, "but I'll make sure he finds out."

The barbershop was cold. Alexander scraped the ashes from the logs and they burst into flames. He added two more pieces of wood to the fire and went upstairs to change clothes. The empty building made him feel sad. He had been alone there many times before, but today it was different. He paused for a moment and looked at John

100

Timberlake's empty bed, then turned and went into his room. As he changed clothes he wondered what would happen to him. Nobody had said anything about his indenture. He wished he could talk to Reverend Sclater. As soon as he had the opportunity, he was going to ask Mr. Cunningham. Maybe he could just continue to live there and work for him.

About mid-afternoon David Cunningham walked into the shop. Before Alexander could ask him anything he said, "James Mennes and James Spence are going to be moving into the shop to live. They'll be bringing their things over in a little while."

"What am I going to do?"

"You'll be staying here too, at least until the court settles John's estate. They'll decide what you'll be doing then. Until they meet, you can't live alone."

"Where are they going to sleep?"

"One of them can sleep in John's bed. The three of you can work out the other details. Maybe tomorrow we can find some answers for you."

Alexander watched Cunningham cross the street and enter the ordinary. He was barely out of sight when Mennes and Spence came into view carrying their belongings. They were laughing and talking as they walked toward the shop. Alexander turned and walked away so he wouldn't have to open the door for them. The two men entered the shop and continued up the steps, never acknowledging the boy's presence. He could hear their jovial conversation as they moved things around upstairs. In a few minutes they came down and Mennes said, "We need to find somewhere down here for you to sleep."

"My bed is upstairs."

"That's going to be my room," said Spence, "so we'll just leave that bed up there. You need to bring your things down here so I'll have room for mine."

Alexander brought his meager belongings downstairs and

placed them against the wall in the back room. He left the shop and walked over to the stable behind the ordinary.

"Cooper, do you have any place here that I could keep my clothes?"

"Why you ask?"

Alexander told him what had happened and said, "There's no place in the shop to keep them. Dinah and Elizabeth don't have much room. I know you'd watch them here."

"Go get 'em. Ain't nobody gonna bother 'em here."

When he returned with the clothes, he sat down and shared his frustrations with Cooper. He didn't want to go back to the barbershop until he had to. Stopping by the kitchen, he went in and sat down at the table. Dinah gave him a bowl of stew and a large hunk of bread. When she wasn't looking, he put the bread in his coat pocket. He would need it later. After eating his stew he talked for a few minutes and left. Dinah looked at Elizabeth and said, "Uh, uh! Somthin' wrong wit' dat boy. He mus' be mighty upset 'bout Mistuh Timbulake."

Mennes and Spence were downstairs talking when he arrived back at the shop. "Since you're going to be down here tonight," said Mennes, "let the fire burn a little longer so it'll stay warm upstairs."

"Yeah," laughed Spence, "and get it going early in the morning. I hate getting up in a cold house."

Alexander went in the other room and lay down on the wooden bench. After they went upstairs he quietly searched for some food. Finding some old bread, he ate it. Going back to the bench he lay down and listened to the two men talking until they went to sleep. When he heard them snoring he got up and went to the fireplace. He took the long iron poker and separated all the logs so the fire would go out. Taking the poker with him he slipped out the door and started walking towards Yorktown.

Even though he was walking as quietly as he could, it

seemed every dog in town heard him and barked. He never slowed his pace. Keeping a firm grip on the poker he stayed alert. He kept expecting one of the dogs to charge him, but none did. As soon as he was out of town things became quiet. The sky was clear and the moon gave enough light for him to see. He walked at a steady pace. He came to a long, straight section of the road and in the distance he could see a dim light. He kept wondering what it was as he walked towards it. The light seemed to be moving towards him. He stopped walking until he could determine what it was. When he heard the horse's hooves he knew it was a carriage.

Some large trees in the nearby woods would provide a place to hide, but a swampy area separated him from them. Quickly retracing his steps he found a dry strip of land and ran into the woods. Standing behind one of the biggest trees he watched the approaching carriage. When it got closer he could see two large dogs trotting along beside it. When they came to the place where he had stopped they began to growl and bark. Tracking him back up the road they were headed straight to his hiding place. He gripped the poker with both hands wondering how he could fight both of them at once. Just as the dogs started into the woods a man called out from the carriage, "Here! Come back here!" Both dogs ran back to the carriage and resumed their positions running alongside. Alexander's entire body was trembling. He sat down on the cold ground and leaned against the tree until he calmed down. When he could no longer hear the carriage he got up and continued walking towards Yorktown.

It was the middle of the night when he stopped at a road that he thought was the one that went to his father's house. If no one was living there, that's where he was going to stay. He hoped the furniture would still be in the house. He would have to wait until daylight to be sure this was the place. A grove of large pine trees stood nearby. He walked into the middle of them and scraped up a deep pile of pine needles. Taking the piece of bread from his pocket he sat down and ate it. He rooted out a comfortable spot with his body and then covered himself with the rest of the needles. In a little while he was asleep.

It was daylight when Alexander awoke. He was cold. In the distance he could hear a man's voice. Getting to his feet, he brushed himself off and quietly walked toward the voice. When he approached the clearing he knew this was the right place. His father's house and the outbuildings were exactly as he remembered them. He couldn't see the grave because it was on the other side of the house. A man was walking from the barn towards the house talking to a little boy who walked along beside him. Somebody was living there.

Retracing his steps to the road, he resumed his walk towards Yorktown unsure what he was going to do. Soon the York River came into view. The abundance of waterfowl like he had seen two years earlier was still there and so were the strange looking birds. As he continued his brisk walk downriver he began to get warm again. He wondered how long it would take him to walk to the Sclaters. He knew he could get something to eat there and maybe spend the night. He didn't want to spend another night sleeping on the cold ground.

He heard a noise behind him. Looking back over his shoulder he saw a carriage approaching. He had no place to hide and he was sure they had seen him by now. Remembering the two dogs running beside the carriage last night he turned again to see if any were with this one. There were none. He kept walking at a steady pace until the carriage was very close and then he stepped off the road so it could pass. When it pulled alongside it stopped. There was nobody in it except the driver, a middle-aged man with a rifle lying across his lap.
"You need a ride boy?"
"Yes sir."
"What 'cha doing out here on the road so early?"

"Going to visit some friends below Yorktown."

"Where you coming from?"

"Williamsburg."

"How long you been walking?"

"Since last night."

"You running away?"

"No sir."

"I don't wanta get in no trouble helping a runaway. Who you going to visit?"

"Reverend Sclater and his family at the Charles Parish glebe."

"What's his wife's name?"

"Her name is Mary. She also has a daughter named Mary. Another daughter is named Martha and their son is James."

"Get in."

Alexander climbed into the carriage, thankful for the ride. Continuing the questioning the man asked, "What 'cha doing with that poker?"

"Brought it for protection. Didn't want any dogs biting me."

"Wanna sell it?"

"No sir, it doesn't belong to me. I have to take it back."

"How you know the Sclaters?"

"Reverend Sclater helped me find a home after my parents died."

"He's a good old man," said the driver. "He's tough. Some of those vestrymen down there tried to run him off but he wouldn't go. He fought them all the way to the Governor, and he ruled in his favor. They finally left him alone."

"Why'd they try to run him off?"

"Same as always. They wanted to run the church. He wouldn't let 'em."

"Want a apple?" said the man, holding one out to the boy. "I have two."

"Thank you," said Alexander. He took the apple and began eating it.

They rode in silence as Alexander ate the apple.

Occasionally, the man would glance at him and smile. When there was nothing left but the seeds and the stem, the boy tossed them out.

"You ate that thing like you was hungry."

"I was."

"You sure you ain't running away?"

"I'm sure."

"How you gonna get back home?"

"Reverend Sclater will take me. We have some things to talk about."

"Yorktown is as far as I'm going. I'll have to drop you off right down the road a bit. You'll still have a long ways to walk."

"Yes sir, I know. I've been there before with Reverend Sclater."

"Maybe somebody else will give you a ride."

When they came to the Yorktown road the man stopped.

"You didn't tell me your name."

"Alexander Stinson."

"My name's William Anderson. You tell Reverend Sclater I gave you a ride."

"I will. Thank you for the ride, Mr. Anderson"

"Here. Take this other apple with you, I probably won't eat it."

Alexander waved as the carriage pulled away and began eating the apple as he resumed walking. Several other carriages passed, but none offered him a ride. He didn't remember it being so far to the Glebe Road and was becoming anxious about finding it when he recognized the turn in the distance. He quickened his pace knowing that it wasn't much further. He was almost running when he turned into the long drive leading to the house. The two girls were in the yard. They watched him approaching and when they recognized him Mary ran to meet him and Martha ran towards the house calling, "Mama! Papa! It's Alexander!"

James came running from the front door closely followed by

Reverend and Mrs. Sclater. "Where on earth did you come from?" asked the woman.

"Williamsburg."

"How did you get here?" asked James.

"Walked."

Everyone was smiling except the minister. "Have you run away?" he asked sternly.

"No sir. I had to talk with you and I had no other way to get here. Mr. Timberlake is dead and I don't know what's going to happen to me. I need you to help me again."

"Let's go inside and talk," said Mrs. Sclater, "it's too cold to stand out here."

Once inside, all four of the children began talking at once. After a few minutes, Reverend Sclater quieted them. "Alexander must be very tired and hungry. You can talk to him while your mother prepares him something to eat. After that, I need to talk to him."

After he had eaten Alexander went into the other room to talk with Reverend Sclater. The minister was seated in the large chair near the fire just the way he had been two years before when he told the boy about his father's death.

"This room doesn't hold any pleasant memories for you, does it son?"

"No sir."

"I'm sorry. I came here because it's warm. Would you rather go somewhere else?"

"No sir. I like this room but it just makes me think about my Daddy."

"Tell me what happened to Mr. Timberlake."

"He got real sick one night and sent me to get Mr. Cunningham. He sent for the doctor and they stayed with him and tried to help him, but he died two days later. He was buried yesterday. When Mr. Timberlake was real sick he said for me to tell you to put in a good word for him because he needed all the help he could get."

"That sounds like John."

"I liked him. He was good to me. I like Mr. Cunningham

too, but he's let his two men come to live in the shop and they took my bed. I don't have anywhere to sleep. He doesn't seem to care what they do. He said the court would decide later what happens to me. That's why I left and came to see you."

"I'm sure Mr. Cunningham is upset over his friend's death. I'll talk to him for you."

As Rev. Sclater continued talking, James appeared in the door. "Papa, Sheriff Tyler is here and wants to see you." Alexander followed the minister from the room and watched as he shook hands with the man standing at the door. After talking to him for a minute he turned and led the man back towards the front room. "James, go ask your mother to get the Sheriff a cup of tea." Looking at Alexander he said, "Let's go back in and sit down. The Sheriff wants to talk to us." After they were all seated the minister spoke again. "Sheriff Tyler came here looking for you. He says you are a runaway. I assured him that was not the situation."

"Reverend, the boy is an indentured servant. He ran away yesterday and Miss Allen notified me. She thought he would come here and it appears she was right."

"I'm afraid I don't understand what Miss Allen has to do with the boy."

"Mr. Timberlake was in business with her so it seems she has to look after his affairs until they can be settled."

"I thought he and Mr. Cunningham were partners."

"They were partners in the barbershop. But Mr. Timberlake was also buying the ordinary."

"The boy was living and working in the barbershop. Wouldn't Mr. Cunningham be responsible for him until the court makes a decision?"

"I talked to both of them. They asked me to come look for him and bring him back."

"We have another problem that I must ask you to check on."

"What's that?"

"You know the laws concerning the care of servants. Mr.

Cunningham allowed two of his men to come live in the barbershop and take this lad's bed from him. He has no place to sleep. That's why he came here to get me to help him."

The Sheriff shifted uncomfortably in his seat. "Is that true son?"

"Yes sir. He has two servants, James Mennes and James Spence. They moved in yesterday after the funeral. One took Mr. Timberlake's bed, and the other one took mine. They told me to go downstairs and sleep but there's no bed down there. They also told me to keep the fire burning late so they could stay warm."

"I still have to take you back to Williamsburg. The court will have to settle this."

"Let me make a suggestion," said the minister. "Since the boy doesn't have a bed in Williamsburg, why not let him spend the night here? I'll be going to Williamsburg tomorrow and I can take him back. That will give you time to inform Miss Allen and Mr. Cunningham that they have broken the law and give them an opportunity to find a place for the boy to live before we get back tomorrow. I don't think the court will be too pleased over the way they have treated this boy."

"Pastor, you present a very persuasive argument," said the Sheriff. He smiled as Mrs. Sclater appeared with some tea.

Reverend Sclater did not appear in any hurry to leave home the next day. Alexander was happy that he had extra time to spend with the children. The drive to Williamsburg was pleasant even though the sky was overcast with an occasional drizzle. It was mid-afternoon when they arrived and went into the ordinary. David Cunningham and Susanna Allen were seated at a table near the fireplace. They both spoke politely to the minister, but only glanced at the boy. Cunningham arose and moved another chair to the table, "Have a seat Reverend," he said to the minister.

Turning towards the back room Miss Allen called, "Elizabeth?" The young girl appeared almost instantly, but stopped abruptly when she saw Alexander.

"Bring some tea for Reverend Sclater."

The girl disappeared into the back room.

Turning her attention to the boy, who was standing uncomfortably beside the table, she spoke to him for the first time. "Where are your things? I understand you moved them from the barber shop."

"Yes ma'am, I did. I didn't have anywhere to put them except on the floor so I put them in the barn."

"Why did you run away?" asked David Cunningham.

"I didn't run away. If I was going to run away I would have carried my things with me."

"The Sheriff said you told him you had no place to sleep. Why didn't you talk to me about it instead of leaving."

"I tried to. When you told me about the others coming to live there, you said the three of us could work it out. They took my bed and sent me downstairs to sleep. There's no bed down there."

Elizabeth appeared with the tea. She sat it on the table and disappeared again. The minister, who had been listening to the exchange of words, finally spoke as Miss Allen was pouring him a cup of tea. "I think we will all agree that this problem could have been resolved differently. Fortunately, no serious harm came to the boy. I hope the court will be understanding about what has happened and give everyone another chance. What we need to agree on today is who will care for Alexander until the court decides."

"Since both of us were business partners with John, we feel obligated to work together to see that he is properly cared for," said Cunningham. "Because there's no room for him at the barbershop Miss Allen has agreed to provide a place for him to sleep here and see that he's fed. We will be sure that all of his lawful needs are met until the court meets. He can still work for me in the shop and also help at the ordinary if he's needed. That was agreeable with Sheriff Tyler. Is it

110

agreeable with you?"

"It certainly sounds fair," said the minister. "I think the court will be satisfied if you make those provisions. Where will he be sleeping?"

"There's a bed in the basement that we don't rent unless we are very crowded," said Miss Allen. "It will serve well for him. You're welcome to see it before you leave."

The minister nodded as he sipped the hot tea.

Turning to Alexander, she said, "Go get your things and take them to the basement."

Hurrying toward the back door, he found Elizabeth standing there waiting for him. She opened the door and stepped outside as the boy followed her. Closing the door, she turned to face him. Tears were streaming down her face. "Why did you leave me?" she sobbed.

Alexander was speechless. He had been so consumed with his own troubles he had not thought about her. He felt awful. "I...was...coming back," he stammered.

"Why didn't you tell me? I didn't know if you were coming back. You're the only friend I have and you left me!"

Tears were now running down his cheeks too and he could hardly speak. He reached out and took her hand. "I'm sorry," he said, barely above a whisper. "I promise I'll never leave you again." He turned and walked towards the barn. His eyes were so blurred by tears that he didn't see Dinah standing in the kitchen door until she spoke. "I sho am glad to see you back home. You come by aftah while an git you somthin' to eat."

Alexander smiled at her through the tears and said, "Thank you Dinah, I will."

When the boy reached the barn, Cooper as usual, seemed to appear out of nowhere. "I heard you were comin back today. You in much truble?"

"I don't think so. Don't guess I'll know 'til I go to court. Hope I didn't get you in trouble for helping me."

He smiled reassuringly. "Don't see how I can be in no

truble. You jest ask me to keep yo stuff. You didn't have nowhere else to keep it. You never tole me you were going 'way."

"Miss Allen sent me to get my stuff. I'll be sleeping in the basement for now."

"That ain't no bad place. It's warm down there but ain't much light."

"You can come visit me there. Maybe we can sneak over to the kitchen for food!"

"Miz Allen ain't gonna let us do much vistin' or eatin' if she can help it," laughed Cooper.

"Maybe she can't help it," said Alexander, as he gathered up his clothes and started back to the ordinary.

When Alexander walked in, Elizabeth pointed down the stairs and said, "They're down there."

Walking cautiously down the stairs, he found the three adults talking and looking at the room. He had never been in the basement before and didn't know what was there. He only knew it was used to store supplies for the ordinary. At the bottom of the steps was a fireplace. Nearby were a table, chair, and bed. On the table was a lamp. At the other end of the room numerous kegs and barrels were stored. The room had a strange smell. Reverend Sclater walked over to the bed, picked up the mattress, looked at it, placed it back on the bed and sat down on it. "I see no reason why this wouldn't be fine," he said, giving a sweeping glance to the group.

"Good," said Miss Allen, as she turned to go back upstairs. She stopped at the bottom of the steps. Looking back at Alexander she said, "You must be very careful with the lamp and the fireplace or you'll burn the place down." Never waiting for a reply she led the group back up the steps leaving the boy alone. He placed his clothes on the bed and stood for a moment studying the room. He liked it. He blew out the lamp and followed the group upstairs.

David Cunningham was waiting for him at the top of the

stairs. "We need lots of firewood here and at the barbershop. You need to get it in before dark. When you finish, see if Miss Allen has anything else that she wants you to do."

"Yes sir," said the boy. He thanked Reverend Sclater for bringing him home, told him goodbye, and went to do his work.

Christmas With The Carys

Alexander adjusted quickly to his new quarters. David Cunningham rarely asked him to do any work in the barbershop except for keeping enough wood and water inside. His two servants, Mennes and Spence, seemed anxious to learn the trade and stayed close to the shop. Susanna Allen was in court October, November and December, trying to settle the business agreement she had with John Timberlake. The court appointed her Executrix for his estate and awarded her custody of his two servants Alexander and Anne Granger, who also worked at the ordinary. Although he would not be learning a trade, Alexander was happy he would not have to be a barber.

Reverend Sclater and his family visited in Williamsburg for a week in early November to celebrate the birth of Henry and Sarah Cary's third child, a boy they named Henry. They came again in December for their Christmas visit. James, Mary, and Martha walked to the ordinary several times each day hoping they would see Alexander and Elizabeth and have time to visit with them. One afternoon as the five children stood in the back yard talking Susanna Allen opened the door. "Alexander and Elizabeth, come here." The two children hurried toward the door. When the three Sclater children turned to leave she called to them, "You three stay where you are."
As she closed the door James looked at his sisters and said, "Now we've gotten them in trouble and she's going to try to get us in trouble for keeping them from their work."

They stood there for several minutes before the door opened again. "You can go home now," said Miss Allen, "your father will be talking with you."

"I told you so," said James as they started toward the street.

"I don't believe Papa will be mad at us for visiting Alexander and Elizabeth," said Mary.

"He will if she tells him we were keeping them from their work," said Martha.

"Merry Christmas!" said a chorus of voices as they stepped from behind the building.

Turning towards the voices, the astonished children saw their parents standing with Alexander and Elizabeth in front of the ordinary door. All of them were laughing.

"We're going home with you," cried Elizabeth, jumping up and down as she spoke. "Your sister and Mr. Cary invited us to supper and Miss Allen said we could go."

As the three Sclater children stared unbelievingly at the group, their father spoke. "I think it would be a fine gesture if all of you would go thank Miss Allen." The excited children rushed towards the ordinary and all tried to get into the door at the same time. James Sclater smiled at his wife and said, "I hope they don't frighten away all the customers."

Snow was falling by the time they arrived at the Cary house. One of the servants met them at the door to take their coats and the three girls hurried off to see the new baby. Three-year old Mary, much to the amusement of her grandparents, ran along behind the older girls trying to keep up with them. Reverend Sclater walked towards the front room where his son-in-law was sitting near the fire as Mrs. Sclater went to check on the progress of the meal. Alexander stood alone in the hall not knowing where to go and wondering where James had disappeared. He walked to the end of the hall and stared at the large table in the dining room that was heavily laden with food. Reverend Sclater called to him from the other room, "Alexander, come join us by the fire."

The two men were seated near the large fireplace. Henry Cary greeted the boy as he entered the room and asked, "How do you like living at the ordinary?"

"Fine. I sleep in the basement. It's warm, but sometimes at night it gets noisy."

"What kind of work are you doing?"

"Mostly I just work around the ordinary and run errands. Sometimes I help Cooper."

"Has Miss Allen ever said anything about hiring you out as a helper?"

"No sir."

"I'm going to need some helpers at the Magazine when the weather breaks. I'm sure I could use you some days if she would allow it."

"Can she legally do that?" asked Reverend Sclater.

"Yes sir. I work several servants regularly, but it has to be with the owner's consent. I can't negotiate directly with the servants or pay them wages."

"Are you still having trouble finding enough laborers?"

"Everyone is. Not many of the freedmen will hire out as laborers. Most of them, unless they are craftsmen, try to eke out a living on the land they receive as freedom dues. Others are moving to the wilderness."

Alexander and Elizabeth would remember that evening for the rest of their lives. The table was piled high with all kinds of delicious foods and everyone ate from china plates, even the children. After the meal they all crowded into the front room and listened to Reverend Sclater read the Bible story about the birth of Jesus. Afterwards, each of the children received a gift from the Carys. Elizabeth was given a little doll that had been carved from wood and had moveable legs. Alexander's gift was a small, wooden spinning top with a metal tip on the bottom. He was embarrassed by his failure to get it spinning after trying several times.

"Let me show you how it works," said Mr. Cary. Taking the top from the boy he wound the string tightly around it. Casting it towards the floor, he set it spinning with his first try. "Now, you try it," he said, handing it back to the boy. After several attempts he also had the top spinning across the floor.

All too soon it was bedtime for the younger children and time for Alexander and Elizabeth to return to the ordinary. They thanked the Carys for allowing them to come and for the gifts they had received. The Sclaters thought it best that James accompany them back to the ordinary although Alexander insisted it was unnecessary. Mary and Martha were pleading with their parents to let them go along also. Reluctantly, their parents yielded to them. They squealed with delight as they grabbed their coats and ran to the door.

"Be sure to tell Miss Allen you are back as soon as you get there," said Reverend Sclater, "and thank her again for letting you come."

"We will," said Alexander.

Stepping out into the night the five children started towards the ordinary. Everything was covered by several inches of new snow. The lights that shone from every window illuminated the snow-covered streets and the Christmas decorations that adorned the doors and gates. The flickering candles and lamps cast eerie shadows across the fallen snow. It was a scene they would long remember and a fitting conclusion for such a wonderful evening.

When they reached the ordinary the three Sclater children stopped at the gate. "We'll come back to see you tomorrow," they promised as they turned back towards the Cary house. Alexander and Elizabeth walked to the rear door and went in. Only a few people were in the ordinary. Susanna Allen, David Cunningham, and his two children David and Jane sat at a table near the fire.

"We're back," said Elizabeth.

"Thank you for letting us go," said Alexander.

"Did you have a good time?" asked Cunningham.

"Yes sir," said the boy.

"Good," said Miss Allen. "Everything is finished for tonight. You need to hurry to bed because I'll need you both early in the morning."

"They gave us both a present," said Elizabeth, holding up her doll.

"What did they give you?" asked Cunningham, looking at the boy.

"A spinning top," he said, as he held it up for all to see.

"Can you make it spin?"

"Sometimes," he said, casting it towards the floor. It was a perfect throw. The top righted itself and sat spinning. It seemed motionless in the dim light.

"I want one!" said little David. "Daddy, will you get me one?"

When they reached the back door Elizabeth said, "Good night."

"I'll walk with you to the kitchen," said Alexander.

"I'm not afraid."

"I'll walk with you anyway."

"I will never forget tonight. I had a wonderful time with your friends. The food was so good. I've never eaten from a china plate before, have you?"

"Once, the week I stayed with the Sclaters. They used them for Sunday dinner."

"Nobody has ever given me a present before either. This is the first doll I've ever had. If I weren't your friend I wouldn't have been invited. I'm glad I could go with you."

"I'm glad you could too. I wouldn't have wanted to go without you."

When they arrived at the kitchen door Elizabeth stopped. Turning to Alexander she said, "Thank you for being my friend." Leaning towards him she kissed him on the cheek, then turned quickly and went inside. The astonished boy stood alone in the darkness staring towards the closed door. His mind was racing as he walked back towards the ordinary.

Spring came late to Virginia that year, welcomed by those who had endured the long, cold winter. With the warm weather came increased activity. Planters were unusually busy because of the late planting season. Building had continued through the winter, but had been greatly hampered by rain, snow, and extreme cold. In Williamsburg, several large projects were being carried on simultaneously. Construction on Bruton Parish Church was entering its fourth year under the watchful eye of Governor Spottswood and was scheduled to be finished soon. It would replace the Middle Plantation Church built in 1683 which stood nearby and was currently being used for worship. Henry Cary, Jr. had almost completed the Governor's Palace after assuming responsibility for it from his aging father. He was also nearing completion of the Magazine. Artisans and laborers were in great demand for these projects.

Construction on a smaller scale was also taking place that spring at Susanna Allen's Ordinary. James Morris, a local carpenter, had been employed to build an outbuilding. To keep her expenses low Miss Allen contracted with him to provide Alexander as his helper. When she told the boy he was excited about the prospects of learning something new. His hopes faded the first day. Mr. Morris was not a pleasant person to work with, was impossible to please, and was unwilling to teach him anything. He also learned that the hours he spent helping the carpenter were not a substitute for the hours needed to do his regular chores which he had to do before or after his new job. He dreaded each day.

As they entered the second week Morris was becoming more difficult to work with. He was irritated that he had not been paid his wages as promised and argued with Miss Allen frequently. Each day he threatened to quit if he did not receive his pay, but always returned the next day. As he began his third week he still had not been paid. When he finished work that day he turned to the boy and said, "I'm going to go get my money," and walked toward the back door of the ordinary. Alexander waited until Morris was inside and then slipped into the building behind him. Angry voices were coming from the next room.

"I've told you I don't have the money," said Susanna Allen, "I can't pay you. I don't have the money!"

"Why did you hire me if you couldn't pay me?"

"I thought I would have the money, but I don't."

"We had an agreement. I did my work and now I want my pay."

"I can't pay you if people don't pay me."

"Well, get it! You pay me today or I'll not work another day for you and I'll see you in court."

"I can't pay you today."

"Then I'll see you in court!"

James Morris came storming through the door almost running into the boy. He paused long enough to give him a hateful look before continuing outside. Alexander watched from the window as the carpenter gathered up his tools and left. He felt sorry for Morris and Miss Allen, but he was glad that his ordeal was over.

Susanna Allen and David Cunningham sat drinking with their friend William Robertson discussing the latest woes that had befallen the ordinary. James Morris, true to his word, filed a suit against Miss Allen to recover his expenses and wages. He was not the only one. She found herself being summoned to appear in the York County Court with increasing frequency as a defendant and almost as often was there as a plaintiff trying to recover money due her.

"I spend as much time in court as I do here," said the woman in a slurred voice.

"Your drinking isn't going to help," said Cunningham.

"Don't start preaching to me again David. I'm in no mood for it."

"You're drinking too much. That's why you can't take care of the business."

"I said don't preach to me! If you don't like the way I run it, you run it. Your friend John was going to solve all my business problems and now I still have my problems and his. It's worse than ever."

"We're just trying to help you," said Robinson. "If things don't get better we probably won't be able to get a license for next year."

"What can I do about it? I owe everybody in town and nearly everybody in town owes me. Nobody pays me...I can't pay anybody else. They take me to court...I take them to court. I try to fix the place up...I end up in court again. What can I do? I get upset...a drink helps me."

"We're not talking about a drink," said Cunningham, "you're drinking all day."

"There you go again preaching. If you don't like the way I am then you can go sleep in the barbershop tonight with your two simpletons."

Alexander and Elizabeth, who were listening to the conversation from the back room, could hardly keep from laughing out loud. Each time they looked at each other they would giggle and hold their hand over their mouths.

"Elizabeth, come here," yelled Miss Allen.

The two frightened children looked at each other. Had she heard them laughing? Elizabeth hurried to the other room while Alexander continued to listen from the back.

"Make sure all the tables are clean before you go to bed," said the woman as she stood up. "Call Alexander and tell him to bring more wood in and fix the fire. These two gentlemen can close up for the night. I'm going to bed."

Business did improve during the summer months. The ordinary was often filled at night and always crowded at mealtimes. Anne was responsible for all the beds and the laundry. Cooper stayed busy caring for the animals and the garden. Dinah and Elizabeth were responsible for the food, and Alexander for the water, wood, and any other chores. Miss Allen was constantly calling him to help the others or run an errand. They were especially busy on market day and when the House of Burgesses was in session.

Alexander liked to spend mealtime and evenings inside the ordinary, listening to people talk. He especially enjoyed hearing conversations about the frontier or wilderness. Boats could travel up the James River to the falls and all the land along the river had become large plantations like Mr. Byrd's, but beyond the falls were thousands of acres of wilderness occupied only by a few frontiersmen and Indians. That's where he wanted to go when he was a freedman. He dreamed of that day.

Some men, like Aaron, had lived in the wilderness. Whenever he ate at the ordinary Alexander tried to get close enough to hear his stories. One evening as he sat with two friends Alexander sat at the next table so he could hear them talk.

"It ain't no place to go without good guns and dogs. You need at least two of each. A man will owe his life to his dog many times. A sleeping man will get attacked by Indians or wolves and not know it 'til it's too late. A dog will smell 'em, even when he's sleep."

"Why you need two dogs?" asked one of the men.

"Something might happen to one. Get killed by wolves or bit by a snake. Wolves will stay away from a man and two dogs. Without a dog you need to leave. Same with a gun. A man can't live there without a gun. If you only have one and it breaks you better leave and hope you can get out."

"What about Indians, you ever see any?"

"See 'em all the time. Most of them don't bother you. Sometimes mean ones come from other places. They'll kill you. They'll kill other Indians too. It's hard to tell one from the other so you have to be careful. Lot of men go into the wilderness and never come back. Nobody knows what happened to them."

"You ever plan on going back?" asked the first man.

"Maybe. If I do I might not go alone. It's hard for one man to take everything he needs and do all the work. It's a big help if you have somebody with you."

Williamsburg was crowded. All the rooms were taken for the weekend and many people were staying as guests in private homes. Everyone wanted to attend the first service in the new church. Alexander and Elizabeth sat in the balcony watching the people crowd into the pews below until they were all filled. Some would have to stand. Empty seats remained in the balcony but they would probably remain vacant because pride would prevent people from sitting with slaves and servants. The Governor entered and was seated in his elegant pew and the service began.

Alexander noticed that Susanna Allen and David Cunningham were not sitting together and wondered why. Cunningham and his two children came regularly but Miss Allen didn't. The ordinary was open late on Saturday nights and she used Sunday mornings to rest. Recently, one of the churchwardens had visited her at the ordinary and warned her about the number of times she had missed. She was very angry when he left. This was the first time she had been since then. Alexander wondered if it was because of the warden's visit or because today was a special day. He studied the people in all the pews and made a game of trying to determine if anyone in town was missing. He could think of nobody. Next, he tried to count how many people were from out of town. Then, he began to count how many people were sleeping and watched to see if anyone would wake them up. When the service was over he was glad. Now he would have some free time to spend with Elizabeth.

The next day Alexander was carrying water to the rooms upstairs. He stopped for a moment at one of the windows to watch the activity on the street below him. Colonel William Byrd came down the steps of his home across the street and started walking towards the Capitol. He lived in Williamsburg when the council was in session, but seldom came at any other time. His servants took care of the house when he was away. Alexander did not like Mr. Byrd. He remembered the visit with Miss Allen to Byrd's plantation and how the man never acknowledged his presence. Occasionally Colonel Byrd would eat at the ordinary or pass the boy on the street, but he never spoke to him. Alexander had noticed with great amusement that he never missed an opportunity to speak to a woman. He laughed softly as he watched Byrd hurrying across the street to intercept two women walking up the other side.

1716
Chapter 13

Planning To Run Away

Alexander was standing at the well when he noticed David Cunningham walking rapidly up the street towards the ordinary. Alexander knew from his gait, and the expression on his face, that something was wrong. He grabbed the bucket of water and hurried towards the house. As he entered, Susanna Allen said, "When you get through bringing in water..." Before she could finish Cunningham burst through the door and walked straight towards them.
"The Governor wants me to go with him," he said to Miss Allen.
"Where?" she asked, with a puzzled look on her face.
"On his trip. His senseless trip to the mountains."
"Why does he want you to go?"
"He wants all of us to go. All of his personal servants and aides. We'll be out there living in the woods like savages for weeks."
"I doubt that. He's certainly not going to live like a savage."
"No he's not. The rest of us will to insure that he doesn't."
"It may be fun David. You'll probably enjoy it."
"Fun! How can it be fun living in the woods like an animal for weeks?"
Susanna Allen began to laugh.
"Why do you think it's funny? I don't see anything funny about it!"
She laughed even harder as Cunningham stormed angrily out of the room.

Governor Spottswood's trip had been the topic of conversations for many weeks. Shortly after becoming governor he had sent rangers to explore beyond the mountains seeking a route to the Mississippi River and the Great Lakes. He himself had traveled extensively and was well informed about Virginia. Now, he was planning a summer trip for himself with more than sixty men to accompany him. His goal was to travel beyond the mountains.

It was late August when the mixed group finally left Williamsburg. The Governor, riding in a coach, was accompanied by no less than sixteen prominent politicians. They were supported by personal servants, soldiers, fourteen frontier rangers and four Meherrin Indian scouts. On the morning they were scheduled to leave David Cunningham came downstairs and awakened Alexander. He had never given up hope that he would not have to go, but now the dreaded day had arrived and he was going.

"I may be gone a month," said Cunningham. "Miss Allen is going to need a lot of help from all of you while I am away. Each of you had better do your part to see that things run smoothly here while I am gone. If any of you cause problems for her you'll answer to me when I return."

"Yes sir," said the boy as he stared up at the surly man towering over his bed.

Cunningham turned abruptly and left. Alexander learned later that he had delivered the same message to the other servants and slaves. Each of them resented the threats from one who had no authority over them but they knew the uselessness of complaining to Miss Allen about his behavior.

It was late September when the group returned to Williamsburg weary from their month-long journey, but elated over their accomplishment. Every gathering provided an opportunity for the participants to tell anyone who would listen about their journey west. They described in great detail how they forded rivers, shot and ate bear, deer, and wild turkeys. They had often cut their way through dense underbrush with axes, disturbing nests of hornets which inflicted great injury to both men and horses. When they reached the crest of the mountains the governor insisted that they go another day's journey. Camping beside a large river they noisily celebrated their accomplishment, firing many volleys into the air with their guns and drinking toasts from the large supply of liquor they had brought. The next day they began their trip home.

Susanna Allen's Ordinary became a favorite gathering place for a regular group of the men that had gone on the trip. John Fontaine, an Irishman, had become good friends with David Cunningham and came almost every evening to visit. Usually, before the night was over several of their comrades would join them to drink and reminisce. The more they drank, the more they talked, and the louder they got. Night after night they would retell and embellish the stories of the trip. Alexander delighted in listening to the men.

"I thought it was a long way to travel just to have a celebration," said Fontaine.

"You had a celebration every night," said Cunningham.

"I only drank enough for protection, David."

"Protection from what?"

"Rattlesnakes! If I got bit, I wanted to be sure I had enough in me to kill the poison. A man never knows when he'll get bit in that wilderness."

"Any snake that bit you would have died from the alcohol," said one of the other men.

"Or at least become too drunk to crawl," said another.

"You mates didn't do so bad yourself as I recall. One reason I drank as much as I did was because of fear."

"What were you afraid of?" asked Cunningham.

"I was afraid the rest of you were going to drink it all."

"At least we didn't lose our gun and have to pay a reward to get it back," said Cunningham, referring to a well-known event that occurred on the trip. Fontaine was the butt of many jokes because he lost his rifle.

"You boys didn't learn a thing from that now did you? I was just trying to teach you something important. I paid a few pence to have someone carry that heavy gun all day and it left my hands free to carry my jug."

Susanna Allen appeared in the room and walked towards the group of men.

"Who gave you permission to be here?" she said loudly, staring at Alexander who was sitting listening to the group.

Every eye turned toward her and a great hush filled the room.

"I was just listening to them talk about the trip," he said, rising to his feet.

"This seat is for customers. It's not for you to sit here listening to them."

Before he could respond she swung an open palm towards his face catching him by surprise. The sound from the slap rang across the room.

"Go downstairs and don't come back in here unless I tell you to."

The humiliated boy hurriedly left the room.

Standing in the semi-darkness of the basement room, he stared at the smoldering embers in the fireplace. After a while he reached down for some wood and tossed two pieces onto the hot coals. In a moment they burst into flames. The longer he stood there the angrier he became. His anger, like the flame, had begun as a smoldering ember and was now like a roaring fire within him. He wanted to charge back up the steps and attack that hussy who had made a spectacle of him in front of all those people. Why had she done that? She stayed angry all the time lately and drank excessively. She had poured her anger out on him before verbally, but tonight was the first time she had hit him. He decided it was also going to be the last.

In his mind he began to go systematically around the room trying to remember who was there. How would he ever be able to face those people again? He knew Elizabeth was there. He hoped she was in the back and didn't see what happened. Everyone in town would know about it by tomorrow. He would be ashamed to see anyone. He wondered how far he could get if he started towards the mountains tonight. Aaron said you couldn't survive in the wilderness without a gun and a dog and he had neither. He had no heavy clothes either. He had nothing. Maybe he could find someone like Aaron who would help him and he could help them. Jumbled thoughts were running through his mind when he heard the door open and someone coming down the stairs. It was Elizabeth. He turned his face back towards the fire and wouldn't look at her as she stopped near the bottom of the steps.

"Are you alright?" asked the girl.

"Yes."

"What are you doing?"

"Thinking."

"About what?"

"Leaving."

"You can't!"

"Why?"

"You promised me you'd never leave me again."

The boy was silent a long time before he spoke again. "I wouldn't care if she hit me for not doing my work, but I've always done my work. She had no reason to shame me like that. If I hurt her I'll go to jail, but I'll never let her do it again. I'd be better off in the wilderness than here."

"What about me?"

Alexander turned and looked at her. She was trembling, and tears were running down her face. He felt ashamed for thinking only of himself.

"I'm not going."

"Promise?"

"Promise. I'll stay until we can both go."

Elizabeth turned around and went back up the steps. Now his thoughts were more jumbled than before. He could think of no way out.

Conditions worsened at the ordinary. Susanna Allen was constantly hounded by creditors and stayed angry all the time. She drank excessively which caused her and David Cunningham to feud continually. Both of them took their spite out on the servants. When Anne Granger's indenture was complete there was no money for her freedom dues. Miss Allen had great difficulty borrowing the money she needed. Anne spurned her offer to remain as a worker and chose instead to accept a job next door at the Raleigh Tavern. Her actions infuriated Miss Allen. She made no attempt to acquire another servant and began to treat the rest of the servants and slaves with utter contempt. Elizabeth was moved inside to take Anne's place which left all the cooking and kitchen work to Dinah. A very demanding Susanna Allen called upon Alexander and Cooper to assume more of the duties that had once belonged to the others.

Alexander and Elizabeth were maturing rapidly. Both of them had outgrown their winter clothing. They knew they had a right to new clothes and could complain to the court if they were not supplied but neither of them was willing to face the wrath of Susanna Allen. Sixteen hours was a normal workday for them. One evening when Alexander was preparing for bed Miss Allen opened the basement door and called to him, "Alexander, come up here." The barefooted-young man bounded up the steps.
"Get dressed and go over to the bakery. You're going to work there at nights."
"Who's going to do my work here?"
"You are. You'll have time."
"When will I sleep?"
"Stop asking me questions," screamed the woman! "Just do what I tell you!"
This time he saw it coming. He was watching her hand and when she swung at him he ducked. Her hand slammed into the door facing. She screamed in pain and began cursing the boy who retreated back town the steps for his shoes. As soon as she disappeared, he moved cautiously up the stairs and slipped out the door.

The bakery was hot and as always it smelled good. Mr. Goodwin the baker was watching an apprentice boy who was busy kneading dough in a large wooden trough. He looked up when Alexander walked in and asked, "Are you ready to go to work, son?"

"Yes sir."

"Let me show you how to fire the oven. You can do that while we work the dough. Later, when it's hot enough you can help us."

The next few hours was spent firing the oven, weighing out hunks of dough, shaping them into loaves, covering them with a cloth, and leaving them to rise. When they were ready, the baker raked the hot coals out of the oven, swept the ashes from the oven floor, and slid the round loaves directly onto it, with a long, wooden shovel.

"Don't you use pans?" asked Alexander.

"Don't need 'em."

"What you call that long wooden thing?"

"This is a baker's peel."

When the last loaf was placed in the oven he closed the iron door and shut off the flue with a damper.

"Now we'll clean up while they bake."

The sun was rising the next morning when Alexander walked home with several loaves of the bread in his arms. He carried them to the kitchen and gave them to Dinah who was already at work.

"Where'd you git dat bread?" asked the surprised woman.

"At the bakery. Miss Allen sent me for it so you don't have to cook any."

"Dat don't sound like her. Wonder what she's up to now?"

Alexander walked unsteadily across the back yard and went inside. Nobody was in sight. He crept down the stairs and sprawled out on the bed with his clothes on. In a few minutes he was asleep.

"Alexander, wake up," said Elizabeth. "Miss Allen wants you."

"What time is it?" said the sleepy boy as he sat up in bed.

"Almost time to serve dinner. She wants you to help. Why

are you still in bed. Are you sick?"
"I worked all night at the bakery."
"Why?"
"Miss Allen's idea. She gets free bread and it pays her bill she owes the baker."
"Who's going to do your work here?"
"Don't ask her that," said Alexander laughing, "it'll make her mad. I asked her last night and she tried to hit me again."
"What did you do?"
"Ducked and she hit the door frame. I hope she broke her hand."
"What did she say?" said Elizabeth, giggling.
"Started cussing me. I ran back downstairs until she left."
Both of them were now trying to stifle their laughter.
"You better get back upstairs," said the boy. "I'll be up in a minute."

Elizabeth was rapidly becoming a pretty young woman and the changes were not going unnoticed by the male customers at the ordinary. Their crude and suggestive remarks grew worse at night after they had been drinking. Some of them were constantly trying to put their hands on her body. Her worst fear was being alone upstairs with any of them. She tried to wait until everyone was gone from upstairs before she worked up there. When Susanna Allen became aware of what she was doing she began to taunt the girl. "You need to learn to be nice to those men honey. You might pick up a few coins from some of them."
"I don't want their money," said Elizabeth, "I just want them to leave me alone."
"You ought to change your mind. You could be good for my business and my business could be good for you."
Elizabeth glared at the woman and said, "You take care of your own business. I want nothing to do with that drunken scum."
She could hear Susanna Allen laughing at her as she walked away.

Elizabeth answered a knock at the ordinary door one morning and found Sheriff Lawrence Smith standing outside. "I need to see Miss Allen," he said.

"I'll get her," said the girl as she went to find the owner.

"What can I do for you Sheriff?" asked Miss Allen.

"I have a warrant for your arrest. You'll have to come with me."

"For what?"

"For absenting yourself from divine services."

"What! Nobody is ever arrested for that."

"They are if they're charged. I have no choice but to enforce the law."

"Who charged me?"

"One of the church wardens."

"Where are you taking me?"

"To see the magistrate. He can send you to jail or set your court date."

"Go get David," she said to Elizabeth. "I need him to go with me."

Racing across the street the girl told David Cunningham who came immediately to the ordinary. As they prepared to leave Miss Allen said to the girl, "Close the ordinary until I get back. Tell Dinah not to prepare dinner. We'll open again for supper."

Elizabeth could hardly wait until they left so she could tell the others. Two hours later an angry Susanna Allen returned to the ordinary with a court date scheduled for mid-December.

Christmas was different this year. Henry Cary and his family went to spend the holiday with the Sclaters. It was a sad time for Alexander and Elizabeth. Except for Dinah and Cooper they only had each other and their cherished memories from last year's celebration. The decorations and gaiety of Williamsburg were far less meaningful to them this year. They were so overwhelmed with work that they had little time to leave the ordinary. Their one respite each week was the Sunday church service. So far, Miss Allen had made no attempt to prevent them from going. Although she had seldom attended before her arrest, she had attended the following Sunday and was making plans to attend the Christmas Day service.

It was Christmas Eve. The bakery was closed but not the ordinary. The crowd was larger than usual and Alexander was helping wait the tables. He glanced up just in time to see Elizabeth recoil from a drunk who had placed his hand on her body. Without hesitation he started toward the man only to be intercepted by David Cunningham.
"Where you going boy?"
"To kill a drunk!"
"Get back to your work."
"Did you see what happened?"
"That happens all the time. Don't pay any attention to it. He's just had too much to drink."
"Then tell him to leave!"
"He's not ready to leave. He still has money to spend. You get back to work."
By now, they had attracted the attention of Susanna Allen.
"Alexander, come here."
The boy walked slowly toward her. The slap in the face was still fresh in his mind. If she tried it again she'd be sorry.
"Is something wrong?"
"Yes it is," he said while watching her hand from the corner of his eye.
"What?"
"That man is putting his hand on Elizabeth."
"Did she complain?"
"She didn't like it. She jerked away from him."
"Then she took care of it. It's not your business. Get back to work."
She made no attempt to move her hand toward him. He turned and walked away.

The muddy streets were almost deserted when the ordinary closed. The drunken man who had put his hands on

Elizabeth was one of the last to leave. Alexander was watching from the back room where he was washing dishes. When the man stood to leave Alexander slipped quietly out the back door. Picking up a large piece of firewood he stood in the shadows until the man staggered past. Raising the wood in front of him he heaved it right into the man's back. The flat side struck him between the shoulder blades. The drunk pitched forward and landed facedown in a large mud hole. Alexander quickly retrieved the wood and disappeared into the darkness. In less than a minute he was back inside washing dishes.

There was a commotion at the front door as the cursing drunk returned covered with mud.
"Someone outside knocked me down in the street."
"Who?" asked David Cunningham.
"I don't know. I didn't see them. They hit me in the back."
"What did they hit you with?" asked Susanna Allen.
"I don't know. I didn't see anything."
"Alexander!" called Miss Allen.
The boy appeared immediately holding a wet cloth in his hand.
"Where have you been?"
"In the back room washing dishes."
Turning to the drunken man she asked, "Are you sure you didn't stumble and fall?"
The man became angry and began cursing again. "I'm not so drunk I can't walk. I know when somebody hits me. If you think I'm a liar then I'll take my business somewhere else," he said indignantly as he headed to the door.

The temperatures dropped drastically during the night and a strong wind was blowing from the west. The muddy streets were frozen as people made their way towards the church on Christmas morning. Alexander and Elizabeth walked briskly, to stay warm.
"You have mud on your shoes," said the girl. "How did you get them muddy?"

"I don't know."

"Maybe you did it last night when you went outside."

He glanced at her and she was smiling.

"I saw you. I'm glad nobody else did or you would have been in trouble."

"For doing what?"

"Hitting that man with a piece of wood."

"How do you know what I hit him with?"

"I saw the muddy piece of wood out back this morning."

"What did you do with it?"

"I burned it before somebody else saw it. Suppose you had hit him in the head and killed him?"

"That's what he needed."

"Don't say that. Nobody needs to get killed."

"He does."

"You got mud on the floor last night too. I cleaned it up before they saw it."

"Thanks."

"Thank you for trying to help me, but please don't do it again. You might get in a lot of trouble next time."

"Mr. Cunningham said that it happens all the time. Does it?"

"Yes. It gets worse every week. I hate it. I wish we could run away."

"We can."

"Where would we go?"

"Only place they couldn't find us would be the wilderness but we don't have what we need to go there. Maybe we could find Aaron and live with him. We could try. He said he needed somebody to help him."

"Suppose we can't find him. What would we do then?"

"Maybe we could find somebody else to help us."

"Suppose we can't?"

"We'll just come back. All they'll do is add more time for us to serve."

"Let's do it."

"We'll have to wait until it gets warmer. We'd freeze in weather like this."

The Whipping Post

Alexander and Elizabeth continued to endure the oppressive conditions at the ordinary as they patiently waited for warmer weather. Each day their resolve to run away grew stronger, but there was no break in the relentless cold during the six weeks following Christmas. They used this time wisely to make their plans and gather what they could for their trip. They found little time to be together during the week so they did most of their planning during their free time on Sunday. The middle of February brought moderation in the weather and a renewed excitement for them. As they walked to church one morning Alexander said, "I've been thinking some more about the gun in the ordinary, I wish we could take it."

"But you said it would be best if we didn't steal anything when we left."

"It would. If we take anything that gives them more reason to come after us, but I don't know how we'll make it without taking some things."

"What would we need?"

"The gun, powder and shot, food, the small ax, a knife, clothes, a cooking pan..."

"We can't do that. Do you remember what they did to that runaway girl that stole some clothes? They branded her! I don't want them doing that to us."

Alexander remembered. When he thought about it he could still hear the screams and smell the burning flesh.

"Guess we'll just go with nothing. I hope we can find Aaron and he'll have everything we need."

"How long do you think it will take us to get to the falls?"

"I don't know, probably two days. We can't leave until the ordinary closes and everybody is sleep. By the time we get out of town we won't get far before daylight. After daylight we'll have to get off the road and stay in the woods. It'll be best to go on Saturday night. Not many people will be out early on Sunday."

Alexander and Elizabeth were almost back home from their Sunday afternoon walk when a carriage passed them and stopped in front of the ordinary. Inside were two gaudily dressed women. Susanna Allen, who had obviously been expecting the women, came rushing outside to greet them. When she saw the boy and girl approaching she said, "Alexander, go find Cooper and get him to help you move these ladies' trunks inside. Elizabeth, go fix us some tea."

Everything began to change at the ordinary after the two newcomers arrived. Elizabeth was moved back to the kitchen to help Dinah and one of the women took her room. Miss Allen told Dinah to start baking bread again since she had help. Some of the customers were complaining about not having Dinah's bread. Several had stopped eating at the ordinary. They said they could get bakery bread anywhere. Alexander would no longer be working at the bakery since the ordinary account was paid and they would no longer need to buy bread. Mr. Goodwin wanted him to continue working, but was unable to pay Miss Allen the wages she asked for.

The greatest change occurred in the environment of the ordinary. When the two women began working there they became an instant attraction to the men of town, exactly like Susanna Allen had planned. Every table was filled for dinner and supper. In the evenings, it became the favorite place in town for the young men to gather for drinks and entertainment. Each of the women had their own room where they could spend time with their male friends if they desired. Everyone in town was talking about it.

Early one morning Alexander was refilling the wood box in the ordinary. Alone in the room, he paused to study the gun in the corner. He did not hear Miss Allen come in and was startled when she spoke.

"Go get Elizabeth and bring her back here. I want to talk with both of you."

"Yes, Miss Allen," he said and hurried out the door towards the kitchen. He returned in just a few minutes with the girl. Susanna Allen was sitting at the table near the fire drinking tea. "Alexander, tomorrow you will start working at the blacksmith shop. You need to be there in the morning when they open so get your work done here tonight. Elizabeth, go tell Dinah that I need you in here and then come back inside to clean upstairs and make the beds."

"I thought you wanted me to help her with the food."

"I do, but the girls need some help in here. They work late at night and it's hard for them to get up early. They need some rest."

Alexander and Elizabeth stood in silence, staring at the woman in disbelief.

"Well don't just stand there. You both have work to do, go do it!"

Without responding, they turned and left the room. Stepping outside, Alexander pulled the door shut behind them. As they walked across the yard he said to the girl, "It's time to leave this place. Let's plan for Saturday night. We'll have two days to save some food. We'll talk some more tonight."

Alexander loved working in the blacksmith shop because he was learning so much. After the first day he wished he could continue working there, but his last day was approaching rapidly. He learned something that day that only made him angrier and more determined to run away. Miss Allen was having the blacksmith make numerous items for the ordinary and paying for them with the boy's labor. When they finished the day's work and closed the shop the friendly blacksmith said, "I'll see you on Monday. We have a lot to do."

"Yes sir," said the boy.

Walking towards the ordinary, he was overcome with guilt.

139

Not only was he planning to break the law, but also he was being deceitful with the blacksmith. He thought about his parents, grandparents, the Sclater family, and the Carys. He knew they would all be disappointed in him. Then he thought of Elizabeth and the conditions at the ordinary. Even though he felt guilty because of what he was going to do, he wanted a better life for both of them. He felt running away was their only hope.

The Saturday night crowd at the ordinary was larger than usual. Everybody was working hard trying to satisfy the demands of the people. After the last customer left there was still a lot of work for Alexander and Elizabeth to do. Susanna Allen and David Cunningham sat at a table talking. "This has been the best day we've ever had," said Miss Allen. "If it stays like this, I'll be able to get out of debt in a hurry."
"The girls have really increased our business," said Cunningham. "Where are they?"
"They're both in their rooms."
"Alone?"
"I don't know. I can't keep up with everything that goes on. I do know I'm tired and will be glad to get in bed. Are you ready to go?"
"I suppose."
When they stood to leave she said to Elizabeth, "When you and Alexander finish work, make sure the fire is fixed and the lamps are out."
"I will."

As the two adults disappeared into their room, Alexander came from the rear of the building where he had just finished washing dishes and asked Elizabeth, "Were you able to get much food?"
"Enough for a few days. I hid it in the back room."
"I have to go downstairs and get my stuff."
"Not yet! Wait until they go to sleep. Help me get everything cleaned up in here."

tonight as they continued their journey towards the falls.

"I hear dogs barking," said Alexander, "it sounds like they are chasing something."
"I hear them too. I hope they aren't chasing us!"
"They're getting closer," said Alexander, as he jumped up and crawled through the hay to the other side of the barn with Elizabeth following him.
"Maybe we can see what they're chasing," he said, as they peeked through the crack. As they watched, three dogs burst out of the woods and headed straight towards the barn. Two men on horses were close behind them. Alexander recognized one of them. "It's the Sheriff! They are chasing us!" he said. "Hide under the hay." Scrambling back across the loft, they quickly covered themselves with the hay. By then, the dogs were jumping against the door trying to get in.

The two men stopped some distance from the barn. "Alexander! Elizabeth! This is Sheriff Smith. I know you're in there so answer me."
"Are you going to answer him?" whispered Elizabeth.
"Not yet. Let's see what he does," said the boy as he crawled from under the hay and peeked out of the crack at the two men. About that time, another man rode up from the house.
"What's going on, Sheriff?"
"Looks like you've got a couple more runaways, Silas. Your barn is like a lodestone. It attracts every runaway that come through here."
"Alexander!" called the Sheriff. "You want me to let them dogs in there? Answer me boy! Are you in there?"
"Yes sir," answered the boy.
"Is the girl with you?"
"Yes sir."
"We're gonna tie the dogs up so you can come out. Both of you come out here when I tell you to. Don't you run or I'll turn those dogs loose."
Alexander and Elizabeth watched as the other man called the

143

dogs and tied them to a tree.

"Both of you come out here."

The scared youngsters climbed down from the loft and cautiously went outside.

"Where do you two think you're going?" asked the Sheriff.

"To the wilderness," said the boy.

"Ha! All you runaways want to go to the wilderness. You ought to be glad I caught you. You would have learned what hard living really is. What do you have with you?"

"Just some food."

"Where is it?"

"In the loft."

"Go show the deputy where it is. Show him everything you have, boy. And don't you lie to me."

In a few minutes they returned with the hidden food.

"Silas, could I hire you to take these two back to town? I should make them walk home, but I don't want to take that long getting back. It would be more punishment for me than for them."

It was almost dark when they arrived back at the ordinary and the evening crowd had begun to gather. The Sheriff proudly marched the two humiliated youngsters inside and loudly proclaimed their return to an angry Susanna Allen.

"I brought your two runaways home. Found them sleeping together in a barn about ten miles from here. Said they were going to the wilderness to live. "

"What did they have with them?"

"Nothing but a little food. You're going to have to pay Silas for bringing them home."

"You should have made them walk back!"

"I decide the best way to get them back. Do you want me to take them to jail or release them to you?"

"Leave them here. They have work to do."

"I'll get a court date set for them tomorrow and let you know when it will be."

The court date was set for March seventeenth. Leaving early

144

that morning, Alexander and Elizabeth were delivered to the York County court by David Cunningham and Susanna Allen. The boy was the first to appear before Judge Lightfoot. After hearing testimony from both Miss Allen and the Sheriff, the judge asked, "What reason can you give the court for this serious action?"

"Because I haven't been fairly treated."

"That's the complaint of all runaways. Be more specific."

"Sometimes I haven't had a bed to sleep in or proper clothes to wear. I have been forced to work for two masters. I work for Miss Allen and then she hires me out to work for others. Sometimes I don't have time to sleep."

"If these charges are true you had recourse through the courts. You should have used it. These are not reasons to break your contract or run away. The court orders that you serve Miss Allen for three additional months after the time of your Indenture order is expired to repay her for what she has expended to have you apprehended. If this happens again, you will find the court dealing much more severely with you. Next case."

Again, Miss Allen and the Sheriff testified against Elizabeth and told how she had run away with Alexander after taking food from the ordinary.

"And what do you have to say in your defense?" asked the judge.

"The working conditions at the ordinary are very bad. I work day and night. I work in the kitchen with the cook and also do the work inside. The drunken men will not leave me alone. They are always touching my body and putting their hands anywhere they please. Miss Allen knows it, but doesn't care. She laughs at it. She has two other women who work there but all they do is entertain men. I have to do all the work."

"Everyone knows that drunken men are difficult to control. You should understand that dealing with them is part of your job. That is no reason to do what you did. Stealing food and running away is a very serious act. Worse than either of these is that you enticed this young man to go with you. It is young women like you who have flooded this colony with bastard children from acts like this. Let me warn you that if you give birth to a child because of this offense you will be dealt with harshly and your child will also be indentured until it becomes of age. For now, I also extend your time for three months after your time of Indenture is expired to repay Miss Allen for what she has expended to apprehend you. In addition, I command that you receive on your bare back at the public whipping post, twenty lashes, to be well laid on by the Sheriff of this County for these offenses."

"But sir, I didn't...."

"You had your opportunity to speak. I have made my judgment. Next case."

Elizabeth was escorted from the court by the Sheriff to be delivered back to Williamsburg for her whipping. When Alexander arrived outside they had already left.

As their carriage journeyed back to town the boy was tormented by the thoughts of Elizabeth being beaten. He had seen this cruel punishment administered to people many times before. He vividly remembered watching a woman's dress being ripped from her body after her hands had been tied to the post. The slow and deliberate beating seemed like it would never end. Each crack of the whip would bring cheers from the crowd as they counted each stroke. He could still hear the taunting words and see their laughing faces as they made crude remarks about her body. The poor woman could barely stand when she was released and was unable to cover her nakedness, much to the pleasure of the crowd. He could not bear to think of such a thing happening to Elizabeth. She had done nothing to deserve such punishment. It was his fault, not hers.

When he could stand the anguish no longer, he spoke to Miss Allen. "Will you talk to the Sheriff when we get to town and ask him if I can take Elizabeth's place? Let him whip me and not her." She turned in the seat and looked at him and laughed loudly. "Now aren't you the gallant one." Saying nothing else, she turned back. Several minutes passed. She looked back at him again with hate-filled eyes and said, "No! She's getting just what she deserves and I'm glad. I wish she were getting more. If you think a whipping will make you feel better I'll see if I can arrange that with the Sheriff." With that she turned again to the front.

When they arrived in Williamsburg, a noisy crowd had already gathered at the whipping post. Stopping in front of the ordinary, Susanna Allen turned to Alexander and said, "Don't you go up there! Go get Cooper and tell him to come get the carriage." Alexander bounded from the carriage and ran through the gate. Instead of going to the barn for Cooper he ran straight to the woodshed and went inside for the ax. When he came out of the door, a strong pair of arms wrapped around him from behind, pinning his arms to his side. He couldn't move his arms. He could move his head just enough to see it was Cooper.

"Let me go, Cooper!"

"Don't be crazy, boy. Put dat ax down. You go runnin' up dare wit dat thing, the Sheriff'll shoot you dead. You won't be no good to nobody den."

"Turn me loose. I've got to help her, it's my fault."

"Ain't yo' fault. Ain't her fault neither. It's jest the way it is. Drop dat ax."

"Please let me go," begged the boy as he began to cry.

"Quit fightin' me, boy, I ain't gonna turn you loose to get yoself killed."

The boy struggled to get free, but couldn't. Finally realizing his struggling was futile, he released the ax and it fell harmlessly to the ground. Cooper moved him several feet forward before releasing him and reached down and picked up the ax.

"I hated to do dat boy, but I don't wanna see you dead."

The noise from the crowd was getting closer. Alexander started towards the gate. Elizabeth came running through the

147

gate towards the kitchen. She was holding her dress up to cover her naked chest. Blood was running from cuts on her back. Three boys were in hot pursuit, laughing and calling her names. Alexander ran between them and the girl and they stopped. The larger of the three stepped towards him and said, "Get out of my way," swinging his fist as he spoke. Alexander ducked. Weeks of built-up anger and frustration exploded within him. With all his might he drove his fist deep into the boy's gut. A strange noise that sounded like howling wind came rushing from his mouth as he fell doubled-over onto the ground. The other two boys turned around and ran back through the gate.

Alexander hurried to the kitchen. Elizabeth was sitting on a wooden stool in front of the fire holding her dress tightly to her chest. Dinah was cleaning her wounds and putting medicine on them. The boy knelt down beside her and began to weep. "I'm sorry," he sobbed, "it's all my fault." Elizabeth turned and looked at him. She wasn't crying. "It's not your fault. It was as much my idea to run away as it was yours. Anyway, it's all over."

"I'll get even with them for this. They had no right to do this to you."

"Don't you go talkin' foolish, boy," said Dinah. "Miz Elizabeth's right. It's all over. Just don't go getting in no mo trubble. Don't you two go runnin' off agin now, you hear?"

"We're not," said Elizabeth. "I'll be free next year. When Alexander gets free, we'll go again as free people." Looking at the boy she smiled and said, "Next time, we can stay in the road and not hide."

Alexander couldn't believe she was smiling and not crying. She didn't even appear angry. "Doesn't your back hurt?" he asked with a puzzled look on his face.

"Yes it hurts!" said the girl. "But I'll never let that hussy inside know it."

"Alexander!" called Susanna Allen from the back door of the ordinary.

148

Opening the kitchen door the boy answered, "I'm out here in the kitchen."

"What are you doing out there? Get in here and go to work! Tell Elizabeth to get in here too."

Alexander ran across the yard to the ordinary. He noticed the boy was gone from the yard and wondered what happened to him.

"Elizabeth has to change clothes. She has blood on her dress, but she'll be here soon."

Several minutes later, a radiant, smiling, Elizabeth, walked into the ordinary and began working. An astonished David Cunningham stared at her. Susanna Allen sat watching her with hatred in her eyes. They had failed in their attempt to run away and had paid dearly for it, but Alexander felt that somehow, they had won a great victory. He couldn't explain why, but he felt good. Maybe it was because of what Elizabeth had said. "It was over." They would continue their life at the ordinary and wait until they were free. The wilderness would have to wait. They still had each other and they had their dream. He knew one reason he felt good. It was because he was so proud of Elizabeth. He had never felt more proud in all his life.

1718
Chapter 15

A New Job For Elizabeth

Alexander held the door open for Miss Allen as she made her way carefully outside and down the steps. He had never seen her dressed so well, even when she went to court. She was a pretty woman. Cooper held the horse's reins, while David Cunningham helped her into the carriage. "You look very pretty tonight," he said.

"Thank you, David. Don't you want to go with me?"

"You know I would like to, but one of us has to stay here. Enjoy your evening"

As the carriage drove off towards the theater, Alexander closed the door and went inside.

"Has she gone?" asked Elizabeth in a low voice.

"Just left."

"Good. Maybe we'll have some peace around here tonight."

"There may not be many people here. A lot of them have gone to the new theater. The Governor went, I saw his carriage go by when I was outside."

"Would you like to go?"

"No!"

Elizabeth laughed and asked, "Why"?

"I wouldn't want to sit with that bunch."

"Wouldn't you like to see the show?"

"Maybe, if I didn't have to sit with them. It doesn't matter, we can't go anyway."

"I'll be able to go in a few months when I'm free."

Alexander stared at her for a moment and said, "That doesn't help me."

He didn't like to hear her talk about her freedom. Her indenture would soon be up, but he had five more years to serve. He was happy for Elizabeth but worried about where she would go when she left. He was also angry about the unfairness of the system. Men like James Spence and James

150

Mennes would be free before him and he had already served more than five years.

"What are you thinking about?" asked the girl.

"Nothing."

"I'll find work. There are lots of jobs in Williamsburg."

"Lots of jobs like this. I don't want you to keep working in a tavern."

"I'll find something else."

"Do you suppose Miss Allen will try to get you to stay for wages?"

"Won't do any good."

"Wonder where she'll get fifty shillings to pay your freedom dues?"

"I don't care, just so she pays me."

"What're you gonna buy?"

"Wilderness land for me and you."

The boy laughed and said, "We have a long time to wait 'til we can own land. You'll need to spend it before then."

"Wait and see."

"Elizabeth," called David Cunningham, "I need you out front."

"Yes sir," said the girl, as she hurried from the room.

The weeks quickly passed and Elizabeth was counting the days until she would be free. Alexander had a difficult time sharing her excitement because she still did not know where she would go when she left the ordinary. Miss Allen had never mentioned the approaching date to Elizabeth but she had heard her discussing it once with David Cunningham when she didn't realize she was being overheard.

"Are you going to try to get her to stay?" asked Cunningham.

"No," said Miss Allen. "It wouldn't do any good."

"You should at least ask."

"I'll not give her the pleasure of refusing me. I think that's what she wants."

When they realized Elizabeth was nearby, they stopped talking.

The church service was almost over and Alexander was glad. It was hot in the balcony with no air stirring. As he and Elizabeth stood to leave, he could see Henry and Sarah Cary directly below them. Mrs. Cary looked up and saw them and smiled. She said something to Mr. Cary, and he also looked up and nodded to them. The crowd moved quickly outside after the service. When Alexander and Elizabeth went out, the Carys were standing a short distance away in the yard as if they were waiting for someone.

"Hello Alexander. Hello Elizabeth," said Mr. Cary.

"Hello," they replied as they walked towards the couple.

"We haven't seen you for a while," said Mrs. Cary, "I hope you are both well."

"We are," said Elizabeth. "How are you and your family?"

"We are also well, thank you."

"How are Reverend and Mrs. Sclater and the children?" asked Alexander.

"They are fine. We hope they'll come for a visit soon. If they do, perhaps you can see them."

"I would like to but I'm working another job now and still work at the ordinary. I don't have much time except on Sunday."

"Where are you working?" asked Henry Cary.

"At the blacksmith shop. I like it, but it's hard work."

"I've been wanting to talk with you about something," said Mr. Cary. Do you think you would have time to come by our house this afternoon?"

"Yes sir, what time?"

"Around mid-afternoon would be fine. Elizabeth, you may come too if you can. You can spend time with Sarah and the children while Alexander and I talk."

"Thank you, I'm sure I can."

"Good, we'll see you then," said Mr. Cary as he took his wife's arm and started towards the carriage.

"I wonder what that's about?" said Elizabeth quietly, as they started home.

"I don't know, but I think she knows. She didn't seemed surprised when he asked us."

152

"He wanted to give you a job once, do you suppose he wants to do it again?"

"Miss Allen would never let me work for him. She hates him because he took her to court to get his money when he worked on the ordinary. She never pays anybody."

"She's gonna pay me, or she'll be in court again!"

"What you lookin' so smug for?" asked Dinah, as the two walked into the kitchen.

"We're not smug, we're hungry," said Alexander.

"You always hungry! Dat ain't nothin' new, but you up to somethin' else. I can tell way you actin', boy."

"We're going over to visit with Mr. and Mrs. Cary this afternoon," said Elizabeth.

"Who said?"

"They did. We saw them at church and they invited us over."

"What for?"

"Mr. Cary wants to talk to Alexander."

"Bout what?"

"We don't know."

"I know we'll starve while you keep asking questions," said Alexander, "let's eat."

"You get ask ovah to rich folk's house, but all you think of is eatin'. Maybe they'll feed you."

"I want to eat now. What's in the pot?"

"Same as always, stew. There' yo bowl and don't eat too much."

Alexander was so excited, he hardly remembered eating. When they were finished, he and Elizabeth went for their usual walk until it was time to go to the Carys. They were surprised to see Sarah Cary answer their knock at the door, instead of one of the servants. Doyley and little Henry came running to the door behind their mother.

"Come in," she said laughing, "Mary and the boys were so excited when we told them you were coming that they wouldn't eat their dinner. I've had to threatened them to calm them down."

"I just had a birthday," said Doyley, "do you know how old I am?" Before they could answer, he said, "I'm six!"

"And how old are you Henry?" asked Elizabeth.

Henry ran behind his mom and hid.

"Henry is almost four," she said. "He's being shy, but he'll be over that in a minute."

"Mr. Cary is in the front room," she said to Alexander. "Elizabeth and I will be in back with the children."

Henry Cary stood up when the boy entered the room and extended his hand. "Thank you for coming Alexander. Have a seat."

"Thank you for asking me, sir."

"I suppose you are wondering why I asked you to come by. Before I tell you, I want to ask you not to discuss with anyone what we talk about today. Will you do that?"

"Yes sir."

"I don't want you to even discuss it with Elizabeth. Can you do that?"

"Yes sir."

"I asked to talk to you, but what I really want is some information about Elizabeth. I've been told that her indenture to Miss Allen will soon be up."

"Yes sir, next week."

"The reason I didn't discuss this with her is that I don't want to create any trouble for her while she is still with Miss Allen. Does she have a place to go when she leaves?"

"No sir. We've really been troubled about what she will do."

"You are quite fond of each other aren't you?"

"Yes sir. We hope to get married some day." He could feel his face turning red.

Cary smiled at the uneasy boy. "How much longer do you have on your indenture?"

"Until I am twenty one and three months. Elizabeth's time was up when she turned sixteen, but we both had three more months added when we ran away last year."

"Can Elizabeth cook?"

154

"As good as Dinah."

"That's quite a claim son," laughed Cary. "Dinah's cooking is legendary."

Alexander smiled as he leaned forward in the chair. "Will you promise not to tell anyone if I tell you something?"

"Certainly."

"She cooks nearly all the bread for the ordinary, not Dinah."

"Are you sure?"

"Real sure. You can't tell the difference in her bread and Dinah's, but we don't want Miss Allen to find out or Dinah might get in trouble."

"Is Elizabeth good with children?"

"We don't have many children around the ordinary, just a lot of drunken men. I know she likes children. She likes your children a lot."

"Do you think she would like to work for us?"

"Yes sir!" said Alexander as he sat up on the edge of the chair.

"Mrs. Cary isn't well and could use some help with the household. We have some good servants, but it's a big job looking after everything. We've wanted to find a responsible person to help her. When we heard about Elizabeth, we thought she would be a good person for the job, but I don't want her to know yet. You can tell her that you talked to me about her need for a job, but nothing else. That should encourage her. You be sure that she doesn't take a job somewhere else until she talks to me."

"Yes sir."

"Mrs. Cary and I will talk with her about details when the time comes. She can live here with us and stay in the little cottage outside."

"That would be wonderful. She would be safe here."

"Let's go see what the others are doing. Remember, don't mention this to her yet."

"I won't."

As they walked back to the ordinary, Elizabeth was telling Alexander about playing with the children and her conversations with Mrs. Cary when she suddenly remembered why they had come to visit the Carys.

"What did Mr. Cary want with you," she asked.

"I'm not real sure. He asked a lot of questions about us and the work at the ordinary. He wanted to know about how much time we had left on our indentures and about Dinah's cooking. All kind of things about us."

"Did he say anything to you about you working for him?"

"No, but I did tell him you would be looking for a job after next week."

"What did he say about that?"

"Not much. He just kept asking questions."

"Well, he must want something from you. He asked you to come talk to him, not me."

"Reckon we'll just have to wait and see what he wants. It may be nothing."

It was only two days until Elizabeth's indenture would be finished and Susanna Allen still had not mentioned it to her. Elizabeth was discussing it with Dinah when Alexander walked into the kitchen.

"You should ask her about it," said the boy.

"I'm not going to."

"She may have forgotten it."

"She hasn't forgotten."

"How do you know?"

"I heard her talking to Mr. Cunningham about it. He asked her why she didn't ask me to stay on for wages. She said she wouldn't give me 'the pleasure of telling her no'. When she saw me she quit talking."

"What are you going to do?"

"Nothing. Wait two days and if she doesn't say anything I'll ask for my freedom dues."

"We sho got two stubbon women on our hands," laughed Dinah. "Whatcha gonna do when two days from now you ain't got nowhere to sleep? You bettah be lookin for you a job if you ain't gonna talk to Miz Allen."

"I'm looking. I think I can get a job at Raleigh Tavern."

"Who told you that?" asked Alexander excitedly.

"I've been talking to some of the girls."

"Promise me you'll not take a job without talking to me about it first."

Elizabeth stared at him suspiciously. "Why are you saying that? You're the one that's been worried about what I would do. Do you know something that I don't?"

"You know how I feel about you working in another tavern. Just promise me you'll talk with me before you accept any job. Will you?"

Alexander knew Elizabeth suspected something by the way she continued staring at him. Finally she said, "I promise, but you know something and I want to know what it is."

"Elizabeth!" shouted Susanna Allen from the ordinary door.

"Yes ma'am," yelled the girl, through the open kitchen window.

"Come here."

Glancing at Alexander as she went out the door, she said, "We'll talk some more later."

Alexander sat down on the stool. His legs were shaking. He had promised Mr. Cary he wouldn't say anything to her, but now she was suspicious. What would he tell her?

"What's da mattuh wit you, boy?" said Dinah, "You sick?"

"No. I just don't want her to keep working at a tavern after she leaves here."

"She gotta work some where. She gotta live."

Suddenly, Elizabeth came running through the door, wide-eyed and breathless. "Tomorrow's my last day. Miss Allen said she had my money! I have to work tomorrow and can spend the night if I want to. She'll give me my money the next morning and I can leave."

"Did she ask you to stay for wages?" asked Alexander.

"No. That's all she said. She's waiting for us to bring the food back in for supper."

"Now, you've got to go see Mr. Cary."

"Why?"

"He may have a job for you."

"Doing what?"

157

"Helping Mrs. Cary and living with them. That's what he wanted to talk with me about last Sunday, but he made me promise not to say anything. He didn't want to get you in trouble with Miss Allen. Don't say anything about it until after tomorrow."

Elizabeth began jumping up and down. "That's too good to be true! I wish I could go talk to them right now."

"Right now, we had better get this food inside or we'll both be in trouble."

"My, my. Da Lawd done looked out fuh you child," said Dinah. "Don't you worry none 'bout getting in no trubble wit nobody."

Two days later, Elizabeth moved her few belongings into the cottage at the Carys and began her new job. Alexander missed seeing her every day. He had very little time to visit her and could only go if the Carys gave him permission. He looked forward to Sundays when they could attend church together and still enjoy their afternoon walks.

Winter came early that year. The first weeks of November were much colder than normal. As Alexander stepped from the yard into the street, he was met by a burst of wind that cut through his thin clothes and made him shiver. The heat from the forge would feel good this morning. As he turned toward the blacksmith shop, he was surprised to see Elizabeth running down the street towards him. He ran to meet her and said, "What's wrong?"

"They've killed Blackbeard the pirate."

"How did you find out?"

"Mr. Cary saw a crowd at the Capitol and went to see what was happening. He came back and told us so I asked him if I could come tell you. He said they were going to have a parade later today. I have to go, maybe I'll see you later."

Alexander could see the crowd gathered outside the Capitol. He wanted to go down there, but turned towards the blacksmith shop instead. When he arrived and told the others, he was surprised that nobody else had heard the news.

"I hope it's true," said Mr. Tuttle. "He's been a curse to many people. If there is a parade, we'll stop work and watch it."

Alexander was excited to hear that and eagerly waited for further word. He didn't have long to wait. One person after another began coming into the shop to spread the news. Soon the streets were filled with people waiting to see the parade that everyone said was going to take place.

"Let the fire die down, son, until we see what happens," said Mr. Tuttle. He had hardly finished speaking when they heard the fifes and drums playing. Making their way to the edge of the street, they could see the crowd approaching.

Governor Spottswood rode at the head of the parade in his carriage, followed by the fife and drum corps. Behind them marched a British Navy Lieutenant in his handsome blue uniform. Later, Alexander would learn that he was Lieutenant Maynard, who had captured the notorious pirate. A group of sailors, his crew who had accompanied him to North Carolina for the battle, followed him. A murmur swept through the crowd as one of the men approached carrying the head of Blackbeard swinging from a pole.

"No wonder they called him Blackbeard," someone said. "Look at that!"

Long, black, curly, hair covered all of the bloody head except a portion of his face. The open eyelids exposed sightless, leathery looking eyes. It was a spectacle Alexander would never forget. Thirteen pirates, bloody and bound, trudged along behind the head of their dead leader.

"You're gonna be next!" yelled a man standing beside Alexander.

"You've killed your last man," said another, "now it's your turn to die!"

"I hope they hang you!" screamed an older gentleman across the street.

Alexander studied the faces of the pirates as they staggered by. They looked like ordinary men. Ordinary men with fear in their eyes. Fear that they were going to die. Their fear was justified. Several days later, gallows were built on Capitol Landing and they were all hanged.

Death Strikes Again

Alexander stood at the upstairs window of the ordinary watching the people pass by on the street below. It wasn't Sunday, but they were all wearing their Sunday clothes. They were going to attend another funeral. He had lost count of how many people had died that winter and many others were very sick. The relentless cold of early winter had abated before Christmas, but with the warmer weather came the sickness they were calling the "raging distemper". Nobody was exempt from it and doctors seemed helpless in treating the sick. When he thought about the possibility that he or Elizabeth may become ill, he quickly put it from his mind. As soon as the last group passed by, he went downstairs to check the fires.

He was adding more wood to the fire, when Susanna Allen came from her room and called Alexander.
"David is sick. Go get Dr. Cocke and ask him to come as soon as he can."
"I think he's gone to the funeral. I just saw him go by in his carriage."
"Go to the church and see if the carriage is there. If it is, wait for him. If it's not, go to his home and leave a message for him to come here when he returns."
As soon as the boy had walked half the distance to the church he could see the carriage parked near the front entrance. Taking up a position near the carriage he waited for the doctor to return. He was rewarded with a short wait as the people soon began to come from the church. He wondered why. It seemed that every funeral service he had ever attended had lasted much longer. His question was answered by a hurried and abbreviated service at the graveside. He watched curiously as the people scurried

away. Nobody was standing around talking like they normally did. Everyone seemed to be anxious to leave. Perhaps they wanted to return to the perceived safety of their home. When the doctor arrived at the carriage, Alexander delivered the message from Miss Allen.

"How long has David been sick?" asked the doctor.

"I don't know, he seemed all right last night. Miss Allen just told me he was sick."

"Get in. I'll give you a ride back."

Arriving at the ordinary, the doctor followed the boy inside and hurried into the bedroom. For the next three days, he returned several times a day to see David Cunningham, but from what Alexander could learn, there was no change for the better. On the morning of the fourth day a very haggard Susanna Allen called Alexander again.

"Do you know where Lawyer Thomas Jones has his office?"

"Yes ma'am."

"Go get him and tell him that David wants to write a will."

The impact of the statement didn't fully hit him until he was almost at the lawyer's office. It was then he understood that David Cunningham was convinced he was going to die. Three days later, he was dead.

Less than a week had passed since David Cunningham's death when Susanna Allen became ill. This time, when Alexander went to get the doctor, he carried with him an emotion he had not known a week earlier. The anger he had nursed for many months was gone and anxiety had taken its place. Suppose Miss Allen died, what would happen to him? What would happen to the two underage children of David Cunningham's that he had left in her custody? What would happen to Cooper, and Dinah, and the ordinary? As much as he disliked the woman, he hoped she didn't die. As he pondered this, the old feeling of guilt returned. He realized that he was more concerned about himself and his friends than he was about Miss Allen. The scene of the previous week began to unfold again. Dr. Cocke came to the ordinary several times a day, but there was no news about her condition improving.

Hardly any customers had visited the ordinary since the outbreak of the illness. Other businesses in town were also suffering because of it. When David Cunningham died the ordinary was temporarily closed. When Miss Allen became ill it had not reopened. The two women employees were spending their time taking care of her. Dinah was cooking only enough food to supply the needs of the folks who worked at the ordinary. Alexander and Cooper had time on their hands. The boy knew that if Miss Allen was not sick that she would let him out for wages to the blacksmith. He thought that day had arrived when one of the women called to him while he was in the yard splitting wood.
"Come inside, Miss Allen wants to see you."
Returning the axe to the woodshed, the boy approached the house with dread. He did not want to go into the room where she was sick and possibly dying. He feared that any message she had for him would not be in his best interest. When he arrived at the door, he found it open. Susanna Allen lay pale and still upon her bed. Seeing the boy standing at the door, she called him to her bedside.
"Do you remember the lawyer you got for David? Go get him for me and tell him I also need to write a will."
"Yes ma'am," said the boy as he turned and left the room. Stepping into the street, he hurried towards the lawyer's office. He could feel his heart pounding as he walked. Another one of his fears was about to be realized, Susanna Allen was going to die. After he delivered the message to Thomas Jones, the man gathered his things together and accompanied the boy back to the ordinary. As they started inside, the lawyer said, "Go across the street and get the two men from the barbershop, I'll need some witnesses."
Hurrying to the shop, Alexander gave the message to James Mennes and James Spence who followed him back to the ordinary. The two men quietly entered the room and stood just inside the door as the lawyer finished writing the will.

Two other men, Samuel Cobb and Andrew Laprade, were also standing in the room. Alexander wondered where they had come from. The boy stood out of sight, just outside the door, listening as the lawyer read the document back to Miss Allen.

"Be sure this is correct before you sign it," he said, "and then we will have it witnessed."

First, the will addressed the care of the two orphans, David and Jane Cunningham and what they would receive. Alexander listened intently and as he heard him mention Cooper, he crept closer to the door. *'I will that my Negro Man named Cooper be employed on the Plantation of the said orphan, David until he comes of age and then I give the said Negro unto the said David and his heirs forever.'* Continuing, he read, *'I will that my servant boy named Alexander Stinson be kept on the plantation for the uses aforesaid or sold by Out Cry at the discretion of my Executors.'* The boy's mind was racing as he tried to determine what this might mean for his future. He might at least end up staying with Cooper unless they decided to sell him by auction. He was wondering who the executors would be. He only had a moment to wonder as the lawyer read on. *'Lastly, I do constitute and appoint my good friends Thomas Jones and William Robertson, Gents, to be Executors of this my Last Will and Testament...whereof I have hereunto set my hand this second day of March in the Year of our Lord Christ 1719.'*

"If this is in accordance with your wishes, you need to sign it here." There was a brief silence and then a shuffle of feet as the four witnesses took turns stepping forward to sign the document. As he waited, Alexander realized that he had not heard the lawyer mention Dinah. Had he missed hearing that part while he was wondering about himself? He dared not ask anyone because he didn't want them to know he had been listening. He slipped out of the door and walked toward the kitchen. Opening the kitchen door and stepping in, he found Dinah crying. Assuming she was upset over Miss Allen's impending death, he said nothing and sat down on the stool at the end of the table. He tried not to appear upset, but his heart was pounding and his entire body was shaking.

"I ben sold," said Dinah, as she looked at the boy and sobbed.

"What?"

"I ben sold. They just tole me. I'll be leavin' tomorrow."

"Sold to who?"

"To da man wit dat other ordinary up the street."

"You mean the Raleigh Tavern?"

"No. Dat other one. Where them fancy folks eat."

"Marot's? Jean Marot?"

"Yeah. She sold me to him."

Now, Alexander understood why he hadn't heard Dinah mentioned in the will.

"At least you and Cooper know where you'll go," said Alexander. "I don't know what will happen to me."

"What you know 'bout Cooper?"

Alexander told her about the will and what he had overheard. When he finished, he went to tell Cooper. Early the next morning, Susanna Allen died.

Alexander was surprised at the large crowd that turned out for Susanna Allen's funeral. Inside the church, everyone sat staring emotionless at the rector as he read the funeral service. Alexander studied the crowd and wondered who would be the next to die. Were any of them pondering the same question? The two Cunningham orphans sat with William Robertson and the two women from the ordinary. Alexander had been jealous of the two privileged children in the past, but now he felt sorry for them. When the service was over, they followed the women closely as they left the church. Once again, an abbreviated service was held at the grave and the people quickly scattered. Elizabeth had not attended, neither had Sarah Cary. Henry Cary was there, but Alexander did not have an opportunity to speak to him. After the crowd left, the boy stood alone in the churchyard, shivering from the cold wind that was blowing. He watched as the casket was lowered into the ground. All the anger and hatred he had once reserved for Susanna Allen was gone. Now, he only felt sadness. He turned and walked toward the ordinary.

Cooper had a blazing fire going in the fireplace. David and Jane Cunningham sat at the table nearest the fire with William Robertson and Thomas Jones. The two women were bringing food and tea to the table. Alexander stood beside the fire warming himself. Cooper stood almost motionless in the next room watching the men at the table and awaiting any command that either may have for him. Mr. Robertson sat quietly sipping on his tea for a few minutes and then turned to look at Cooper.

"Miss Allen stated in her will that she wanted you to go to Mr. Cunningham's plantation to work. For the present time, you will stay here and care for the animals until we can dispose of them." Turning to Alexander he said, "She wanted you to go there too unless we can find something else for you. For now, you will continue at the blacksmith shop. We may be able to have your hours increased there for wages. When you are not there, I expect you to be here. You are still responsible for the water, the wood, and the fires. When you are not here Cooper will take care of them. These two ladies are going to stay here temporarily to care for the children and prepare the meals. They will have something for both of you to eat later and will call you. For now, you may be excused to go to your places, just be sure you keep the fires going."

"Yes sir," said Cooper, as he moved towards the rear door.

"Yes sir," said the boy, and walked towards the basement steps.

The fire in the basement room was almost out but the room was still warm. Alexander placed several pieces of wood on the coals and they blazed into flames, casting eerie shadows about the room. He sat down on the stool and stared into the flames. He thought of the day at Reverend Sclater's house when they sat by the fire. That was the day he learned that his father was dead, killed by two worthless robbers. It had been only a short time since his mother's tragic death on the ship, brought about by selfish, evil men. He thought about John Timberlake, a talented, fun-loving man, who enjoyed living. His life was quickly snuffed out by some unknown illness. Next, it was David Cunningham and now Susanna Allen. So many people that were important to him were dead. Was it his fault? Was God punishing him for some wrong he had done? If so, who would be next? "Oh God," he whispered, "please don't let anything happen to Elizabeth!" A strange feeling crept over him when he realized he had prayed. He couldn't remember praying since he had lived in America and he knew why. He was angry with God. Why had God let all these bad things happen to him? Why? Reverend Sclater had tried to answer that question for him, but now he couldn't remember what he said. He only remembered that the Pastor said, "God loves you and does care what happens to you. You must ask Him to help you and believe that he will." The boy sat staring into the fire for a long time, his eyes blurred by tears. Finally he whispered, "God, please help me."

For the next few weeks, nothing changed at the ordinary except that Alexander's hours did increase at the blacksmith shop. He liked working there and was quick to learn the skills. He wished he could finish his time there and become skilled at the trade, it would be helpful to him when he moved to the wilderness. When he wasn't helping the smith, he usually spent his time making nails. One day, as he was busily making nails, he glanced up to see William Robertson talking with the blacksmith. He had been so absorbed in his work that he had not seen Robertson enter, but now he watched them talk and wondered if the conversation was about him. After about five minutes Mr. Robertson left and Mr. Tuttle resumed his work. He never mentioned the visit to the boy as they finished their work for the day.

Arriving at the ordinary, Alexander went inside hoping supper was ready and that Cooper had plenty of wood split and carried inside. William Robertson and Thomas Jones sat at a table talking. When they saw the boy, they called him to the table. This time it was Mr. Jones who spoke.

"Miss Allen gave us the responsibility of determining how you would fulfill your obligation to her. One of our options was to sell your indenture and that is what we have decided to do. We have someone interested in purchasing it and we have agreed to terms that we feel are fair to everyone. Miss Allen had a lot of debts that have to be resolved. This will help us settle her affairs and bring some resolution for you."

Alexander's mind was racing. Was it Mr. Tuttle at the blacksmith shop? He hoped it was, but it might be Mr. Goodwin at the bakery. He wished the man would hurry.

"Mr. Henry Cary, Jr. has made us an offer that we feel is acceptable. You may know Mr. Cary, he is a builder. You will be able to learn some building skills while finishing your time with him. This is pleasing to the Vestry and they have approved it. We notified Mr. Tuttle today that you will not be returning to work there, but instructed him not to say anything to you about it until we had talked to you."

"When will I begin?"

"Mr. Cary would like to talk to you after supper," said Mr. Robertson, speaking for the first time. "Do you know where he lives?"

"Yes sir," said the boy, who was having a hard time not smiling.

"After you eat, go to his home. He will be expecting you and will tell you when and where you will be moving. I expect he will want you to move tomorrow. As soon as you have an opportunity, it would be appropriate for you to go back and thank Mr. Tuttle."

"Yes sir, I will."

"The ladies are out in the kitchen. You can go out there and eat. Any questions?"

"No sir."

"Go eat, and then go see Mr. Cary."

Alexander walked quickly to the back door and stepped out into the yard. He was smiling broadly as he walked to the kitchen. He couldn't believe his good fortune. "Thank you God," he whispered, "thank you!"

Alexander hurriedly ate his supper and started for the Cary house. He was surprised when Henry Cary answered the door, and more surprised when he wasn't invited in. Stepping outside, Mr. Cary spoke in a low voice. "I apologize for not inviting you in, but Mrs. Cary is sick so I will be brief. Do you know where my father's property is on England Street?"

"Yes sir."

"Good. That's where some or my men live and where you will be moving to. I want you to move tonight. John Winfree is one of the men and he knows you are coming. John is one of the best men I've ever seen with horses. He's going to teach you to handle a team. I want you and him to leave for Yorktown at daylight to tell Reverend and Mrs. Sclater that Sarah is sick. You will take the large carriage so that if Mrs. Sclater wants to come back you can bring her. I'm not sending for her, I only want them to know Sarah is sick, but she may want to come back with you. Any questions?"

"No sir. I'm sorry about Mrs. Cary."

"Thank you. Do you need any help getting your things moved?"

"No sir, I can do it."

"Good. I'll see you tomorrow when you return from Yorktown," said Cary as he turned toward the door.

"Mr. Cary."

"Yes?"

"Thank you for helping me."

"You're welcome. I'm glad it's worked out this way."

Returning to the ordinary, Alexander gathered up his few possessions and started toward England Street. As he walked toward his new home, he wondered about Mrs.

Cary's illness. How sick was she? Did she have the same illness that killed Susanna Allen and so many others? One minute he was worrying about Mrs. Cary dying and Elizabeth getting sick, and the next minute he was trembling with excitement about the opportunity he now had to begin a new life. He was also excited about the trip to see the Sclaters tomorrow and the opportunity he would have to learn to handle horses.

Wedding Plans

Alexander could see Elizabeth waiting for him just inside the Cary's gate. They both looked forward to their Sunday afternoon walks together. It was one of the few times they saw each other during the week. They strolled past the Capitol and turned onto Duke of Gloucester Street, walking toward the college buildings they could see in the distance. When the came to the ordinary, Elizabeth stopped at the gate. For several minutes she stood staring at the small kitchen, sitting deserted in the back yard.

"Do you want to walk over there?" asked Alexander.

"No. I was just thinking about some of the things that have happened since I lived here. Mister Cunningham died. Miss Allen died. Sarah Cary died, and now, Mr. Cary has married again."

"He sure didn't wait long, did he?"

"No. Not long at all."

"Do you like his new wife?"

"I do. The children like her too, but I really miss Sarah. She was like a sister to me."

"She was young enough to be your sister. How old was she?"

"She was only twenty four."

"Do the children mention her often?"

"The boys don't, but Mary does. She still cries for her Mama."

"I wonder why she died?"

"I don't know and I don't think the doctor knew. She hadn't been well since I lived there, but she never complained. We talked about a lot of things, but she never talked about herself."

They stood in silence for a few more moments, and then resumed walking.

"Mrs. Cary is going to have a baby," said Elizabeth.

"Did she tell you?"

"No. She hasn't mentioned it yet, but I can tell."

"Wonder what the children will think about a baby?"

"They'll love it," said Elizabeth, smiling. "Children love babies."

"I wonder how the Sclaters will feel about it?"

"I don't know. I felt so sorry for them when Sarah died. Her mother hardly left her side the week before she died. I don't think she ever slept."

"They are a very close family. They had another daughter that died when she was nine years old."

"How do you know?"

"Reverend Sclater told me. He said his wife nearly grieved herself to death."

"They haven't been back to visit since Mr. Cary married Miss Edwards. The children miss them and keep asking their daddy when Grandma and Grandpa are coming to see them."

When they reached the end of the street, they turned left. When they came to Ireland Street, they turned left again and walked to Queen Street, passing the house where Alexander and some of the other workers lived. John Winfree was standing outside and they stopped to talk with him. Although he was much older than Alexander, they had become good friends. Just as Mr. Cary had said, John was an expert with horses.

"Alexander told me you were teaching him about horses," said Elizabeth.

"That I am, and he's a quick learner. I'm worried he may get my job," laughed Winfree.

"You don't have anything to be afraid of," said Alexander with a chuckle.

Turning left again on Queen Street, they walked one block to Francis Street, turned right, and started back towards the Carys.

As they drew closer to the house, they could see the three children playing in the yard under the watchful eye of their stepmother, Anne Cary.

"Does she enjoy the children?" asked Alexander.

"She does. She spends a lot of time with them every day. I think that pleases Mr. Cary. When she's with the children, she expects me to oversee the household work."

"Do the slaves resent you doing that?"

"No. We all work together, just like we did with Dinah and Cooper at the ordinary."

Mary was the first to see Alexander and Elizabeth approaching. She ran to the fence waving and calling to them. Her two younger brothers followed her.

"Can we go meet them?" asked Mary.

Both boys began jumping up and down, pleading for permission to go.

"Let's all of us go," said Anne Cary, opening the gate and stepping out into the street. "Your father doesn't want you in the street alone."

Alexander felt like a celebrity as the three children came rushing up the street with their stepmother following closely behind them.

The happy group made their way back to the yard and closed the gate behind them.

"Can Alexander stay for supper?" asked Doyley. Immediately, the other two children joined in, repeating the request. Caught off guard by the question, Anne Cary stumbled over her words while trying to come up with an answer. Alexander was embarrassed as the children continued their verbal barrage so he began to try to excuse himself from the awkward situation.

"If we have a vote on this, it's quite obvious who will win," said Henry Cary, who had been watching from the porch, unobserved by the others.

"Can he stay?" cried Mary, redirecting the question to her father.

"He's welcome to stay unless he has other plans, but you'll

have to help the women with the food."

"I'll help," said Mary.

"We will too!" said the boys.

Anne Cary was trying to follow the rapid exchange of words. Finally she said, "Well now that it's settled, lets go get everything ready."

"The children and I will do it," said Elizabeth, "the food is already prepared."

"That's an excellent idea," said Henry Cary. "Alexander, why don't you join me and Mrs. Cary inside while we wait for them?"

Alexander felt very uncomfortable as he followed the couple into the house. He had never felt that way before during his visits when Sarah was living. Neither had he felt insecure in the past when he and Mr. Cary had talked, but things were different now. Before, he was there as a friend of the Sclaters, or for business. Now, he was a servant being entertained by the master and his wife. A wife he did not know well enough to feel comfortable with. He wondered how she really felt about him being there.

Mr. Cary waited for his wife to be seated and then took a seat beside her. Without looking at the boy, he said to him, "John tells me you are doing well with the horses. Do you enjoy working with them?" Before Alexander could answer, Cary turned, and seeing the boy still standing said, "Have a seat."

"I love working with the horses," said Alexander as he settled himself uneasily in a chair across from the Carys. "I've enjoyed everything I've done since I began working for you. I like learning to do different things."

"Do you still plan to go to the wilderness to live someday?"

Alexander wished he hadn't asked that question. He was afraid he would appear ungrateful if he said he did, but it had been his plan for years. It was more than a plan; it was part of his dream. Not only his dream, but also Elizabeth's dream.

174

"Yes sir," said Alexander, avoiding looking the man in the eyes.

"Why would you want to do that?" asked Anne Cary.

Alexander looked at her and knew that her question was asked in sincerity. She was not being reproachful, but truly could not comprehend why anyone would want to live in the wilderness. He smiled and said, "I can be a landowner there. There's a lot of free land and some cheap land in the wilderness. It's good land that has never been tilled. Lots of game for food and clean, pure, water. It's a healthy place to live and raise a family."

"What about Indians? And wolves, and bears, and outlaws? And how will you make money?"

"Those questions will take more than a few minutes to answer," laughed Henry Cary. "Maybe we had better wait until after supper for that. I think they have the food ready."

Unlike the indentured years Alexander spent in the barbershop and ordinary, the months now seemed to speed quickly by. His interesting work kept him busy six days a week. On Sunday, he would usually sleep a little later, meet Elizabeth at church, and after dinner, spend the remainder of the day with her. He never grew tired of her company. One Sunday morning as he waited outside Bruton Parish Church, the hour arrived for the service to begin and she was not there. Neither were the Carys. As the service started, Alexander slipped out the gate and began walking toward the Cary's house, sensing something was wrong. His concern was justified when he saw the doctor's carriage parked out front. He dared not go in, but he wanted to know what was wrong. Circling the house, he went to the cottage in the back yard, but found Elizabeth was not there. His anxiety was increasing as he hurried to the kitchen. Two slaves were busy at the fireplace.

"Where's Miss Elizabeth?" he asked.

"Inside, helpin' da doctor."

"Who's sick?"

"Miz Cary. She's havin a baby and it ain't her time."

Alexander stepped back outside and just stood there. He knew there was nothing he could do, but he didn't want to leave. He was trying to decide what he should do when Henry Cary came to the door and motioned for him. He hurried across the yard as Mr. Cary stepped down from the porch and waited for him.

"Do you know what's going on inside?" asked the man.

Alexander was afraid to answer. It was none of his business and he had intruded, but he could not lie. "Yes sir. I was worried when you didn't come to church so I came to see what was wrong. I asked the cooks and they told me. I'm sorry."

"Thank you. Would you like to help us?"

"If I can," said the frightened young man, wondering what he could do to help.

"Will you take the children for a walk and keep them away for a few hours?"

"Yes sir. I'll take care of them for you."

"Good. I'll get them ready and send them out to you. When you come back, check with me before you let them come inside. They know what's going on, but try not to discuss it with them. If they bring it up, change the subject."

"Yes sir."

"I'll tell Elizabeth you are here, but you will have to wait until later to see her," said Henry Cary as he walked towards the house.

Anne Cary gave birth to a little girl and they named her Anne, after her mother. She struggled courageously for her life, but died when she was only two days old. They buried her the next day at Bruton Parish Church. The small group of people who attended the burial service would stand in sharp contrast to the next group that would assemble there. A few days later, Dr. William Cocke, Governor Spottswood's physician, died suddenly while attending General Court. His funeral was attended by all the principal gentlemen of the entire country who, along with the Governor, showed a great display of emotion over the loss of one held in such high esteem.

The death of the Cary's baby girl was not the end of the sorrow the family would face that year. A short time later, Henry Cary, Jr. was notified of the death of his father, who had also been a prominent builder in the area. The courthouse of York County, the fort on York River, the first Capitol at Williamsburg, William and Mary College, and most of the Governor's Palace were among the public buildings contracted by the senior Mr. Cary. Although both men owned property in Williamsburg and spent much of their time there, they still called "The Forest" their home. The plantation was located about twenty miles southeast of Williamsburg on the peninsula between the York and the James Rivers. It was the western half of the Warwick plantation, part of a patent received by Henry Cary Senior's father, the immigrant, Miles Cary. As soon as he received word of his father's death, Henry Cary left for "The Forest."

Alexander had just returned from the mill with a load of lumber and was helping the men unload it and carry it into the building. John Winfree looked towards an approaching carriage and said, "I wonder when he came back?"
Glancing in that direction, Alexander saw Henry Cary driving towards them.
"I don't suppose his wife was able to go to the funeral, so he was probably anxious to get home to see how she is doing," said one the men.
"He had to come back to be sure you were working," said another. They both laughed.
Mr. Cary climbed down from the carriage, spoke to the men, and walked into the building. When the foreman saw him, he came straight to him and they began talking. As they talked, they walked about the building, examining the work that had been completed in the past few days. After looking at some of the lumber Alexander had delivered, Mr. Cary returned to his carriage and drove away. When the material

was unloaded, the men returned to their work and Alexander climbed into the empty wagon to move it away from the building. Just as he sat down and reached for the reins, the foreman approached. "We won't need the wagon any more today. Take it back, unhitch the team, and feed and water them. By the time you do that, it'll be quitting time so you can go home. After supper, Mr. Cary wants to see you at his house."

Alexander nodded, and said, "Yes sir."

As he drove away, he wondered why Mr. Cary wanted to see him.

Unlike his last trip to the Cary's, Elizabeth met him at the door and ushered him into the front room where Mr. Cary and his wife were sitting. Alexander was not expecting to see Mrs. Cary there. It must have been evident by the expression on his face since she smiled and said, "You seem surprised to see me, Alexander."

"Yes I am...but I'm glad you're well...I mean, I'm glad you're feeling better."

"Thank you. I am feeling better. I just need to regain my strength. Elizabeth has been taking real good care of me, especially while Mr. Cary was away for his father's funeral."

"I was sorry to hear about your father."

"Thank you Alexander. He had lived a good, full life and accomplished a lot."

"If you two will excuse me, I am going to lie down and rest," said Anne Cary, as she slowly stood. Her husband also stood as Elizabeth hurried to her side to escort her from the room. Stopping in front of Alexander, who was still standing, she said, "Thank you for helping with the children that day. Henry told me about it."

"You're welcome. I was glad to do it."

After the women had left the room, Mr. Cary said, "Sit down. I have something I want you to do and I need to talk to you about it."

Alexander sat down facing Mr. Cary.

"Reverend and Mrs. Sclater attended my father's funeral. It's the first time I've seen them since I remarried. They were upset because I married so quickly after Sarah's death so they haven't come to visit us. I knew they were disturbed by it so I haven't been there either. It has been terribly unfair to both them and the children, but I didn't think I would be welcome. Now, they want the grandchildren to come visit them for a fortnight. This would be a fine time for them to go while Anne is recovering her health. I want you to take the carriage and carry them tomorrow. You may spend the night and return the following day. I would allow Elizabeth to go with you, but we really need her here now. Perhaps she will be able to go with you when you return to pick them up. Mr. Winfree has assured me that you are capable of doing this; otherwise, I would never trust the lives of my children to your care. Please believe me that it is not without apprehension that I do this. I hope that you will take every precaution to insure their safety."

"I will. I'll be very careful and if it would cause you less worry, I'll return tomorrow evening so that you will know they are safe."

"No, that's not necessary. I know you'll be careful and you will enjoy your time with the Sclaters. And please, don't discuss with them what I just told you about them being upset with me about my marriage. That's behind us now and I think we will be able to rebuild our friendship. They are fine people and I want them to be able to enjoy a good relationship with my children."

It was shortly after daylight when Alexander arrived at the Cary home with the carriage. He had never seen three children more excited than the ones he found waiting for him inside. They were all talking at once and each one was clinging to their baggage. The children received their final instructions from their father before they loaded up to leave. Elizabeth had tears in her eyes and Henry Cary seemed deeply moved as the carriage pulled away from the gate. Alexander remembered another day, long ago, when another wagon, driven by his grandfather, drove away from his weeping grandmother, into the early morning mist. He quickly put the thoughts from his mind so he could concentrate on driving. He remembered his promise to Henry Cary.

It was a beautiful day and the trip was uneventful except for the powerful memories that flooded his mind at various points along the route. Most of them concerned his night walk from Williamsburg to Yorktown. The first was the place where he had hidden from the approaching carriage and had the close encounter with the dogs. The next was the road to his father's house and grave, and the grove of trees where he slept. Then he passed the place where the man had given him a ride and fed him the apples. Finally, he came to the street leading to Yorktown where he had arrived on the *Bristol Merchant*. He would not allow himself to dwell on any of these memories, but forced himself instead to concentrate on the children and their safe delivery to the Sclaters. Their arrival was like a well-rehearsed play. As the carriage turned into the lane leading to the Sclaters, the family suddenly appeared outside to greet them. Alexander stayed seated with the reins held tightly in his hands as the children climbed from the carriage into the waiting arms of their grandparents. He was afraid the commotion might cause the horses to bolt. It wasn't until everyone had moved away from the carriage that he climbed down to unload baggage and receive his own greetings from the family.

The two weeks passed quickly and it was time for Alexander to return to Yorktown for the children. True to his word, Henry Cary allowed Elizabeth to travel with him. For weeks, she had been totally devoted to the care of Anne Cary who was now greatly improved. It would provide a much-deserved break for Elizabeth. For both of them, it was symbolic of a life they had never known, but one that they had dreamed about and believed would one day be theirs. It was a trip that they would always remember. The Sclaters treated them like family and did everything within their power to make the brief stay a pleasant one. Mary was the only one of the Sclater children still living at home. Because of their closeness in age, her and Elizabeth shared a room and spent most of the night talking.

After breakfast the next morning, Alexander asked, "Do you remember the things that I left with you that belonged to my mother?"

"Yes," said Mrs. Sclater, "we still have them."

"May I see the dress?"

"Certainly, I'll get it for you."

A hush fell over the room. Elizabeth and Mary glanced at each other with puzzled looks on their faces. Mary knew about the things, but Alexander had never told Elizabeth. It had always been too painful for him to talk about the dress, but now he knew what he wanted to do with it and he needed to see it again. In just a minute, Mrs. Sclater returned with a package, wrapped the way it had been for years, and handed it to Alexander. His hands were trembling as he unwrapped the dress and lifted it from the package. He looked at it briefly and handed it to Elizabeth. "Stand up and hold it in front of you." Carefully unfolding the dress, the girl held it against her body.

"It's beautiful," said Mary.

"It certainly is," said Mrs. Sclater, "and well made."

"My mother and grandmother worked on it a long time. She wanted to wear it for my Daddy. She hadn't seen him for over five years and wanted to look pretty for him."

The three children sat spellbound, looking at the dress and listening to Alexander.

"I believe it will fit Elizabeth," said Reverend Sclater, "she must be about the same size."

"Why don't you try it on?" asked Alexander.

"I couldn't do that."

"I want you to."

"Try it on!" said the children.

Elizabeth was blushing as she turned to Mary and said, "May

181

I use your room?" The two girls disappeared upstairs and returned in a few minutes with Elizabeth wearing the dress. It was a perfect fit.

"I want that to be your wedding dress," said Alexander.

Elizabeth looked shocked.

"Is there some news that we don't know about?" asked Reverend Sclater with a smile.

Alexander's face reddened as he answered. "When I am a freedman, we plan to be married. I would like to be married here instead of Williamsburg and for you to perform the ceremony."

"I see no reason why we can't do that."

"We would be honored," said Mrs. Sclater. We will make sure you have a nice wedding."

With tears streaming down her face, Elizabeth asked, "Will you keep the dress for me?"

"If that's what you want."

"I do," said the girl, as she turned and left the room.

Free At Last!

Alexander had just arrived at the job-site when the foreman told him to take the wagon and go to Henry Cary's house. Cary was watching for him and met him at the gate. "I want you to drive me to Yorktown," said Cary, as he climbed into the wagon. "The *Cary Gally* came in late yesterday and I'm suppose to have a large shipment on board. If everything came that I ordered it will be more than I can bring home in the carriage."

As Alexander turned the horses towards the Yorktown Road, he asked, "What's the *Cary Gally*?"

"It's one of the ships that belongs to my family."

"Do you have family members there who send you what you want?"

"No, I order through Noblett Ruddock, a merchant I know in Bristol. He has many trading interests and usually finds what I need. He is a fair trader and happy to receive Virginia tobacco for payment."

"How often does your ship go back and forth to Bristol?"

"Normally it goes twice a year."

"Does it carry passengers too?"

"It can carry a few comfortably."

Moored to the dock, the little ship rested motionless in the still water of the York River. It was much closer to the shore than the *Bristol Merchant* had been able to approach.

"Stay with the wagon until I check the Bill of Lading and see what we have," said Henry Cary as he climbed down from the wagon. In a short time he returned smiling. "We have a wagon full. Some of the men will help you load it."

For the next two hours the men loaded the wagon with iron, pewter, rugs, stockings, hats, linen, several varieties of cloth, saws, nails, gunpowder, sugar, blankets, tin ware, linens, horse harness, saddles, shoes, gloves, cutlery, lead shot, tobacco pipes, port wine, and haberdashery. The team strained at the heavily laden wagon as they climbed the bluff road from the harbor and started the slow journey home.

Alexander and Elizabeth were counting the slow-passing months until they could marry. They could hardly contain their excitement. Henry Cary found much pleasure in teasing them, especially Elizabeth. Arriving home one evening, Cary found the young woman sitting in the dining room, holding his year old son, Archibald, and talking with his wife, Anne. After exchanging greetings with his wife, he turned to Elizabeth and said, "Well, it seems you will have to put off your wedding plans for another year."
"Why?"
"I learned today that Alexander's indenture paper is wrong. He has another year to serve."
Elizabeth laughed. "I know better. I've read that indenture too many times."
"And what does it say?"
"December 9, 1722."
"But don't forget, he had another year added to it when he ran away."
"It wasn't a year, it was three months. His time is up in March."
"Surely you'll want to wait a few more years before getting married?"
"We have no reason to wait."
"You need to wait until Archibald is old enough to remember your wedding."
"I'll tell him about it."
"When do you plan for the wedding to be?"
"In March."
"I'm sure that will not be a good time. Reverend Sclater will probably be much too busy preparing for Easter. You'll also be busy here so I think it would be better to wait a few months. Have you ever considered a Christmas wedding?"
"We've already waited long enough."

"Well, I must warn you. If you insist, we can only let you have one day off from work."

Anne Cary, who had listened quietly to the amusing exchange, finally spoke. "I think the spring season is a wonderful time for a marriage."

"Is this some kind of conspiracy? Has my own wife turned against me? I shall talk to the Parish Minister tomorrow about your disobedience!"

"You'll feel better after you've had your supper dear," said Mrs. Cary, rising to her feet. "You sit here and spend some time with your son while we see if it's ready."

Everyone laughed as she took the baby from Elizabeth and placed him in Henry Cary's arms.

Christmas decorations had already begun to appear on the streets of Williamsburg. Alexander loved the Christmas season although some of them had not been good. He would never forget his first one in Williamsburg. It was the worst Christmas he could remember. As he recalled the year when he and Elizabeth were guests of the Carys he smiled. But this year would be a special Christmas for him. It would be his last one as a servant. In a few months, he would be free, and then he would be married. For years he had dreamed of this day. Stopping briefly near the Barber Shop, he stared at the window in the upstairs room where he slept his first night in Williamsburg and thought about the sights and sounds of that night. It was the first time he went to sleep while dreaming his dream. Across the street, the ordinary that was once a hub of activity, sat deserted. He remembered the first time he saw Elizabeth there and how he had immediately included her in his dream. She had been an important part of his life and his dream for almost ten years. Soon she would be his wife and another part of his dream would become true.

"Mr. Cary said for me to invite you to supper on Christmas Day," said Elizabeth as they walked to church the Sunday before Christmas.

"Good. I love being there at Christmas. I often think of our first Christmas there."

"Me too. The Sclaters will be there this year too."

"Really? They haven't been since Sarah died."

"I know. It will probably be very hard for all of them. They've never met Mrs. Cary but I'm sure they will like her."

"And she will like them too. They are all wonderful people."

"I hope we can talk with Reverend Sclater about our wedding."

"What's there to talk about?"

"When it will be. Whether we can stay with them awhile or if we need to come back here after the wedding."

"Oh. I never thought about that."

Elizabeth looked at him and smiled, but said nothing.

On Christmas Day, Alexander watched the Sclaters and the Carys as they interacted with one another. They seemed very comfortable in each other's presence, but one thing really concerned him about Reverend Sclater. There was something different about him since the last time he had seen him. He did not appear well and seemed to be weary. Perhaps he was just tired from the trip. After supper, the three men sat by the fire talking.

"Alexander tells me you've agreed to marry him and Elizabeth," said Henry Cary.

"Unless they've changed their mind," said Reverend Sclater, with a sly smile.

"I've been trying to get them to, but I haven't had much success."

"I understand. Sometimes it's hard to get young people to listen to reason."

"I think I might persuade Alexander, but Elizabeth is the stubborn one."

"No sir, you can't persuade me either," said Alexander.

"When do you plan to get married?" asked the minister.

"As soon as we can after the ninth of March."

"What's so important about that date?"

"That's when I'll be free."

"And you've decided to give up your freedom again so quickly?"

"See! I told you he has lost his sense of reason," laughed Henry Cary.

"That's certainly a serious decision. Obviously we want to help if you insist on going forward with your plan. I'll talk to Mrs. Sclater and we'll work out all the details before we return home. I'm sure you'll be able to stay with us for a while. But remember, you have three months to change your mind. If Henry can convince you, be sure to let me know!"

Alexander smiled, but said nothing. Secretly, he enjoyed the teasing from the two men.

On the first Sunday evening in March, Henry Cary arranged a meeting with Alexander and Elizabeth after supper.

"Alexander, in a few days you will be a free man. I have several things that I need to discuss with you. I know the plans that you and Elizabeth have for marriage and we will discuss that in more detail shortly. I also know of your desire to go to the wilderness. That's what I want to discuss with you first. Is that something the two of you plan to do immediately or later?"

"Later. We will need a lot of things to take with us and we have nothing. We plan to work until we are able to get what we need. I don't know how long that will take."

"That's a wise decision. Most people try to go too quickly and suffer for it because they are ill prepared. Would you like to continue to work for me?"

"Both of us?"

"Both of you."

"Yes sir."

"Mrs. Cary and I would love for Elizabeth to continue working for us just as she does now. You can also continue working for me except that we both will have more freedom in our decisions about what you do. I will pay you fair wages, but you will be responsible for your own keep. Does that sound fair to both of you?"

"Yes sir," said the two of them in harmony.

"Would you like to continue to live in the cottage, or do you think it's too small?"

"I love the cottage," said Elizabeth. "It would be perfect for us."

"Then we can continue to allow it to be part of your compensation." Turning to Alexander, he smiled and said, "Young man, you're lucky. You don't have to pay rent. That's more money you can use to buy wilderness supplies."

"Have you ever been to the wilderness?" asked Elizabeth.

"Only a short distance beyond The Falls."

"What's it like?"

"It's quite different. It is mostly forestland with different kinds of trees from what we have here. The air seems cleaner and there are many swift streams of clear water. Although I didn't see any Indians, they still live there. They are from a different tribe than our Indians, they are Monacans. There are many wolves and some bison. Not many people live there, but there are lots of wild animals."

"That sounds like a scary place."

"It's not a place for the faint-hearted, but it is a place with promise. The future of this land lies in our ability to conquer the wilderness and move further west. Frankly, I'm disappointed that it has taken our people so long to settle this land. It has been well over one hundred years since Jamestown and we have scarcely moved beyond The Falls."

"I have a question for you too," said Alexander. "Doyle told me that he was going to our wedding next week, is he?"

"I'll have to talk to that young man. He's giving away our family secrets. I suppose he heard me talking about it to my wife. Yes, we're all going. That was the final thing I wanted to talk with you about this evening. Reverend and Mrs. Sclater want us to come. We will all go there Friday and the wedding will be Saturday morning at Charles Parish Church. The Sclaters are preparing dinner for everyone afterward. That's the part I'm looking forward to!"

"I can hardly believe it," said Elizabeth, with tears in her eyes, "I'm so glad you're going."

"There's more. We were coming home Saturday afternoon, but the Sclaters want us to stay and attend church with them Sunday. They said that you could also stay if you would like to, but I thought you may want to come back here to your cottage."

"I want to come back here," said Elizabeth.

"Me too," said Alexander.

"That's fine. If I were you, I would come back too. You may drive the small carriage and you can return at the appropriate time. I will notify the servants of your plans. Do you have any other questions?"

"Not me," said Elizabeth.

"Me either," said Alexander. "I just want to thank you for all you've done for us. I can never repay you, but I want to try. You will not be sorry for giving us this chance."

"God has been kind to me. My life circumstances have been very different from yours, through no merits of my own. It is only by His grace that I can be the helper and not the helped."

As Henry Cary stood, Elizabeth jumped to her feet and hugged his neck. "Thank you," she said, with a quivering voice. Briefly overcome by emotion, the man wiped a tear from his eye with the back of his hand and said, "Both of you are welcome."

Alexander and Elizabeth were only expecting to see the Sclaters and Carys at their wedding, but were pleasantly surprised to see others. They were especially glad to see James Sclater and his sister Martha with their spouses. More than a dozen parishioners from Charles Parish had also attended, in addition to John Winfree and two other workers who lived with Alexander. The traditional service was simple, moving, and over quickly. Outside the church, the small crowd of people filed past the young couple, giving them their best wishes before dispersing. The only ones left was the group that was returning to the Sclaters.

"Elizabeth, you look perfectly beautiful," said James Sclater.

"I love that dress!" said his wife.

189

"Thank you," said the new bride.

"That's the dress that Alexander brought with him from England," said Mary. "It was his Mother's dress."

"It looks new," said Martha, who had been listening to the exchange.

"It's the one your parents kept for me," said Alexander. "My mother and grandmother made it. Mum never did get to wear it."

"I'm sure she would have looked lovely in it also," said Mrs. Sclater. "She would be very pleased if she could be here today and see how perfectly it fits her daughter-in-law and how lovely it looks on her."

"Thank you," said Elizabeth, blushing. "I think it's wonderful that I could wear it today since it's what Alexander wanted."

The huge dining room table was laden with food, and every seat was taken. It was a joyful occasion for all of them. The two families seemed delighted to show their support to the young couple who had endured so many hardships in their brief lives and were now beginning a new life together. There was no hint that there had ever been a broken relationship between the Sclaters and the Carys and Anne Cary seemed to be accepted unconditionally by all the members of the Sclater family. Seeing James and Martha again was a special treat for the newlyweds and an opportunity for them to reminisce about their childhood memories

"Ladies and gentlemen, we are having a delightful time," said Henry Cary, "but we need to show some consideration to Alexander and Elizabeth. They have a long trip ahead of them and if we detain them much longer, they will have a cold and dangerous trip back to Williamsburg after dark. I propose a final toast to them for safe travel, and suggest we dismiss them."

"A thoughtful proposal," said Reverend Sclater. "I suppose the rest of us are so content with our current state that we aren't thinking about the well being of others. The truth of the matter is that I had forgotten they planned to leave!"

"You are welcome to stay if you would like," said Mrs. Sclater, "we have room."

"Thank you," said Elizabeth, "but I suppose we need to follow our original plan. You have done so much for us already that we will never be able to repay you."

"The happiness we have seen in your eyes today more than repays us."

"Enough of this talk about paying for acts of kindness and love," said the minister as he rose to his feet. "We need to do as Henry said and get these folks on the road."

Elizabeth waved to their friends one last time as they turned from the Glebe Road towards Yorktown and were soon out of sight.

"I'm glad Mr. Cary said what he did about us leaving," said Alexander, "I was wondering when we would get away."

"Me too. I was afraid if it got too late, they would insist we stay. How long do you think it will take us to get home?"

"We should get there before dark."

"It's going to be cold by then. I'll get a fire started while you take care of the horse."

"I don't think I'll want any supper. I'm stuffed."

"Everything was so good. I think food tastes better eaten from fine china. They were beautiful plates."

"I remembered them, they use them every Sunday. When I get rich I will buy you some."

Elizabeth laughed. "I guess I'll have to wait a long time."

They rode in silence for several minutes.

"What are you thinking about?" asked Alexander.

"Us."

"What about us?"

"Everything. How we met and how long we've been friends. The hard life we had for so many years. Our dreams and how long we waited to be free. How good God has been to let us live when so many people around us have died. I hope He let's us live many more years together. I never want to live without you. Remember that time you ran away and left me?"

"I remember but I don't like to. I came down here to get Reverend Sclater to help me."

"I didn't know where you were. I was afraid you wouldn't come back. When you did come back, I was mad enough at you to kill you!"

"See that clump of pines over there? That's where I slept that night. I nearly froze."

"You deserved it for not telling me you were leaving."

"I couldn't tell you. If I had, you could have gotten in trouble."

"You're the one that's going to get in trouble if you leave me again," said Elizabeth as she poked him in the ribs with her elbow.

"Yes, Mrs. Stinson," he said, laughing.

"Oh that sounds funny."

"It does, doesn't it?"

"I love it!"

"Mr. and Mrs. Stinson will take some getting used to."

"You know what I'm looking forward to?"

"What?"

"Sitting downstairs at church with all the gents and their ladies."

"Tomorrow?"

"No. We'll sleep late tomorrow and then I'll fix your breakfast."

"I like that plan."

It was beginning to get dark when they pulled up to the Cary house. The first thing Elizabeth noticed was smoke coming from the cottage chimney. "Someone's in the cottage," she said. Alexander tied the horse to the post and hurried across the yard. As he reached for the door, it opened. There stood Mandy, one of the older slaves.

"Praise da Lawd, ya'll home safe. I'm so happy for ya'll chilluns I could shout!"

"What are you doing here?" asked Elizabeth.

"Mistuh Cary tole me to be here with a fire goin' when you got home. He said if you didn't need nothing else fuh me to get my self out of here and don't come back."

"Thank you Mandy," said Elizabeth as she gave the old woman a hug.

"Ya'll want any supper?"

"No. We've had plenty to eat."

"Den I'll see ya'll tomorrow," she said, as she shuffled off across the yard.

Elizabeth went inside and Alexander went back to the carriage for their luggage. When he returned, Elizabeth was standing by the fireplace weeping.

"What's wrong?" asked Alexander.

"Look on the table."

Turning around, he saw why she was weeping. On the table were two beautiful china plates, two settings of silver, and a bottle of wine. A wedding gift from the Carys.

He reached out and took her by the hand and tried to think of something to say, but nothing seemed appropriate.

"I'll be back as soon as I take care of the carriage and horses."

When he returned, Elizabeth was standing by the table, examining the china and silver. Her tears were gone and she was smiling.

"I'm glad to see you happy."

"I've never been happier in my life."

"It's amazing what two china plates can do!"

"And I didn't have to wait until you got rich."

"We'll be the only two people in the wilderness eating from china plates with silver."

She sat the plate down on the table and walked towards her husband. Stopping with her face just inches from his, she said. "My happiness is not because of china plates, but because I have you. I love you."

He took her in his arms and they kissed. "I love you too," he said.

She leaned over and blew out the light. Only the flickering flames from the fireplace lit the room. She took him by the hand and led him towards the bed. "Tomorrow, we eat breakfast from china plates, but now, we go to bed."

More Sickness and Death

Alexander rubbed his hands briskly together as he walked from the stable to the cottage. He was glad to get home and was looking forward to sitting by the fire for a while until he got warm. He had been cold all day while working on the new building at the college. Some of the men he worked with were saying it was the coldest January they could remember. In addition to the miserable weather, the Williamsburg area was under the pall of another extended period of sickness and death. Someone had died almost every week since winter began. Every day, news came of another person being sick, and most never recovered.

Reverend Sclater was one of the first to become ill and die when the mysterious illness began in November. The ensuing weeks had done little to dull the pain Alexander felt when he thought about the death of his friend, to whom he owed such a great debt. The minister had become an advocate for the boy when there was nobody else to look after his well being. He often wondered how different his life would have been if Reverend Sclater had not been there for him. When Alexander needed him, he had always been there, but now he was gone.

Stepping quickly into the cottage and closing the door behind him he turned to greet Elizabeth. She was sitting at the table crying.
"What's wrong?" he said, rushing to her side.
"Mary's sick."
It seemed as if all his strength drained from his body when he heard those words. Dropping down on one knee beside his wife, he took her by the hand.
"Very sick?"

Elizabeth nodded her head up and down. "Doctor Blair has been here twice today."

"What did he say?"

"What do doctors ever say?" said Elizabeth angrily. "He doesn't know. He said she has a fever and anybody can tell that."

"Is Mr. Cary here?"

"He's been home all day."

"Do you think I should go over there?"

"No. The doctor said to keep everyone away except the family."

"Have you been over there?"

"I was there earlier today, but they said for me not to come back unless they sent for me. Mandy and Maude are over there. I'm so scared. I'm afraid she's going to die."

"She'll probably be better in the morning," said Alexander, trying to be encouraging, but thinking all the time how hollow and unconvincing his words sounded. He was afraid too, but wouldn't admit it or allow himself to cry.

"She's almost like my child," sobbed Elizabeth. "I've spent so much time with her."

Alexander wanted to make a proper response, but could think of nothing to say. There was a light knock on the door. Jumping to his feet, he stepped to the door and opened it. There stood Mandy.

"Mistuh Cary wants lil' Archabald to come ovah here and stay with ya'll. They gettin' his things together now."

"I'll come over and get him," said Alexander.

"No suh. I'm gonna go back and git him now. Mistuh Cary don't want ya'll over dare," said the woman as she turned back toward the house. In just a few minutes, she was back with the three-year old boy in her arms. Following close behind was Maude, another slave, with her arms filled with things for Archibald.

"We couldn't get him to eat no suppah," said Mandy.

"He can eat with us," said Elizabeth. "We were just getting ready to eat."

Reaching out to Elizabeth, the smiling little boy threw both arms around her neck. Sitting down again, she began to take off his little coat and hat. Alexander took the other items from the women and they hurried back to the house.

Having the little boy to care for during the evening hours gave the young couple some respite from thinking about Mary's grave condition. When they did remember, it was with mixed feelings of guilt and fear. Guilty that their concern could so easily be diverted from Mary's serious illness and fearful about it's outcome. When bedtime came, they climbed into their bed with the happy young lad snuggled securely between them. For a long time, Elizabeth lay awake praying silently for Mary. Alexander, who was also unable to sleep, would occasionally glance toward his wife. Neither of them spoke for fear of waking the sleeping little boy. Around midnight, Alexander slipped silently from the bed and put more wood on the fire. Shortly after returning to the warm bed, he went to sleep.

The knock on the door failed to awaken Alexander, but he awoke with a start when Elizabeth sat upright in the bed.
"What's wrong?" he asked.
Before she could answer, the knock sounded again. Rushing to the door, he found Mandy standing outside, wringing her hands.
"Mistuh Cary want you to go git Doctor Blair quick as you can. Miss Mary is worse."
Alexander hurriedly dressed and ran through the streets to the home of Archibald Blair. When he knocked on the door, a servant answered. Alexander began to deliver the message, but before he finished, the doctor was standing at the door.
"Tell Henry I'll be there in a few minutes," he said, and disappeared into the darkness.
Retracing his steps to the Cary home, he rapped at the front door. Mandy came, followed by Henry Cary.
"Doctor Blair said he would be here in a few minutes. Is there anything else I can do?"
"Just take care of my little boy, I'll send Mandy if I need

you."

Alexander stepped back into the darkness and waited. His entire body was shaking, but he knew it wasn't from the cold. In just a few minutes the doctor arrived and went inside. Alexander stood staring at the door, wanting to go in but knowing he shouldn't. He walked slowly back to the cottage.

Elizabeth was standing by the fire, visibly shaken. "Did you find out what's wrong?"

"No. The doctor is there, but I didn't go in. I asked Mr. Cary if there was anything else I could do and he said for us to just take care of Archibald."

Walking across the room, Alexander hung his coat and hat on a wall peg and turned to look at the little boy who was sleeping peacefully in the middle of the bed. When he looked back at Elizabeth he saw that she had started crying again. Crossing the room, he took her in his arms and held her close to him. She began to sob.

"Oh please God, don't let anything happen to little Mary. Please don't let her die."

Alexander could no longer hold back his tears. It had been a long time since he had cried, but now, he was blinded by the burning tears that ran freely down his cheeks. They stood by the fire embracing until a movement across the room interrupted them. Archibald was tossing about in the bed. Rushing to the bed, Elizabeth lay down beside him. Placing her hand on his back, she began to pat him gently He soon settled down and went back to sleep. Alexander added more wood to the fire before returning to bed. The young couple was up as soon as the first light of morning appeared and took turns looking out the window towards the house for a hint of what was happening inside. After breakfast, Alexander reluctantly prepared to go to work. He didn't want to leave with all the uncertainty surrounding the household. Besides, he wasn't sure if Mr. Cary wanted him to work or stay there with Elizabeth and Archibald. If Mr. Cary wanted him on call, then he shouldn't leave. His question was answered by the appearance of a very tired-looking Mandy. When he saw her leave the house, he rushed out to meet her. "How's Mary?"

"No bettuh. Da doctor's still here. Mistuh Cary said to tell you to stay home today. He mite need you here."

Elizabeth joined them in the yard. "What is the doctor doing for Mary?"

"Mostly just sittin' there with Mistuh and Miz Cary. They all look real troubled. I'm gonna go get them some food, all they doing is drinking tea."

"Can I help you do something?"

"No ma'am. Jest take care of dat baby and pray for Miz Mary."

Alexander and Elizabeth turned and walked back to the cottage. They had just sat down for breakfast when Mandy knocked again. This time she was sobbing.

"Miz Mary is gone. That po child is dead," she moaned. "Mistuh Cary wants Miz Elizabeth to come over dare."

Without saying a word, Elizabeth hurried across the yard ahead of Mandy and disappeared inside. Alexander stood staring at the house for several moments before closing the door. Walking over to the table he sat looking at the little boy, sleeping so innocently nearby. He slid the chair back from the table and turned it towards the fire. Leaning forward in the chair, he sat staring for a long time at his folded hands. When someone quietly opened the door behind him he turned in that direction. Expecting to see Elizabeth, he was surprised to see Henry Cary. He started to get to his feet, but Cary motioned for him to stay seated. Walking softly over to the bed, the man stood looking for a long time at his young son. When he turned around, tears were streaming down his face. Without speaking, he walked to the fireplace. Locking his fingers together, he placed his forearms on the mantel and laid his forehead on them. Alexander could see his body trembling as he wept.

"Why God?" he groaned. "Why?"

Alexander could not control his tears nor did he try. He hoped that little Archibald would not wake up at that

e in a deplorable state because the previous two
have been negligent of their duties. The Burgesses
t and have just relieved the last man of his job.
f the arms are unusable and must be returned to
condition. The safety of the colony depends upon

going to do it?"
old him I would. Obviously, I do not have the time
ysical means to repair the arms, but I told him I
responsible for getting it done. I want you to help

examine each weapon. Those needing no repair,
clean and keep in good order through regular
. Those needing repair you will take to John
gunsmith, and return them when they are finished.
ntain the records. It will be a good opportunity for
ake some extra money and learn some new skills
erve you well in the wilderness. Would you like to
o that?"
love to," said Alexander, smiling. "When do we

k. We will need a full day to do the inspection so
know which day it will be. I will have to choose
en I can be away from the work at the college for
ay.
pend the night with Alexander and Elizabeth?"
hibald shyly as he came to the table and stood
father.
ght son, they will be busy taking care of their

ps all the time. They don't have to take care of

bably wish that John slept all the time," laughed
y, "but he doesn't. Maybe you can stay another
he gets older."
can," said Alexander. "And maybe your mother
ou back to see baby John tomorrow."

moment and find them both crying. After a while the man
became calm, but still continued to lean against the mantel
and stare down into the fire. After a long interlude, Henry
Cary turned and walked over to the table. Sitting down
across from Alexander, he said, "I apologize for that display
of emotion, I had no right to subject you to that. I needed to
get away from the house for a few minutes and also wanted
to check on my son."
"You owe me no apology, sir. I've asked that same question
before."
"Did you find an answer?"
"No."
"Why is there so much death in this wretched place? I don't
understand it. I'm going to move my family, away from
here."
Alexander stared at him in surprise. "Where?" he asked.
"West. Upriver. Away from towns."
"The wilderness?"
"Maybe not that far, just where there are less people. Over
250 people live crowded together in this town. I think it's
unhealthy so I'm going to move."
"When?"
"I don't know. I have no plan, just the desire. Don't
mention it to anyone yet."
"I won't."
"I need to get back over to the house," said Mr. Cary as he
stood up and walked toward the door.

The next few days were appalling. Many of the friends and
neighbors who normally would have been so responsive to
the needs of the Cary family stayed away because of fear.
The weary family and household workers had additional
duties piled upon them because of the funeral, burial, and the
visitors who did come. The January days that followed
Mary's death remained unchanged from the gloomy ones
that had preceded it. Alexander and Elizabeth continued to
care for Archibald who seemed to be unaware of the unusual
events that were taking place around him. Twelve-year-old

"Right now, we need to go home," said Mr. Cary. "We've taken enough of their time tonight and it will soon be your bedtime."

The young couple said goodnight to their friends and bolted the door. They walked across the room to the crib and stood gazing at their tiny baby.
"Guess who else is going to have a baby?" said Elizabeth.
"Who?"
"Mrs. Cary."
"How do you know?"
"She told me today."
"When?"
"Early November."
"What will Archibald think about that?"
They both laughed.
"We'll probably never see him over here after that," said Alexander.
"I pray that things go well for them. I hope they have another little girl."

On Wednesday of the following week the two men spent the day at the Magazine inspecting the weapons and documenting what they found.
"Why don't you take these two rifles over to John Brush now," said Henry Cary. "They don't require as much repair as some of the others and we can get them back quicker. We'll save the worst for last."
"Does he know I'll be bringing them?" asked Alexander.
"Yes. I told him we would have some there before he closed today. I'll finish the paperwork while you take the guns."
Outside, they had just finished changing the guard. Alexander stepped through the door carrying the two rifles and started for the street.
"Halt!"
Turning towards the voice, Alexander froze in his tracks. A young British lieutenant was aiming a cocked pistol directly at him.

203

"Where are you going with those weapons?" he asked in a loud voice.

"To the gunsmith," responded Alexander.

"And who gave you permission to remove weapons from this magazine?" said the officer, still holding the pistol only a few feet from Alexander's face.

"I did," roared Henry Cary as he stepped outside the magazine. "Put that pistol down!"

"And who are you?" said lieutenant, never flinching.

"I'm Henry Cary, the new Keeper of the Magazine. I authorized this man to deliver these guns to the gunsmith for repair. Put that pistol away."

"You have no authority to remove weapons from this magazine on my watch. My guards have orders to protect these weapons. Neither do you have authority to give me orders," said the man, still unmoved by Cary's words.

"Perhaps you need the Governor to explain it to you," said Cary, as he stepped toward the officer, stopping only a few feet away.

The lieutenant's face reddened as he glared at Henry Cary in silence for a moment before lowering the pistol.

"How do I know you are telling me the truth?" said the officer angrily. "Do you have papers to prove you are the Keeper? I can't take the word of anyone who appears and say they have the authority to carry off weapons. Prove it to me!"

"Indeed I will, sir. I'll have the Governor prove it to you as quickly as I can locate him. And I'm sure he'll not appreciate you hindering his new plan to provide more safety for the colony. Neither do I appreciate you endangering the life of my armorer when he is obeying my orders! If you care enough to step inside and examine the book, sir, you will find I have documented the removal of these guns. Also, if you are through harassing this young man, I suggest you apologize to him and allow him to continue his work."

"I will not apologize to anyone. I am following my orders."

"Very well. Will you give him permission to leave?"

The officer glared angrily at Henry Cary and nodded his

head.

"Will you please tell him he may leave without his life being endangered?"

"You may leave," said the man, glancing quickly at Alexander before returning his angry glare to Henry Cary.

"Thank you," said Cary. "If you have no further need of my services, I too shall leave."

"Show me the book."

"Gladly," said Cary as he turned towards the magazine with the young officer following.

Alexander was still shaken when he arrived at the gunsmith shop. When he entered, John Brush looked up from the workbench. "Are those the rifles from the magazine?" he asked.

"Yes sir."

"Good. Mr. Cary said he was going to send some, do you know how many he has?"

"About a dozen. He's saving the worst ones for last."

"That's a wise plan. Do you know what's wrong with these?"

"Yes sir. The ramrod is missing on this one and the other one has a broken hammer."

"I'll have them ready late Friday. You can bring me two more and pick these up."

"Do you let people watch you when you work on guns?"

"If they don't ask too many questions," said the gunsmith, laughing. "Why? You want to learn about guns?"

"Yes sir. I'm going to the wilderness to live and I want to learn all I can about fixing them."

Brush laughed again. "When you going?"

"In a few years."

"You have a family?"

"A wife and a baby boy."

"It's hard living in the wilderness. Dangerous too."

"Have you ever been there?"

"No. But I talk to a lot of people who have. Mostly they come to have guns repaired or to ask questions about what kinds of guns they need to take with them."

"What do you tell them?"

"More than they want to hear, I suppose, because most of them don't do what I recommend." He stopped and stared at Alexander before continuing. "Most of them don't have enough money to buy all they need. Neither do they want to carry more than they have to. When they get there and something breaks or gets stolen, they are in trouble and have to come back, if they can get back."

"What do you recommend?"

"Guns or otherwise?"

"Both."

"I recommend they carry at least three guns. You should have four."

Alexander was shocked. "Why would I need so many?"

"See? That's the way everyone thinks. First, you need a good rifle; you can't make it without one. You also need a pistol because there'll be times when you can't carry a rifle and do your work. Now suppose your rifle breaks. Most of the time you can't fix it in the wilderness because you don't have what you need. That's why you need two rifles, if one breaks, you still have one."

"Why should I have four?"

"What will you be doing out there? Will you stay home all the time?"

"No. I'll probably be trapping, hunting, planting crops, or cutting wood."

"Exactly. When you're gone, your family needs a gun at home for their protection. So if you only have two, and one breaks, you can't leave home. What would you do then?"

"What kind of rifles do you recommend?"

"The same kind," said the man smiling.

"What do you mean?"

"Identical rifles. I recommend smoothbores. They are lightweight; you can use small shot for small game, and a round ball for large game. That way, you don't have to worry about different sizes of rounds. Most people want a big rifle and a fowler. You need both, but if one of them breaks, you have a problem. You really don't need a big rifle, a smoothbore works fine."

"How much do you charge to make one?"

"You don't want me to make you one."

"Why?"

"It's better to buy them from England, they are made better and readily available. You need to buy two identical ones, three if your family is going with you. Don't go to the wilderness until you have what you need. Don't go there unprepared."

"That's a lot to carry."

"That's why you also need a wagon. Another mistake people make is trying to take all they need on foot or even on horseback. You can't do it. Take your time and get what you need before you go. You'll never regret it and it may save your life."

Alexander pondered the words of the gunsmith as he walked home. A smile crossed his face as he remembered the childish attempt that he and Elizabeth had made to run away to the wilderness with practically nothing. The smile disappeared when he thought of the days that followed their ill-fated venture. Elizabeth still had scars on her back from the beating she received at the whipping post.

It was their dream that had driven them toward the wilderness and a new life. That dream was still very much alive and one day they would go, but he now realized how important it was to be prepared. He remembered the words of old Aaron years before in the ordinary. He had lived in the wilderness and spoke from experience. "It ain't no place to go without good guns and dogs. You need at least two of each. Something might happen to one." John Brush had reinforced these words about the guns, but had never mentioned dogs.

Alexander made some decisions that night as he walked towards home. They would not go to the wilderness until they were well prepared. They had been saving their money to buy some land, but he realized now he was going to need a lot more. He knew he would need a horse, but hadn't thought about a wagon. At least he had some experience with horses and wagons, but it was too early to think about buying either of them. He still wasn't sure he needed so many guns, but what John Brush said made sense. He was eager to spend more time with the gunsmith and learn more about guns, but was also anxious to receive more of his wise advice. There was one thing he could do now; he could begin to look for a young dog. Maybe two. He had a lot to tell Elizabeth tonight.

Elizabeth listened intently as Alexander told her about the events of the day. She was frightened when he told her about having the pistol pointed at him by the lieutenant but was soon laughing about how Mr. Cary had bullied him into submission.

"Do you think he'll really tell the Governor?" she asked.

"I think so. I've never seen him that mad before. He marched right up to that officer and told him to 'put that pistol away'."

"Were you scared?"

"Not at first because it happened so fast. But after I stood there looking at that gun and listening to him arguing with Mr. Cary, I was afraid he might accidentally shoot me. When I left, my legs were shaking so badly I could hardly walk!"

After he told her about his conversation with John Brush, she grew very quiet.

"It sounds like he knows what he's talking about, doesn't it?"

"It does. I was just surprised about needing so many guns. I would have made the same mistake he said everyone does. I would have bought a fowler and a rifle."

"You should go ahead and get you two now. Exactly alike, just like he said."

Alexander stared at her. "I don't need them yet."

"Yes you do. You need to get them and use them. Make sure they are what you need. If they are, then you can learn

208

to use them well."

"Spend our money on two new guns?"

"Some of it. We'll have to do it sooner or later. Do it now and you can practice with them."

"I thought about trying to find a dog, maybe two, but not about getting guns."

"You need to do that too so you can train them. You can probably get some puppies for nothing."

Part Three: Moving West

1727
Chapter 21

Journey To Falling Creek

Alexander could hardly wait to get to the house to tell Elizabeth the news. She knew it was time for him to come home from work and was watching for him from the window. When she saw him hurrying across the yard she was alarmed and rushed to the door to meet him.

"What's wrong?" she asked.

"Nothing. What makes you think something is wrong?" he said, grinning.

"Because you were walking so fast. You look like you're in a hurry".

"I am. I have something to tell you," he said, as he stepped inside and closed the door.

"What?"

"The Carys are moving."

"Moving! Where?"

"Henrico County. Seven miles below The Falls on the south side of the river, to the Falling Creek plantation Mr. Cary inherited from his father. He's going to move the family up there to live."

Elizabeth, stunned by the news, sat down at the table and stared at her husband.

"When are they going to move?"

"Soon. He started telling people today."

"What's going to happen to us? We'll have to find another job."

"We're going with them!" said Alexander, as he pulled Elizabeth to her feet. He grabbed her up in his arms and lifted her off the floor, swinging her around in a circle. "He

211

wants us to go too!"

John, who had been watching their antics from across the room, began crying. Alexander sat Elizabeth back on her feet and she hurried over to pick up the baby.

"Did Daddy scare you acting so silly?"

Alexander reached out and took his young son in his arms. The little boy gazed at him for a moment and then smiled as his daddy sat down and began to bounce him up and down on his knees.

"Mrs. Cary never mentioned it to me today," said Elizabeth, "do you think she knows about it?"

"She knows. He wanted to tell all the men who work for him first so they didn't find out from someone else."

"Will they lose their jobs?"

"No. He's going to keep working here. He has some more large buildings to build at the college."

"How's he going to work here and live in Henrico?"

"He's going to keep his houses here and come back and forth as he needs to. It isn't that far to ride a horse and the boats go up and down the river nearly every day."

"Who'll take care of the houses here?"

"He'll leave some of the slaves here to take care of things."

"That's going to be hard on Mrs. Cary and the children."

"That's why he wants us to go with them. We'll be up there with the family when he's down here. With baby Judith and those three boys, she's going to need a lot of help from you, and he wants me to work on the plantation."

"Aren't you going to work here anymore?"

"Maybe, but I think he wants me up there most of the time, especially when he is gone. He says there's a lot of work for me to do up there."

"I wonder what kind of houses are there?"

"He didn't say. They must be nice if he plans to take his wife and children, especially a little baby."

"I wonder if we'll still have our own house?"

"I don't know, he just said there were 'some houses' on the land. He talked like it was a large place."

"Do you think it's dangerous there? It's so close to the frontier."

"I don't think so. A lot of people live on the lands along the river on both sides."

"Aren't you glad you went ahead and bought your guns last year."

"I am. I love those guns. If it hadn't been for you encouraging me to, I never would have bought them."

"Your guns and your dogs. Sometimes I think you love those dogs more than me!"

"That's because they mind me better," he laughed, jumping back to keep her from hitting him.

"If you like them so well, maybe you'd like to sleep with them tonight!"

"I like sleeping with you better," he said, stepping towards her. She pushed him away.

"I'll remember what you said about me. I'll show you how well I can mind you!"

"I'm sorry."

"Too late. I'll get even with you."

"I hope you don't start by not feeding me supper."

"Oh! I was so excited about the news, I forgot about the food!"

Elizabeth hurried to the fireplace and began to get the food ready for the table while Alexander played with John and continued to talk to her.

"I wonder what else we'll need to get before we leave?"

"Why don't you talk to Mr. Cary and see what he suggests."

"I will. There may be some things already there. I know there's a trading post at The Falls. I think we can buy a lot of stuff there, but it's on the other side of the river."

"What about our plans to move to the frontier?" asked Elizabeth, with a troubled look on her face.

Alexander laughed. "We're still going. We'll be closer to it there than we are here and I'll probably save money quicker after I get you away from these shops in town."

Elizabeth frowned at him, pretending to be angry. "You're

213

the one spending all our money on guns and things!"

"It was your idea," said Alexander, smiling.

The plans for the move developed quickly. During the next few weeks, Alexander carried several wagonloads of household items to Warwick so they could be loaded on a boat to be shipped up the river. When he returned from the last trip, Mr. Cary went down to supervise the loading of some more household items from the family home at The Forest. He returned the next day.

"Everything is loaded," he said to Alexander. "I'll go with the women and children on the boat. You take the wagon and go ahead so you can meet us there to help unload."

"Can I go with Alexander in the wagon?" asked Archibald.

"Not this time, son. It's going to be a hard trip. Alexander will probably have to spend the night at The Falls and may have to sleep in the wagon or on the ground. He also has to take the horses and wagon across the river on the ferry. Maybe you can go with him another time."

"Is the ferry near The Falls?" asked Alexander.

"There are several ferries between here and The Falls. You'll use the last one before you get there. It will land you near the plantation. The ferrymen will give you directions. You may not get there in time to cross the same day you leave here, so be prepared to spend the night. Also be prepared to protect yourself from rogues."

After Mr. Cary left, Elizabeth said, "That sounds dangerous. Sleeping in the open and having to protect yourself from rogues."

"Nobody will get close to me without me knowing it because my dogs will be with me. You'll finally have your revenge. I have to sleep with my two dogs, just like you wished!"

Early the next day Alexander started towards The Falls with a lightly loaded wagon and his two dogs trotting alongside. He reminisced as he traveled west on the river road, remembering the night that he and Elizabeth had run away from the ordinary and began their fateful walk along this same road going to the wilderness. Soon he came to the place where they hid and rested when daylight came. Nearby was the barn where the Sheriff found them with the tracking dogs.

Alexander smiled as he recognized some of the landmarks that Susanna Allen had pointed out to him on the trip he made with her. He was just a child, but he sat in the front seat holding the old fowling piece as she drove the carriage. He felt so grown-up and important. She had made him direct her back to Williamsburg to see if he could remember the way and he did. He thought about the cold rain that fell and his thin clothing that didn't keep him dry or warm. He remembered Dinah feeding him supper that evening in the ordinary kitchen and how good the warm fire felt. That was the first time he ever ate any of her bread and stew. It was also the first time he saw Elizabeth. That was the night he began to include her in his dream. God was good. He had helped them survive and pursue their dream.

He thought about how badly he wanted to learn the way to Westover so that one day he would be able to drive himself there. That seemed so important to him then. He longed for the freedom and the means to go places and to be no man's servant. When he passed the entrance to Westover, he glanced down the road, but had no desire to go there. He was on a new road now and it felt good. He glanced at the fowler lying at his feet; it was loaded with shot. The other one, lying across his lap, was loaded with a round ball. The two dogs trotted happily alongside the wagon. The only feeling of anxiety he had was when he thought about the ferry. He had never seen one and could only imagine how it must feel riding on one. He didn't know how he would get the horse and wagon loaded and wondered what would happen if the horse became frightened and bolted? What if the ferry sank in the river? He couldn't swim.

When he arrived at the ferry, the ferrymen were there but the large boat was firmly secured to the bank.

"We're not crossing today, friend," said one of the men, "the river's too high. It's been dropping all day so I think it'll be fine tomorrow. You can spend the night here if you like, but if I were you I would go up to the Trading Post, it's only a little further up the river. You can get a hot meal and a bed if you want to and provender for your horse. They have reasonable prices."

"Thanks. I've been wanting to visit there anyway, but I'll probably sleep in the wagon. Don't want to leave my stuff."

"Don't worry about that. They have somebody to watch it for you so you can rest. Nobody will bother you or your stuff while you sleep. They'll see to it."

"What time do you start operating tomorrow?"

"Whenever our first customer gets here. We'll be here about daylight. As soon as it's light enough to see the other side, we'll be ready."

Alexander had been hearing about the Trading Post at The Falls for years. Colonel William Byrd's father had started it and now Colonel Byrd owned it. He welcomed the opportunity to see the Trading Post, but hoped he didn't see Mr. Byrd who had recently returned from England after being gone for five years. As soon as he was out of sight of the ferry, he stopped. He took the gun lying in the floor and wrapped it in a blanket so it would be concealed. He didn't know how he would manage going into the trading post and leaving everything outside, but he certainly didn't want to take both rifles inside.

The Trading Post was much larger than he thought it would be. He was surprised to see two buildings instead of one. The first one was a large stable. A man was standing outside the door watching him approach.

"Greetings," said the man.

"Greetings."

"My name is Dixon and I operate this place. If you're going toward the frontier it's the last bit of civilization you'll find so we try to make it enjoyable."

"My name is Stinson. I'm headed across the river, but have to wait until tomorrow for the ferry."

"We have two other men waiting here for the same thing, but still have room for you if you want to spend the night. We have everything you need, a bed for you, stable for your horse, food for both you and your animals, and any supplies you might need. We charge regular ordinary rates."

"I don't need a bed. I'll sleep in the wagon, but I could use a stall for my horse."

"I have one. There's also room for your wagon inside the barn, out of the weather. I have an armed man here all the time to watch after things. You don't have to worry about your stuff if you want to go inside."

"You mentioned food for me."

"Got one of the best cooks in the colony. Tonight we're eating venison stew, fresh baked bread, and apple pie."

Alexander laughed. "Show me where to put my horse and wagon."

The large stable had three stalls on each side. The three on the left side had horses in them, but the other side was empty.

"Pull your wagon over there," said Dixon, "and put your horse in any of those stalls. There's food for your horse over there in the barrels. You can feed him yourself or we'll do it for you."

"I'll feed him."

"When you're ready, come on over to the other building. James will keep an eye on your stuff," he said, motioning with his head toward a man standing in the far corner of the building. "James, this is Mr. Stinson, he's going to be spending the night. You help him if he needs anything."

"Yes sir, Mr. Dixon."

Alexander unhitched the horse and placed him in the stall. It was clean. Walking over to the feed barrels, he opened one and was surprised to find it well stocked with quality food. He was impressed. After taking care of the horse, he walked back to the wagon and fed the dogs that had been trailing along behind him everywhere he went. After they gulped down their food, he snapped his fingers over the edge of the wagon and said, "Get in." Both dogs jumped into the wagon.

"Lie down," he said. Both dogs lay down. "Stay."

He picked up the rifle from the front seat of the wagon and turned toward James who had been watching attentively from the corner.

"I'm going inside for some supper. I'll be back after I eat."

"Take your time, I'll watch everything for you. Do them dogs bite?"

"Only if you bother something in the wagon. Just don't let anyone near the wagon."

"They won't get off that wagon will they?"

"Not until I tell them to. They won't bother you."

"Good. We'll get along fine as long as they stay on that wagon."

Dixon was waiting for him when he walked inside. "Supper's ready anytime you want to eat. I thought maybe you might want to look around some before you eat, we have lots of stuff."

"I'll eat first."

"Have a seat anywhere you choose."

Two men sat at the first table eating. Alexander spoke to them as he walked by and took a seat at the next table. Almost as soon as he was seated, a pretty young woman came from the rear of the building carrying a plate and sat it on his table. On the plate was a bowl of stew and a large piece of bread.

"Hi, I'm Ginny. Mr. Dixon said you were eating with us tonight, I hope you enjoy this."

"Thank you, it looks good."

She quickly disappeared to the back room.

Alexander tasted the stew. It was delicious. The bread tasted a lot like the bread that Dinah and Elizabeth made, just a little coarser. The flavor was outstanding. As he ate, he was aware of the two men watching him. He thought it was strange that they had not returned his greeting and now he noticed that they didn't carry on any conversation as they ate. He supposed the other two horses in the stable were theirs. They must be the ones that Dixon said were waiting to cross the river. As soon as he finished eating, Ginny appeared again.

"Would you like some more?"

"Mr. Dixon said you also had apple pie. I want to hear more about that before I decide."

"Fresh baked today. Sweet, spicy, and still warm."

"The stew and bread was delicious. I could eat more, but I think I want the pie now."

"Be right back with it." Scooping up the plate and bowl, she disappeared again in the back. In a few moments, she returned with a generous serving of apple pie on the plate.

"You like coffee?"

"I love coffee," said Alexander staring at her with a surprised look on his face. "Why?"

"I just made some. Mr. Dixon drinks it every evening. We have extra if you want a cup." Bending over she whispered, "But it'll cost you half of what your meal cost."

"Bring me a cup anyway," he laughed.

In just a minute she was back with the coffee. She sat it on the table and disappeared again. It smelled wonderful. He took a sip, and it was good. He took his time finishing his pie, relishing every bite. As he ate, he looked around the large room with amazement. It was like an ordinary, general store, and livery stable, all in one. He couldn't believe they also sold coffee. It was a remarkable place considering it was so far removed from civilization. When Alexander finished his coffee he walked over to the counter where Mr. Dixon was standing.

"Do you want me to pay now or wait until I'm ready to leave tomorrow?"

"Tomorrow will be fine. We're having bacon and eggs for breakfast, are you going to eat with us before you leave?"

"I'll eat," said Alexander, smiling.

"Why don't you look around? You may see something you need. I have a little bit of everything here: guns, shot, lead, and powder. We also have some clothes and shoes, pots and pans, and a lot of other things. You can pay with sterling, tobacco, hides, anything you have of value."

"Thanks, I'll look."

He noticed the two men were still watching him. As he walked into the store part of the building, they kept their eyes fixed on him. The store was fascinating. Anything that he would need to take to the frontier was here. A backwoodsman didn't have to go back to tidewater to buy supplies; he could find anything he wanted here at the Trading Post.

"I can see why you keep a guard on duty," said Alexander, "you have a fortune invested here."

Dixon laughed. "The area is growing. People need goods and I want to provide them at a fair price. Didn't you find anything you wanted?"

"Not now. Most of my stuff will be brought upriver tomorrow by boat. I have the rest of it in the wagon, but I'll be back when I need something. I'm sure you'll be seeing a lot of me."

"Where are you going to be living?"

"On the Cary Plantation down the river on the other side."

"Henry Cary's place?"

"Yes sir. Mr. Cary and his family are moving up here to live. My wife and I work for them."

"Then you're going to be Mr. Byrd's neighbor."

Alexander looked puzzled. "Which Mr. Byrd?"

"Colonel William Byrd."

"I thought he lived at Westover."

"He does, but he owns a plantation near Mr. Cary at Falling Creek. He has another one on the Appomattox River and also some property here at Shockoe. He usually comes up here about every three months. He owns a lot of frontier land too."

"We plan to be moving to the frontier in the next year or two so we'll be back to stock up before we go."

"Don't wait that long, you drop by anytime."

"I will. When my wife finds out about this place, she'll want to come over."

A voice behind him asked, "What's your wife's name?"

Alexander turned toward the sound of the voice and saw Ginny. She had come back into the room and was listening to the conversation.

"Elizabeth."

"Do you all have any children?"

"We have one little boy a year old."

"Where will you be living when you go to the frontier?"

"Don't know yet. It depends on where we can get some good land."

"Maybe you can buy some land from Mr. Byrd," said Dixon.

"I wish he would move to the frontier," said Ginny.

"Ginny doesn't like Mr. Byrd," laughed Dixon.

"He doesn't like me either, but I don't care. He thinks the Almighty has put all women on this earth for his pleasure. I've let him know that this woman isn't!"

"I'm afraid you may give Mr. Stinson a bad impression of his neighbor."

"I already have my impression of Mr. Byrd," said Alexander.

"You know him?"

"I lived across the street from his home in Williamsburg. He was there often."

"I hope Ginny's remarks haven't offended you. I would consider it a favor if you would not mention them to your neighbor or Mr. Cary. Ginny can be outspoken at times."

"You don't have to be concerned about that, I'm in total agreement with Ginny."

"Do you think your wife will like living on the frontier after living in Williamsburg and here on the plantation?" asked Ginny.

"I think she will. She's as anxious to go as I am. It's been our dream for a long time."

"It's good to have dreams. I hope your dream comes true. I'm anxious to meet your wife."

221

"Thank you, I'll tell her about you."

"Breakfast will be ready about daylight," said Dixon, "that will give you an early start."

"I'll see you then," said Alexander. When he turned to leave, he noticed the two men at the table were still watching him and listening to everything that was said.

When Alexander came to breakfast the next morning, the two men who had spent the night inside, were not there. When he returned to the wagon their horses were gone. As he was hitching his horse to the wagon, Mr. Dixon came out and talked with James. As soon as he finished his conversation, he approached Alexander.

"Son, I don't want to cause you any undue worry, but all of us are concerned about those two men who spent the night here. We don't know who they are and have never seen them before. We think they are up to no good so be careful and watch out for them. I certainly wouldn't trust either of them if you run into them anywhere."

"I was wondering about them too. Thanks, I'll watch out for them."

When Alexander arrived at the ferry, the boat was leaving the other side of the river. He watched as it slowly crossed and pulled into the shore.

"You ready to go?" called one of the ferrymen.

"I'm ready. Tell me what to do."

"You walk your horse on the ferry, he'll do better with you than a stranger. We'll block the wheels for you. Keep the dogs off until we get the wagon tied down, we don't want them to scare the horse."

Alexander patted the horse and talked to him a moment. Taking hold of the bridle, he started leading him slowly toward the ferry. The horse walked very calmly to the ramp, pausing only a moment before stepping onto the boat and following Alexander until they were told to stop. The men blocked the wheels and secured the wagon to the ferry with ropes. Alexander whistled and the dogs scrambled on board.

On each end of the ferry was a device used to adjust the rudder which ran beneath the boat. As they cranked the rudder, the boat began moving slowly away from the bank.

"Do you know those two men we just took across?" asked one of the ferrymen.

"No sir. They spent the night at the Trading Post, but didn't do any talking. Mr. Dixon didn't know them either."

"I tried to get them to wait until you got here, but they were in a hurry. They got mad at me and didn't want to wait. They insisted I carry them over before you got here. After I took them across, they went down the river a little ways and stopped. They're still hanging around over there just inside that grove of trees. We've been watching for them to leave and they've never left. They're up to no good, I can promise you that. If I were you I'd watch out for them. There are some scummy people drifting through here now. All they want to do is grab something from somebody else. I don't want to scare you, but you'd better be careful of those two. You'd better watch your back too, going through those trees."

"Mr. Dixon felt the same way and told me to watch out for them."

"You have another gun besides that rifle?"

"Yes sir."

"Make sure it's loaded and you can get at it."

"It is."

When they landed on the other side, the two men secured the boat and removed the chocks from the wagon wheels. When they untied the ropes, the horse walked calmly off the boat and onto the shore. The ferrymen kept looking downriver to see if they could see the two men. Alexander stuck his pistol into his belt, checked both rifles, and climbed into the wagon. The ferrymen waved as he started down the narrow road beside the river with the dogs running alongside. He kept one hand on the rifle which was lying across his lap and one on the reins. As he entered the woods, he continually scanned both sides of the road and also kept watching the

223

dogs. They would probably be aware of someone close by before he would. Suddenly, both dogs ran forward growling, with the hair on their backs bristled up. As he rounded a curve in the road he saw the men. One of them was lying on the ground and the other was standing beside him. When he drew closer, the man on foot held up his hand. Alexander stopped about ten paces away.

"I need you to help me. My friend fell off his horse and I think he's hurt bad."

Alexander stood up in the wagon. "He does look like he's hurt bad, I think the best thing to do is put him out of his misery. I'll do it for you," he said, as he raised the rifle to his shoulder.

The astonished man's eyes grew wide and his mouth dropped open as if he were going to speak. The man on the ground opened his eyes and started moving like he was going to get up. Alexander fired. The rifle ball plowed into the dirt about two feet from his head, showering him with dirt and leaves. He began screaming and jumped to his feet yelling he had been shot. The man on foot almost fell as he recoiled back from the ball that had landed near his feet. Before they could recover, Alexander yelled to the dogs, "Get 'em!"

Both dogs lunged towards the men, snapping at their heels as they tried to mount the panicky horses. Alexander reached down into the floor of the wagon and picked up the other smoothbore that was loaded with shot. By now the men were in the saddles and the dogs were nipping at the hocks of the jumping horses. Alexander whistled and the dogs immediately ran towards him. The two men were riding downriver as fast as they could. The distance was perfect. They were too far for the shot to kill them, but close enough to burn the hide of both man and beast. He fired again. Both men came up out of their saddles as the horses lunged faster down the road. Alexander quickly reloaded his rifles while the two dogs stood by the side of the wagon happily wagging their tails.

"Good dogs," he said as he hopped down from the wagon

and patted their heads. "You did a good job."

The rest of the trip was uneventful, except for fits of laughter that he had when he thought of the funny spectacle he had witnessed. He wondered if he would ever see the two men again and decided he would not say anything about what had happened. He did not want to alarm Elizabeth and was afraid Mr. Cary may not approve of what he had done to the two strangers. The Cary's boat arrived early in the afternoon and they began to unload their belongings and carry them into their new home.

Exploring A New Land

Alexander was walking toward the house when he noticed the sloop approaching. He stopped in the yard and watched the boat slowly making its way up the river. Anne Cary had also seen the boat and was walking towards the dock with the children. She was expecting her husband to be on board. Henry Cary spent most weeks in Williamsburg, usually returning to the plantation for the weekend. He had recently accepted the contract to build The Presidents House at William and Mary where he already had two other buildings under construction. These projects would take several years to complete and would probably delay the starting of his new home at Falling Creek. As the sloop came closer, Alexander could see Mr. Cary on the deck, waving to his family. As they drifted toward the dock, Alexander crossed the yard and went into his cottage.

Life on the plantation was different from Williamsburg but nobody seemed to miss the convenience of living in town. They stayed well supplied from the boats coming upriver and with what they were able to get from the Trading Post. Many changes were taking place in the colony. A few months after they moved to Falling Creek, a new county was formed from Henrico County. It was named Goochland County in honor of Sir William Gooch, the new Governor of Virginia. Travel was also increasing. People who lived along the river were noticing an increase in the number of settlers passing through the area going west and recently there had been talk of a town being built at The Falls.

Alexander and Elizabeth still clung tenaciously to their dream of moving further west and having their own place for their growing family. The year after they moved to Henrico, their second son, Joseph, was born. They knew how difficult it would be to relocate with two small children and carve a new homestead out of the wilderness. They also knew that the longer they waited, the less options there would be for good land. One of the things they dreaded most was leaving the Carys, who had been so good to them. They were beginning to despair of ever seeing their dream come true.

The sloop arrived at the dock and tied up for the night. Henry Cary disembarked and embraced his wife and children. After exchanging greetings with everyone, he turned to young Archibald and said, "Son, go find Alexander and tell him to come down here to the boat."

"Yes, Papa," said the boy as he turned around and ran towards the group of houses. In just a few minutes, he returned with Alexander.

"Archibald said you wanted to see me."

"Yes I do. I have some things for you and I didn't want to leave them on the boat. If you will take them home, I'll come by and talk with you about them later. Right now, I need to accompany the Captain to the house. Archibald can carry something if you need help."

Alexander followed Mr. Cary onto the boat.

"This lead, shot, and gunpowder is for you to take home," said Cary.

"What are they for?" asked Alexander.

"We may need them. I'll be over to see you tomorrow and we'll talk about it then."

"Yes sir."

It was early Saturday afternoon when Henry Cary stopped by the cottage. Alexander offered him a seat as Elizabeth went to make them some tea.

"I suppose you must be wondering what all the mystery is surrounding the things I brought and my unwillingness to discuss them yesterday," said Mr. Cary, "they are for the frontier."

"Who's going to the frontier?"

"Me and you."

"When?"

Elizabeth stopped pouring the tea and was staring at Henry Cary in amazement. Mr. Cary laughed. "I'm not being fair to you am I Elizabeth? Maybe I had better wait for you to finish our tea! I'll keep talking while you prepare the tea and then you can sit with us since this also concerns you. I wanted to discuss this with Mrs. Cary before I talked to you, which is why I waited until today. She is in complete agreement with what I am planning to do and what I will propose to you. I am considering a trade of my paternal home at Warwick for 12,000 acres of land in Henrico County. It's about fifty miles west of The Falls near the foot of the Willis's River. I haven't seen the property, but plan to go see it next week. Alexander, I want you to go with me. We should only be gone a few days. If I am pleased with what I find, I will complete the trade when I return. I didn't know how much powder and shot you had, that's why I bought more."

"Are you planning on moving there?" asked Elizabeth.

"Probably not, at least not now. Living here is convenient for my work in Williamsburg so I'm going to build a new home here, hopefully very soon."

"What do you plan to do with so much land?" asked Alexander.

"I may sell some, or give it to my children, I don't really know. What I do know is that large portions of land are disappearing fast. Frontier land is cheap now, but the day is coming when there will be no more large portions and what is left will not be cheap."

"If you get the land, will you sell us some?" asked Elizabeth.

"Maybe," said Henry Cary, laughing, "but you're getting ahead of me. I had another idea that I wanted to discuss with you. If I get the land, I will need someone to live there and oversee it for me. I thought you might want that job. Many people are going to the frontier without owning land and they are settling on other people's property. There are also a lot of trappers out there because trapping is very profitable right now. Many of them have no qualms about trespassing and trapping on other people's land. If I purchase the property, I do not intend to allow that kind of exploitation on my land. I can't control it without someone living there that will look out for my best interests. We could work out an agreement where you could continue to work for me there and earn your land. It wouldn't be easy and may be dangerous but frontier living is going to be that way anywhere you go. I really hate to see you leave here, but I know that it's something both of you have dreamed of doing for a long time. Does that sound like an offer you would be interested in?"

"Yes sir!" said the young couple.

"Good. There is no use discussing details with you until I know I am going to get the land. We'll plan to leave early Monday morning. I can be away from the college for a while, do you see any problem with you being away from the work here for a few days?"

"No sir. Everything is going well and I'll be sure everyone knows what they are to do while we're gone."

"Then we'll plan on leaving early Monday by horseback. We can make better time and we don't need to carry a lot of stuff. I understand there are some good buildings on the property, and one is a cabin where we can sleep. I want to see what kind of condition they are in."

After Henry Cary left, Alexander and Elizabeth stood looking at each other silently. Suddenly, she burst into tears. "What's wrong?"

"Wrong? Nothing is wrong. I just can't believe this is happening to us, it's too good to be true. When so many bad things have happened to others, God continues to let good things happen to us."

It was shortly after daylight on Monday when the two men headed west, carrying little more than weapons and food. As they rode, they talked.

"Will we have to cross the river to get to the land?" asked Alexander.

"Not the James River, the property is on this side, but there are some smaller streams we'll have to ford. That should be no problem on horseback."

"Have you been that far west before?"

"No. Most of this will be new territory for me too. I'm depending on directions I've received from those who have been."

"Do you think we'll see any Indians?"

Cary laughed. "I don't know, but they'll probably see us. I don't think we'll have to worry about them. There are not many left and I understand that most of them are friendly."

"What about animals?"

"We might see anything. Again, I don't think they will cause us any problems."

"Have you ever seen a buffalo?"

"No. But there are still some here. Our neighbor, Mr. Byrd, has seen some; in fact, he has eaten some buffalo meat. Two years ago when he surveyed the line between Virginia and North Carolina, they killed one and he ate some of it. He said it tasted a lot like beef."

The two men rode steadily along the rutted road, stopping occasionally to rest themselves and the horses. They met few travelers and only occasionally saw the smoke from a settler's cabin. Late in the day, as they neared their destination, they could see the distant mountains on both the western and northern horizons.

When they came to an unanticipated fork in the road, they stopped. They were trying to determine which road to take when they saw two gentlemen approaching from the west on horseback. Alexander sat watching them come closer and listening to their strong British accent as they talked. His hands tightly gripped the rifle with his thumb resting on the hammer. As they grew closer, Henry Cary called out, "Joseph Mayo! Are you lost out here in this wilderness? What are you doing so far from Powhatan's Seat?"

"Henry Cary! I thought that looked like you, but I couldn't

convince myself that you would be out here wandering around in the wilderness. I should ask you the same question!"

"You certainly don't look like you're surveying."

"I'm not. I'm enjoying the wonderful hospitality of my dear kinsman and we are looking for more frontier land to patent. Henry this is Joseph Hooper."

"Mr. Hooper, I'm Henry Cary of Warwick, and this is Alexander Stinson. We are here to look at property owned by Colonel Wilson Cary of Richneck, and are searching for a cabin that is located on his property."

"Well, you're not far from your destination. We'll pass by there on the way to my house. If you two would like to ride along with us I'll be glad to guide you there."

"That would certainly be helpful. You seem to know the area well, have you lived here long?"

"Nearly seven years now. I patented land here and would like to secure more."

"Henry, are you related to Colonel Wilson Cary?" asked Mayo.

"Yes, he's my cousin."

"He owns quite a bit of land here. Do you think he may be interested in selling any of it?"

Cary smiled. "Actually, that's why I'm here. I'm discussing the possibility of acquiring land from him."

"If your plan does not work, will you be kind enough to let him know of our interest in the land?"

"I will."

"You two gentlemen failed to tell me how you know each other," said Hooper.

"Henry is my neighbor," said Mayo. "He is formerly of Warwick, but is now living at Falling Creek, on the opposite side of the river from me."

"Then you are William Byrd's neighbor?"

"I am. Are you a friend of Colonel Byrd?"

"Not really," laughed Hooper. "I only know of him through Joseph and his brother, William. I suppose you could say they were his friends."

"I suppose," said Mayo laughing. "I know he considers William his friend, but I don't know about me. I accompanied him for part of the trip surveying the Dividing Line. It was not a pleasant experience."

As the road passed a glade, they could see the cabin and several outbuildings on the far side of the clearing. They turned and rode toward the buildings.

"Do you gentlemen plan to spend the night in that cabin?" asked Joseph Hooper.

"We do. I was told that it was in an inhabitable condition."

"I suppose it still is, although it hasn't been inhabited for many months now."

"The barn seems to be in good shape," said Mayo, as they rode past, "and there's some dry firewood under that shed."

The four men dismounted and entered the cabin. It was one large room with a ladder to a loft. Rough beds made from hewn poles were built against each sidewall and a large rock fireplace adorned one end of the room.

"It seems to be in a livable state," said Cary.

"Yes it does, but I'm not sure how comfortable it will be," said Hooper. "You gentlemen would be welcome to be guests at my house if you desire."

"That's kind of you, but these quarters will serve us fine. You have already done us a great service by directing us here."

"It was my pleasure. How long do you plan to be here?"

"We plan to explore some of the property tomorrow and return home the following day."

"Would you be kind enough to join us for supper at my house tomorrow evening? Mr. Mayo and his wife will still be here. It would give us an opportunity to become better acquainted."

"I'm afraid that would be too great an imposition."

"Absolutely not! You would do me a great favor by coming. We seldom have guests here to entertain. It would also give us a chance to hear the latest news from Williamsburg. I insist upon it. And on second thought, plan to spend the night with us tomorrow so you don't have to return here in the dark. You can begin your journey home from our place."

"I must remind you, sir, that we are traveling light. We brought no proper clothes with us for such an occasion, only what we are wearing."

"And I remind you, Mr. Cary, that this is the frontier. We seldom have need of formal attire. Please come as you are. My place is only a short ride northwest of here."

"Since you insist, we accept your offer and look forward to an evening with you. And if you would allow me to have a few more minutes of your time before you leave, I would appreciate any information you could give me about the property boundaries and anything else you think may be helpful to us tomorrow."

For the next thirty minutes, the three gentlemen talked about the area, its landmarks and its people. While they talked, Alexander unloaded their things, took care of the horses, and started a fire.

Early the next day, Henry Cary and Alexander set out to explore the land.

"Mr. Hooper says there's a small Indian village a few miles west of here," said Cary.

"Are they friendly."

"Very friendly, but seldom seen unless you go to the village. They blend into the forests so well, that they see you, but you don't see them."

"Do you think any of them are watching us now?"

"Maybe."

"I wonder if they have guns?"

"I'm sure some of them do."

"You don't plan to go to their village do you?"

"No, I had not planned to. Why, do you want to go?" laughed Cary.

"No. I'll wait until I meet one out here."

Alexander looked uneasily about them as they rode, and would occasionally glance back to see if anyone was behind them, but they never saw another person all day. They found several areas where the trees had been girdled and were standing dead. The vegetation around them had been cleared away to allow grass to grow. As they approached one of these areas, Henry Cary, who was riding in front, suddenly stopped and whispered, "Look!"

Grazing silently on the far side of the clearing were four buffalo, a large male, two cows, and a yearling.

Alexander raised his gun. Cary held up his hand and shook his head. "Don't. We can't use the meat if we kill one, it would only waste."

Apparently hearing his voice, the animals stopped feeding and stared in their direction for a moment, grunted, and disappeared into the woods. Returning to the cabin in mid-afternoon, they examined the buildings and the spring closely before leaving. Although he noted some improvements that should be made to the cabin, Henry Cary was well satisfied with what he had found.

When they arrived at the Hooper house, the two men were surprised to see a nice home located in such a remote area. Joseph Hooper met them at the door.

"Gentlemen! We're honored to have you. I trust you've had a profitable day?"

"It has been a good day for us, and I hope likewise for you," said Cary.

"Indeed it has and we are looking forward to a fine evening together. Come in and meet the ladies. This is my wife Elizabeth, and this is Joseph's wife, Mrs. Ann Mayo. Ladies, this is Mr. Henry Cary and this young man is Alexander Stinson."

After exchanging greetings with the ladies, Mr. Cary said, "Your husbands were very kind to us yesterday when they found us wandering around in the wilderness and led us to our destination. I'm afraid Mr. Hooper has gone beyond usual courtesy by inviting us here for the evening, but he is a very persistent man. We are not properly dressed or otherwise prepared for such a splendid reception as this, for that I apologize.

"You need no apology, Mr. Cary, our home is always open to guests," said Mrs. Hooper. "We are excited about the possibility of you becoming our neighbor."

"Indeed we are," said Joseph Hooper, "but let us be seated and we will get you something to drink before we continue our conversation."

For the next hour, the conversation rapidly changed back and forth between all present. The Hoopers and Mayos were seeking news from The Capitol while their two visitors were trying to learn more about wilderness living. Occasionally, the two ladies would excuse themselves to go check on the slaves who were preparing the meal. After one such exit, Elizabeth Hooper returned to announce that supper was ready.

"Gentlemen, let us not keep the ladies waiting," said Joseph Hooper, "we can continue our discussions after we eat. Please follow Mrs. Hooper to the table."

Alexander felt very tense as he followed the others to the dining room. The large table was crammed with food. It reminded him of some earlier meals he had eaten with the Sclaters and the Carys. The hosts had a special gift of making their guests feel at ease and soon everyone was enjoying the fine food and continuing their earlier conversations.

"The Indians aren't a problem for us," said Joseph Hooper. "The problem people are those scoundrels who pass through here and have no respect for other people or their property. Many of them are runaways from Tidewater heading further west. Most have nothing more than the clothes on their backs and will steal anything they can carry."

Alexander was very uncomfortable as he listened to the conversation.

"We also have some problem ones who are permanent residents. I wish they would also head further west. I'm referring of course to the trappers. Not all of them, but there are some who have no respect for boundaries. They think that because this is the wilderness, they have a right to trap anywhere they please."

"That is one of my concerns," said Henry Cary. "Does the Sheriff do anything about that?"

"He tries, but he can't be everywhere. This is a big county. He has to have evidence to arrest someone. Finding a trap is useless unless you can catch someone working the trap, then they can be arrested for trespassing. Trappers often don't check their traps every day, depending on the weather, so it's difficult to catch them."

"Can't you destroy the traps?" asked Alexander.

Hooper laughed. "We destroy them when we find them and so does the Sheriff, but it's useless. It only lets them know that we are aware of their presence. They simply relocate and build another trap."

"What kind of traps do they use?"

"Deadfalls and snares, made mostly out of logs and saplings. They can cut what they need to build a trap anywhere in the woods. We have one trapper here who is especially bad about trespassing, his name is John Payne. He is probably the best trapper in the area, or at least he catches more animals, but he traps anywhere he pleases."

"With that information, it seems he would be easy to arrest," said Cary.

"Arresting him would be like arresting the wind," said Elizabeth Hooper.

Her husband laughed and said "Exactly! They say he is a Scotsman, but he's more like an Indian than a Scot. He's rarely seen except when he brings in his wolves for bounty or goes to sell his pelts."

"I've never seen him," said Mrs. Hooper, "I'm beginning to think he's a myth."

"He's no myth," said her husband. "We would be better off if he were."

"Do you think he would teach me to trap?" asked Alexander.

Everyone stared at him like he had committed the unpardonable sin.

"Goodness no!" said Hooper. "He's the most unfriendly

236

man I know of. Actually, I would even consider him dangerous. You would want nothing to do with him. If you move here and want to learn to trap, I have a slave named Ben who knows about trapping, he will teach you. Have nothing to do with John Payne!"

Early the next morning, Alexander and Mr. Cary began their journey home. As they rode, they talked.
"I'm pleased with what I've seen," said Cary.
"The bottom land along the river seems rich enough to grow anything. I'll bet it would grow good tobacco," said Alexander.
"I'm sure it would, but getting it to the market would be the problem. It's useless to raise large amounts if you can't market it. That's a big problem that has to be resolved."
"What do you think the Hoopers do?"
"They don't raise much tobacco because they're not dependent on it for their livelihood. They raise enough food and livestock to be almost self-sufficient. Other things have to be brought in by wagon."
"They seem to be happy that someone may be moving there."
"They are. They would make wonderful neighbors. Do you think you would like to live there?"
"I really would."
"I intend to go forward with my plans to trade for the land. I talked with Mr. Mayo about surveying it and establishing the boundaries and he's willing to do that for me. Barring something unforeseen, the transaction should be complete by the end of summer. After the crops are in, I would like for you to move up there for a few months and do the necessary repair work before winter. You could become more familiar with the land and learn a little about trapping while you kept watch for trespassers. Elizabeth and the children could stay at Falling Creek while you were gone and you could come back home before Christmas. After that, if you decide you would like to live there, you can take your family and move. You would probably want to wait until spring. We will work

out a fair exchange of land for your services."

"I would like to do that."

"Talk to Elizabeth about it when you get home and see if she agrees to it."

"I hate to be away from my family that long, but I think she will agree to it."

"I believe a man could support his family well there. You could raise a lot of your food and also hunt and fish. Trapping and raising some tobacco would provide enough money for you. You wouldn't get rich but you could live well."

Alexander smiled and said, "I'd like to try it."

Danger In The Forest

Alexander was making final preparations to leave for the frontier. It was early October and the days were already turning cooler. He was anxious to leave because he knew how much work he had to do before the weather turned cold. One evening he told Elizabeth, "I'm going to the trading post tomorrow to buy a cooking pot to take with me."

"I'm going with you," she responded. "I need a larger one for us. You can take our old one and I'll go pick out a new one to use here."

"I can do it so you don't have to go."

Elizabeth looked at him and smiled, "If you go, I'm going with you. Besides, I have something else I want to get."

"What?"

"You'll see."

"Are you going to take the children?"

"No. I'll get someone to keep them, we won't be gone that long."

"Do I need to take the wagon to get your 'something else'?"

"No. We'll ride the horses."

Early the next morning, the young couple left for the trading post. When they arrived at the landing, the ferry was approaching their side of the river. They watched as it landed and an elderly couple in a carriage came ashore. In just a few minutes, Alexander and Elizabeth boarded and were on their way to the other side of the river. When they arrived at the trading post, nobody was in the store except Mr. Dixon.

"What a pleasant surprise to see you again Elizabeth. Your husband has been keeping you on the other side of the river too much."

"It's not his fault, I've been busy with the children and the work."

Ginny came hurrying out of the back room when she heard their voices and hastened to Elizabeth to give her a hug. "It's been so long since I saw you," she said.

"I know, I need to come over more often. It's just easier to let Alexander come by himself."

"When are you leaving for the frontier?"

"Alexander is leaving in a few days, but the rest of us will wait until later, maybe spring."

"Don't you need to get some things for your trip, son?" asked Dixon.

"Yes sir, that's why we're here, we need a new cooking pot. I'm taking our old pot so Elizabeth wants to pick out a new one."

"I've got some nice ones. Come over here Elizabeth and choose one. Alexander, you look around and see if you can find anything else you need. You're going to be a long ways from things when you get out there. You better be sure you have everything you need before you go. How about powder, shot, lead, flints, those kinds of things?"

"I have enough. Mr. Cary stocked me up on those."

"Well he didn't buy them from me!"

"I think he bought them in Williamsburg," said Alexander, smiling.

"I'll have to get after Henry when I see him, he knows better than that."

Elizabeth chose the pan she wanted and handed it to Mr. Dixon. "I'm going to look around a little more," she said.

"That's fine! You take your time and I'll keep your husband busy so he doesn't bother you," laughed Dixon. Turning back to Alexander he asked, "Are you planning on doing any trapping while you're out there?"

"Yes sir. I want to learn to trap. I have someone that will teach me."

"Good! Just remember, if you get any good hides, be sure to bring them back to me. I'll give you top price for them if you handle them right."

"I'll have to learn to do that too. I may just try to trap

wolves. They pay 200 pounds of tobacco for bounty on a grown wolf and you don't have to cure the hides, just turn in the scalp."

"Yeah, but those things are smart and not easy to trap."

"That's what I hear. I guess I'll find out when I get there."

Ginny and Elizabeth were laughing and talking on the other side of the store. When they came over to where the men were standing, they were carrying a sack of coffee beans.

"Who are they for?" asked Alexander.

"You," said Elizabeth.

"For what?"

"To take with you."

"No. They cost too much."

"They'll last you a long time. You love coffee and I want you to have them."

"You'd better listen to her son," said Dixon. "It's bad enough to have to eat your own cooking. You'll need an extra treat and will be glad you have them when you get there."

"That's easy for you to say because you're selling them, but I have to pay for them!"

"Not this time," said Elizabeth, "I'm paying for these. You can't refuse a gift."

"I don't have any way to carry them home."

"Hold them in front of you on the horse. I can carry the pot."

"Looks like you've lost the argument son, and I've gained a sale," said Dixon, smiling. "What about a coffee mill? I've got some good ones. Good price on them too."

"No sir, I have one I can carry."

As they were leaving, Ginny followed them outside. "I have a favor to ask both of you and I didn't want Mr. Dixon to hear me. When you get to the frontier, if you ever meet a good man who's looking for a wife, don't forget me. You may think I'm crazy, but I think about you two all the time. I would love to have a life like you have. I don't want to spend my life working here or in some ordinary. I hate for men to make rude remarks to me and try to use me. I want a husband and family, but I am not going to get married to just anybody. I want somebody that will treat me the way you treat each other. Just remember that, will you?" Tears were running down her cheeks as she spoke.

Elizabeth embraced her and said, "You'll find a good husband."

"We'll remember," said Alexander.

It took almost two days for Alexander to make the trip in the heavily loaded wagon. Arriving in early afternoon on the second day, he spent the remainder of the day unloading the wagon, arranging his stuff, and getting enough wood to last through the night. For the next few days, he worked from daylight to dark repairing the buildings and getting wood for the winter. When that was complete, he visited the Hoopers and made arrangements for Ben to begin teaching him to trap. It wasn't until his second week that he had time to become familiar with the land. After breakfast, he would take the dogs and walk his little trap line. When he finished checking the traps each morning, he would walk over a new area, studying the terrain and looking for signs of animals or people and searching for new locations for traps. Although he saw many animals, and shot some smaller ones for food, he saw no signs of other humans. On the third week, after he had become familiar with the land closest to the cabin, he began to travel by horseback so he could range further from home. By now, the dogs had become accustomed to the routine and were anxious to go each morning. Alexander always kept them close, never letting them range too far ahead.

Small footpaths ran throughout the area. Some were easy to distinguish as animal trails while others seemed to be smooth and well worn as if they were being used regularly by humans. Alexander was following such a trail through an area with brushy terrain on either side. Looking ahead, he could see that the trail led through an open area under a large tree and then continued up a small hill, disappearing again into the brush. In the clearing, another trail crossed the one he was on. On the left side, the path wound around the side of the hill and down to a small creek, disappearing from view beyond the creek. On the right side, it dropped quickly from sight between two steep hills into a dark, wooded ravine. He had paused as he entered the clearing and was looking around. All of a sudden, the dogs began to move forward cautiously with the hair on their backs bristled up. Alexander grew tense until he saw what was disturbing them; a dead wolf was in a deadfall trap beside the path. Swinging down from the horse he walked forward to examine what he had found. While he was looking at the dead animal the dogs began growling again. He made them be quiet until he determined the source of their agitation; someone was coming up the trail from the creek. He softly called the dogs and hurried back to the horse. Leading the animal out of sight in the brush, he tied him to a small tree and made the dogs sit. He checked the pistol stuck in his belt, it was ready. Holding the rifle tightly with his thumb on the hammer, he waited.

A man riding a horse came into view; Alexander hoped he was alone. A large, yellow dog trotted alongside the horse. When they reached the clearing, the dog rushed toward the trap and began sniffing the ground where Alexander's two dogs had been. Hopefully, he wouldn't follow their scent back to where they were hiding. The man swung down from the horse and stood looking at the wolf, ignoring the dog's unusual actions. He was a big man, several inches taller than Alexander and probably twenty pounds heavier. He had large hands. His pistol was stuck under his belt with the handle to the left side, indicating he was left-handed. Alexander reminded himself to remember that. The man tied his horse and leaned his rifle against a tree. The mongrel dog continued to busy himself trying to sort out the different scents as the man walked to the trap and easily lifted the big log off the dead wolf.

Alexander cocked his rifle, stepped quietly out into the path, and aimed it at the trapper. "Looks like you caught one of my wolves," said Alexander. At the sound of his voice, the man spun on one heel, stopping in a crouched position, with both feet planted firmly on the ground. His hand was only inches from the pistol when he saw the cocked rifle and froze.

"What do you want?" he snarled.

"I want to talk with you."

"About what?"

"About trapping on somebody else's land."

"What business is it of yours?"

"This is Henry Cary's land. I work for Mr. Cary."

The man's face reddened with anger. "Mr. Cary is like all the other rich men who own wilderness land. He never sets foot on it and doesn't want anyone else to. You can tell Mr. Cary to come chase me off."

"That's why I'm here. Mr. Cary sent me to chase you off."

A low growl came from the yellow dog as he eased slowly towards Alexander.

"Call your dog."

"Can't remember his name," said the man, smiling. He had never moved from the crouched position he had stopped in and his hand was still only inches from the pistol.

Alexander knew what he was thinking. If the dog attacked him, the man would grab the pistol and shoot. If Alexander shot the dog, then the man would shoot him. This man was dangerous. He was willing to sacrifice his dog for a chance to kill. Alexander whistled and his two dogs came charging down the path, ready to defend their master. The yellow dog stopped, thoroughly confused by the change of events. Alexander, who had never taken his eye off the trapper, saw the smile disappear from his face.

"You through talking to me?" he asked defiantly.

"Not yet. I want to know your name."

"Why you want to know, so you can run to the Sheriff and get a warrant?"

"Maybe, maybe not."

244

"I don't like to talk with a rifle sticking in my face."

"I'm not going to put the rifle down and let you shoot me with that pistol."

"Put it down and we'll talk. I won't shoot you," said the man as he stood upright and dropped his arms by his side.

"Give me your word?"

"You have it."

Alexander lowered the rifle, eased the hammer down to a safe position, and leaned it against a tree.

"My name's Payne. John Payne. Now what else you want to talk about?"

"Since I'm going to be your neighbor, I would also like to be your friend, but you will have to agree to stay off of Mr. Cary's land."

"I don't need any friends. If you are a friend of Cary, you are no friend of mine. This is wilderness land, not Cary land."

"This is Cary land and Mr. Cary is my friend. He's a good man."

"Glad you like him, I don't. If you ever see him again, you can tell him," said Payne, as he started moving towards Alexander with clenched fists.

"You gave me your word!"

"Only that I wouldn't shoot you. I didn't give you my word that I wouldn't beat your brains out."

Alexander took a step backwards, as the man continued towards him, his big left hand cocked and ready. He swung and Alexander ducked. Losing his balance, the man lurched forward. Before he could recover, Alexander hit him as hard as he could behind the left ear. The man fell forward over the edge of the bank, landing on his hands and knees. Dazed, Payne shook his head for a moment, and then jumped to his feet. Like an enraged bull, he charged up the bank towards Alexander. Instead of clinched fists, both hands were open to grasp his foe. Alexander knew he would be no match for this man if he fell into his grip. He had one chance, and his timing had to be perfect. With all the strength he had, he swung at the man's nose, putting every ounce of his weight behind the punch. He connected. Excruciating pain shot up his arm, through his elbow and into his shoulder. Payne seemed to hang in mid-air for a moment and then dropped to his knees. He tried to catch himself again as he fell forward, but this time his arms would not hold him and his face plowed into the forest floor.

Alexander stepped back and waited, trying to decide what to do when the man got up. He knew from the pain in his right arm, he would not be able to hit him again like that and he had far less power in his left hand. He would have to resort to the pistol to save his life. His concern was unnecessary; the fight was over. After several minutes of lying crumpled on the ground, Payne slowly pushed himself up on his knees and sat back on his heels. Dirt and leaves were stuck to his face and he was trying to clear his eyes so he could see. Blood was streaming from his nose and mouth and running down onto his pistol, which was still stuck under his belt.
"You're bleeding all over your pistol," said Alexander.
Payne leaned back and pulled the pistol from his belt and laid it on the ground in front of the man he was trying to kill a few minutes earlier. Alexander picked up the pistol and emptied the blood-soaked powder from the pan. Pulling a piece of cloth from his bag, he began to wipe the blood off the weapon.
"Give me that rag," said Payne.
"It's not clean."
"It'll do."
Alexander handed him the piece of cloth and Payne used it to try to stop the flow of blood from his nose. After several minutes, he rose unsteadily to his feet.
"You need some help?"
"No. There's a spring down that path, I'm going down there."
The yellow dog, which had kept his distance throughout the fray, followed his master down the path.
Alexander removed the wolf from the trap and examined the deadly device. It was simple, but far superior to the one that

246

Ben had taught him to make. Perhaps that explained why he had caught nothing. He studied it closely until he saw Payne staggering back up the path. Alexander picked up his rifle and waited. The bleeding had stopped, but his nose looked as if it had doubled in size and his eyes were beginning to swell. Alexander handed him the pistol.

"I cleaned the blood off, but had to take the powder out, don't forget to reload it. I took the wolf out of the trap, but didn't reset it."

"Take the wolf with you and turn it in for bounty."

"That's your wolf."

"Take it! I don't want anybody seeing me looking like this. It'll be rotten before I can turn it in."

"You need any help?"

"No. I'll be alright."

"I still want to talk to you some more."

Without looking at him, Payne said, "I'll come by to see you later."

"Do you know where I live?"

"I know."

After he returned home, Alexander placed the wolf in a secure place in the shed, deciding he would deal with it the next day. His arm was throbbing and he could hardly use his hand. Since he was planning to spend the rest of the day at home, he busied himself cooking a pot of stew, enough to last for several days. The dogs barking startled him. He grabbed his rifle and hurried to the door. Two men on horseback were approaching. A quick glance confirmed that his other rifle was sitting close-by in easy reach before he stepped outside to meet them.

"I'm George Payne, Sheriff of Goochland County," said one of the men. "This is Daniel Stouer, my deputy."

"I'm Alexander Stinson. Moved here from Falling Creek to work for Mr. Cary."

"I know. I saw Henry last week in Williamsburg. He told me you were here and asked me to drop by when I was over this way."

"Would you like to come in?"

"Not today. We need to get back to the ferry before dark. Just wanted to say hello and tell you to be careful. We have a trapper here named John Payne, no kin to me, thank God. He causes a lot of trouble trespassing. You let me know if you see him on Cary property."

"I've already met him."

"Where?"

"I was out riding one day."

"Did you talk to him?"

"I did. He said he would come by and see me later."

"Ha! I wouldn't count on that. If he causes you any trouble, let me know."

"I will. Before you leave, will you certify a wolf kill for me?"

"Glad to, where is it?" The two men followed Alexander to the shed, certified the wolf, and left. As soon as he went back inside and lay the gun down, the dogs started barking again. He grabbed the gun and returned to the door. John Payne was riding into the yard. His face was swollen and his eyes were almost closed. Alexander wondered how he could see.

"I appreciate that," said Payne.

"What?"

"Not telling the Sheriff you beat my face in. Most men would have bragged about it."

"What were you doing eavesdropping?"

"I can learn more by listening than by talking. You still want to talk with me?"

"I do. Tie your horse and come in."

Payne cautiously entered the cabin, scanning everything inside through his half-closed eyes before seating himself at the table. Tilting his head toward the fireplace, he said, "Anything in that pot?"

"Stew. You want a bowl?"

"If you have extra."

"There's enough for both of us," said Alexander as he ladled two bowls from the pot and sat them on the table. He

248

returned to the fireplace for the bread, hoping it was done. It was. He cut them each a chunk and placed it on the table. They ate in silence with Payne gobbling his down, pausing only long enough to breathe through his mouth. He seemed unable to breathe through his badly swollen nose.

"Where'd you learn to make bread like that?"

"From my wife."

"You got children?"

"Two boys. You have a family?"

"No. What's in the stew?"

"Squirrel."

"I use rabbit, catch them in a snare, saves powder and shot."

"You want more?"

"You have enough?"

"I have plenty."

Payne said nothing and shoved the empty bowl back toward Alexander. After refilling both bowls and cutting more bread, the conversation continued as they ate.

"Where'd you learn to fight like that?" asked Payne.

"Been fighting since I was a lad. When you're an orphan, you have to learn to fight."

"You didn't learn to fight like that fighting children."

"You fight like that when you're fighting for your life. You were trying to kill me."

Payne looked at him, but made no reply.

After they finished eating, Alexander asked, "You want a cup of coffee?"

"Coffee? You have coffee? Been over a year since I had a cup."

"It's a gift from my wife," said Alexander as he poured them each a cup.

"What'd you want to talk about?" asked Payne.

"Trapping."

"Thought we'd already talked about it."

"Not yet. I want you to teach me to trap."

Payne stared at him in silence. After taking a sip of hot coffee, he said, "Why?"

"Because I want to learn, and I hear you're the best."

"You want me to teach you to trap so you can catch animals on land that I can't trap on? You must be crazy."

Alexander laughed. "I want you to teach me on Cary land. What do you think about us working together while I learn? With two of us working, we could set more traps."

"Now I know you're crazy. Cary will have both of us arrested. The Sheriff is just waiting to catch me on that land."

"Mr. Cary has put me in charge of his land and has given me permission to trap."

"He didn't give me permission. You'll be out of a job when he learns about your scheme."

"It's not a scheme. I need to learn to trap. I looked at your trap this morning and saw how well it was made and you caught something."

Payne smiled. "I've seen your traps too, they're pitiful. Only way you'll catch anything is if they stumble over it and break their neck."

"They're not that bad!"

"What've you caught?"

"Nothing. That's why I want you to teach me."

The two men talked until Payne said he needed to go home. It was getting dark and his eyes were almost closed. He was complaining of feeling chilled even though the cabin was warm.

"Are you going to be able to see well enough to get home in the dark?"

"I don't know, I suppose so."

"Why don't you spend the night here and leave after daybreak?"

"You don't mind?"

"No. I have an extra bed."

"All I'll have is a cold cabin and a busted nose."

"You can sleep over there. Go to bed, I'll take care of your horse."

Payne appeared to be asleep when Alexander returned to the cabin. He banked the fire and went to bed although he wasn't sleepy. His mind was in turmoil as he recalled the day's events. Now, he understood what people meant when they talked about the dangers of wilderness living and why some people disappeared and were never heard from again. Earlier, he had faced a man who tried to kill him and now that man was sleeping across the room from him. The turn of events was unbelievable. His aching arm and Payne's moaning assured him that he would not sleep well tonight.

1730
Chapter 24

Indians! Friend or Foe?

Alexander lay quietly waiting for daylight. The glowing
coals in the fireplace gave enough light for him to see John
Payne lying in the bed across the room. Payne had been
restless most of the night, but for the past few hours had
grown quieter. Alexander had slept very little and was
anxious to get out of the bed and move around. At the first
sign of light he got up, put more wood on the fire, and filled
the coffee pot with water. His failure to get more water
before dark irritated him because now, the bucket was almost
empty. He decided to wait until Payne was awake before
going to the spring, although it was only a short distance
from the cabin. Walking quietly to the door, he opened it.
All three dogs were lying on the porch, but not together.
They stared at him suspiciously, but none of them moved.
He eased the door shut to stop the cold air that was rushing
in and sat down at the table to wait for Payne to wake up.
When the coffee water was hot, he added a handful of coffee
grounds and waited for it to steep. As the time slowly
passed, he began to move about nosily in hopes that Payne
would awaken, but he didn't. It was full daylight when
Alexander walked to the side of the bed and looked at Payne.
His face was more swollen than before and his skin looked
dry and flushed. He seemed to be having problems breathing
through his parched lips.

"Do you want something to drink?" asked Alexander. Payne
did not respond.
"Wake up," said Alexander as he shook the man's arm. Still
no response.
Shaking him vigorously he called out again, "Wake up and
drink some water!"
Payne groaned and tried to open his eyes. He muttered

something and fell asleep again. Alexander touched his face and found he was hot with fever. Hurrying to the water bucket, he remembered it was empty. Sticking the pistol under his belt, he rushed out the door to the spring for some cold water. One of his dogs jumped from the porch and followed him. Alexander filled the bucket, and hurried back up the path to the cabin.

He was about thirty steps from the door when all three dogs went charging across the yard barking. Three Indians were standing in the edge of the yard near the woods; one of them had a rifle. After pausing for a moment, Alexander continued walking toward the cabin as if he were not concerned about their presence. He would be no match for them if they were looking for trouble. He wanted to get to the cabin and his rifle as quick as possible, but did not want to appear to be alarmed. The Indian with the rifle stood a short distance in front of the other two. Moving slowly, he laid the rifle on the ground and stepped forward a few paces and spoke. Alexander did not understand him. He pointed to a leaf in his hand and held it up for Alexander to see. It appeared to be stained with dried blood. He then pointed towards the woods and spoke again. This time, Alexander understood the word "Payne." By now, Alexander was only a few feet from the cabin and feeling more comfortable about his situation so he stopped. Payne's yellow dog had trotted over to the Indian and stood there wagging his tail like they were old friends. The Indian pointed to the blood-covered leaf again and then to the dog and said "Payne."
"Are you looking for John Payne?"
The Indian nodded his head and said, "Payne hurt," holding up the leaf again.
Alexander pointed to the cabin and motioned for the Indian to follow him inside. He felt safe with one unarmed man but he would not risk letting more than one enter. Once inside, the Indian rushed to Payne's side and tried unsuccessfully to rouse him. Alexander was watching the Indian closely as he poured the cold spring water into a pan. Through the open

door, he could still see the other two Indians in the yard, they had not moved. Abruptly, the Indian in the house, who appeared to be the headman, turned and rushed to the door, yelling something to the two in the yard before returning to Payne's side. Alexander could see one of the Indians running away into the woods. The other one picked up the gun and positioned himself in the edge of the woods and continued watching the cabin. As Alexander carried the pan of water to the bedside, the Indian looked at him and said, "Doctor," pointing towards the woods.

"Doctor?" asked Alexander with a puzzled expression on his face.

The Indian nodded his head as he dipped his hand in the cold water and began wiping Payne's face. Alexander found a small piece of cloth and handed it to the Indian. Dipping it in and out of the water, he continued wiping Payne's face, neck and arms while talking to him. Alexander sat at the table waiting and wondering where they would find a doctor. He positioned himself so he could watch the Indian working on Payne and still see the one in the edge of the woods.

Only a short time had passed when two Indians emerged from the woods, hurrying towards the house. One was the man who had left earlier and the other was a woman. She appeared to be about fifty years old and carried a small buckskin bag. Alexander walked to the door and stepped out onto the porch to meet them. The man stopped a short distance from the cabin. The woman hesitated for a moment, and then nervously approached the porch. She hurried into the cabin and went directly to Payne's bed. Alexander followed her inside. The two Indians talked rapidly as the man pointed to Payne's nose. The woman stooped down and studied his nostrils. Alexander moved closer to see what she was going to do. Reaching inside her bag, she brought out a small smooth stick with deep, opposing notches cut in one end. She pushed the notched end into one of his nostrils until it met resistance. Twisting it slowly, she gradually withdrew it from his nose. Something was attached to the end. The astonished Indians chattered as they examined it. Alexander immediately recognized it as a piece of the dirty rag that he had given Payne yesterday after the fight. Payne had apparently torn off a piece of it and packed it into his nose to stop the bleeding. The same procedure on the other nostril revealed yet another piece. Payne moaned and tossed about in the bed each time the wads were removed from his nose. The Indian woman returned the stick to the bag and removed a small hollow reed about six inches long. Reaching into the bag again, she brought out a little clay bowl and something that looked like finely ground brown powder. She placed a pinch of the powder into the bowl and then inserted some it into one end of the reed. Stooping down, she blew it into one side of Payne's nose with a quick puff. His entire body trembled and he began to sneeze. After sneezing several times, fresh blood began flowing slowly from the treated side of his nose. After he became calm, the same procedure was repeated on the other nostril. Reaching into the bag again, she withdrew some small dried leaves and began rubbing one of them between her finger and thumb, catching the particles in her other hand. When the leaf had been finely pulverized, she inserted the material into the corner of his mouth between his lip and teeth. She then crushed another leaf in the same manner and placed it in the opposite side of his mouth. When she had returned the other items to her bag, she took the cool water and rag and resumed wiping Payne's head and face. Each time she dipped the rag into the cool water, she would wipe his lips first, leaving them excessively wet, especially at the corners where the drops of water would slowly ooze into his mouth. After watching her repetitious acts for a while, Alexander decided there was no need for his further observation. His time would be better spent preparing some food since it seemed he was going to have company for a while. There was some stew left in a bowl from the night before, but not enough for five people.

Filling the stew pot with water, he realized he would now

need more. He was a little anxious about leaving the two Indians alone in the house, but was beginning to feel more comfortable in their presence. They had been watching him curiously as he prepared the pot and hung it in the fireplace. When he started toward the door with the water bucket, the Headman reached out and took the bucket from him. Stepping to the door, he called out to one of the Indians in the yard, who came running to the cabin, took the bucket and started toward the spring. In a few minutes he was back with the water. After a brief exchange between the two men, the one from the yard left. Alexander watched him as he spoke briefly to the other one outside and then disappeared into the woods, just as he had when he went for the Doctor Woman. Alexander wondered what that conversation was about as he returned to the task of trying to find enough ingredients for the stew.

By the time the water was hot, the Indian was back with two rabbits. He handed them to Alexander, pointed at the stew pot and said something. He smiled and returned to the yard. The rabbits had been dressed, but still had their feet and head attached. Alexander removed the feet and heads and tossed them out to the dogs, much to the amusement of the Indians. Separating each rabbit into six pieces, he placed them into the pot with the other ingredients and put more wood on the fire. Hearing a bump outside, he walked to the door and looked out. The Rabbit Man was bringing more wood from the shed and stacking it on the porch. The Yard Man was still standing at the edge of the woods with the rifle, watching all the activities.

Normally, cooking a pot of stew was an all-day process over a low fire as you went about other activities. Since Alexander was limited in what else he could do, he kept the fire burning briskly under the pot and tended it carefully. By early afternoon the stew was ready and so was a pan of bread. The rabbits were thoroughly cooked and the meat had fallen from the bones. The other ingredients had all been transformed into a thick, tasty, broth. Having only four bowls, Alexander decided to feed the Indians first. They watched curiously as he filled the bowls and placed them on the table with a spoon and a piece of bread beside each bowl and motioned for them to eat. The Headman and the Doctor Woman chatted noisily for a moment, apparently discussing the appropriate response to the strange situation they found themselves in. The man stepped to the door and called into the yard. In a few moments, Rabbit Man appeared at the door. Alexander gathered that they wanted him to eat with them and let Yard Man eat later. Awkwardly, they all sat down and began eating. In just a few minutes, the tension eased and everyone appeared relaxed as they enjoyed the food. Alexander was greatly amused by the Indians as they chatted and laughed between bites and wished he could understand what they were saying. When Rabbit Man had finished eating, he hurriedly exited and was replaced in a few minutes by the Indian from the yard. This was the first time he had been inside. His eyes scanned the room as he eased his tense, muscular body onto the seat at the table. He watched suspiciously as Alexander sat the bowl of stew and bread in front of him. Like the others, he began to relax as he ate and was soon laughing and talking with them.

There was no visible change in Payne as the day passed. Shortly before dark, the Head Man tried to tell Alexander their plans for the night. Alexander understood that some of them were going to leave, but that the Doctor Woman and one of the men would stay. He watched as the three men stood in the yard talking. After a brief conversation, the Yard Man took up a position near the cabin and the other two disappeared into the woods. It had been a long tiring day and the stage was now set for a long night. It was time for a cup of coffee. Alexander thought about Elizabeth and how insistent she had been that he brought the coffee. He really missed her and the children. Placing a handful of the coffee beans in the grinder, he began to turn the handle. After placing the ground coffee into the pot of water,

257

Alexander picked up some of the coffee beans and gave them to the Doctor Woman had had been watching his every move. "Coffee," he said. Placing several beans into the grinder, he cranked the handle and ground them, handing her the results. "Coffee," he said again. She examined the ground coffee for a moment and then tasted it. Alexander laughed as he sat the grinder back on the shelf and returned to the table to wait until the coffee was ready. When he poured himself a cup, he offered one to the Doctor Woman but she refused it.

The hours passed by slowly. Alexander felt it must be near midnight and there was still no change in Payne. The Doctor Woman continued to bathe his face and neck with the cool water. Alexander had removed the pot of stew from the fire and let it cool before placing it outside on a high shelf where it would not spoil and be safe from animals. There was nothing left for him to do but keep the fire burning brightly so they would have enough light to see. He was beginning to feel the effect of the lack of sleep the night before and the two stressful days he had endured. Every muscle in his body ached. He decided to stretch out on the bed and rest until the fire needed more wood. From where he lay, he could see the door, the fire, and Payne.

Alexander woke with a start and wondered how long he had been asleep. His heart was racing as he quickly scanned the room. He apparently had not slept long because the fire seemed to be burning as brightly as it had been before he went to sleep and the Doctor Woman had not moved from Payne's bedside. As he watched her through half-closed eyes, he could see she was examining one of the coffee beans he had given her. After studying it a few minutes, she placed it in her mouth and began to chew it. When it was gone, she ate another one. She turned and looked towards the door, which was slowly opening. Alexander's hand moved rapidly down to the pistol stuck in his belt, but stopped when he saw Yard Man entering with more wood for the fire. Silently, he came in, put the wood on the fire and left as quietly as he had come. That explained why the fire was still burning brightly even though Alexander had been asleep. He smiled as he thought about all that had happened in the last two days and wondered if anyone would believe him when he told about it. The life or death battle with John Payne and the strange circumstances that had brought Payne to this house, perhaps to die. And now, Alexander lay sleeping while Indians moved freely in and out of his house. It was unbelievable.

The long night finally passed and it was beginning to get light. Alexander was preparing his coffee when he heard the Indian woman speaking excitedly. Payne was awake and staring at her with a confused look on his face as she continued to speak to him. He shifted his gaze to Alexander for a moment and then back to the woman.

"Glad you finally woke up," said Alexander, as he walked over to the bed.

"What's she doing here?" asked Payne.

"Trying to keep you from dying."

"How did she know I was here?"

"The Indians came here looking for you and then went for her."

"How long have I been here?"

"Today's the third day."

Payne stared at him unbelievingly and then spoke to the woman who chatted excitedly with him as she gave him a drink of water.

"Any of that coffee left?" asked Payne as he returned his attention to Alexander.

"A new pot, I'll get you a cup."

Cradling the cup in both hands, Payne was sipping gingerly on the hot brew when the door slowly opened and the Head Man slipped inside the house. When he saw Payne was awake he let out a yell and ran to the bed. Immediately, the other two Indians appeared at the door. One of them had two rabbits in his hands. Four chattering Indians in the house was a bit unnerving for Alexander so he stepped back a few feet to give them some space. He was amused by the noisy show, but frustrated by his inability to understand the conversation. He poured himself a cup of coffee and sat down on the side of his bed to watch and listen. He was amazed that Payne not only understood them, but also responded to them in their language.

The chattering stopped and all of them looked at Alexander. The Yard Man turned back to Payne and said something, and they all laughed. Payne responded to them and they laughed louder. Alexander knew the discussion was about him and he wanted to know what they were saying. Recognizing Alexander's predicament, Payne said, "They wanted to know how I got hurt, they thought the deadfall log fell on my head. I told them you hit me. They wanted to know what you hit me with. I told them you hit me with your fist. They think it's funny."

The Rabbit Man spoke to Payne who relayed the message to Alexander.

"He says you are a good fighter and also a good cook."

"Tell him it was because of those fine rabbits he brought me."

When Payne conveyed the message, Rabbit Man responded and they all laughed again.

"He said you threw the best parts to the dogs."

Alexander laughed, but made no reply. The Indian spoke to Payne again.

"He wants to know how you make that good bread."

"My wife taught me. She can make it better than I can."

When Payne told them, more chatter and laughter erupted from the Indians.

"They want to see your woman."

"So do I. I'm tired of my own cooking and tired of sleeping alone."

Laughter exploded again from the group when Payne told them what he said.

"Where does he get those rabbits?" asked Alexander.

"Catches them each night in snares."

"You know how to do it?"

"Not like he does."

"Tell him I want him to show me how to catch rabbits."

"He'll show you."

It was seven days before John Payne's strength returned sufficiently for him to go back home. The Indians, who were maintaining the trap lines, came each day to bring food and report on the catch. The week provided valuable time for the two men to talk.

"So you want me to teach you to trap in exchange for trapping rights on Cary land. What makes you think Mr. Cary will approve of that?" asked Payne.

"I think he'll approve when I explain why."

"I'd be crazy not to do it. I have nothing to lose, but you do. When Cary runs you off his land don't blame me for it."

"I don't think that will happen, he's a reasonable man. I'll talk to him as soon as I get home. I'm going home for Christmas so that gives us six weeks to work together."

"That's only half of the trapping season. You coming back after Christmas?"

"That wasn't the plan. I'm supposed to come back in the spring and bring my family."

"Can't you bring your family back after Christmas?"

"I don't know. I'll have to discuss it with Mr. Cary and my wife."

"How does your wife feel about coming to the wilderness to live?"

"She's ready. We've been dreaming about it for years."

"I wish I could find a good wife."

"Have you tried?"

"Where would I find one willing to live here except an Indian woman?"

"I know one, but she wants a good man," teased Alexander. "One that will love her and treat her well. I'm not sure if you know how to do that, you have such a bad reputation."

Payne stared unblinkingly at him trying to determine if he

261

was serious.

"I think you're lying."

"About what? You do have a bad reputation!"

"About knowing someone."

"I'm not lying. If I wasn't married and wanted a wife, I'd go after her tomorrow. She's pretty, she's a good cook, and she wants to marry a good man and raise a family."

"Who is she?"

"Her name is Ginny and she works at the Trading Post."

Payne grew strangely silent. He never mentioned their conversation again.

Alexander was a quick learner. His improved traps and newly learned skills quickly produced results. Together, the two men were regularly collecting wolf bounties and accumulating many fine pelts for market, but they were careful not to reveal they were working together. As the time approached for Alexander to leave, they discussed the future possibilities.

"You may be back in a few weeks, you may not be back until spring, or you may never come back when Mr. Cary learns about me," said John Payne. "What am I supposed to do until I find out? I can't work both trap lines alone."

"Why don't you stop working the traps on Cary land until I come back. That will keep the Sheriff from catching you and arresting you for trespassing. You've already had a good season and your other traps will keep you busy for the rest of the year."

"I'm going to need some things from the Trading Post before spring. If I knew you were coming back, I'd get you to bring them. Since I don't know, maybe I'd better go down and get them while you're here to work the lines. If you don't come back, I'll have what I need. I'll take the hides I have ready to sell now and you can take yours when you go."

"If you're going to do that, you need to go as soon as you can so I can get home before Christmas."

"I'll leave tomorrow."

Several days passed and John Payne had not returned. Alexander was concerned that something had happened to him. He was working from dawn until dark each day collecting the animals from the traps and skinning and preparing the hides. If Payne didn't return soon he would have to quit resetting the traps. He returned from the trap line about noon on the fourth day, tired, cold, and hungry. After building-up the fire, he sat beside it and ate, enjoying its warmth. He was so tired; he hated to move, but knew he had to get started on the day's catch. Just as he stood, the dogs started barking. Someone was coming, perhaps it was Payne. Picking up his gun, Alexander walked to the door and looked out. A woman on horseback was riding towards the cabin. He sat the gun down and stepped out on the porch. As she rode into the yard he recognized her.

"Ginny! What are you doing here?" he asked as he stepped down from the porch.

"I came to see you!" she said as she dismounted and threw her arms around him. "I was hoping I could find you."

"Why are you looking for me, is anything wrong?"

"No, everything is fine. I just decided I was coming to the wilderness to live so I came to see you. Aren't you going to invite me in?"

"Of course," said Alexander, stepping aside and motioning her towards the porch.

Taking him by the arm, Ginny bounded up the steps, practically dragging him with her.

Once inside, she removed her coat, tossed it on the table, and walked to the fireplace to warm herself. She stood there studying every detail of the room. "I love your cabin," she said.

"Thank you, I like it too. What are you planning to do here," said Alexander nervously.

"Live here," said Ginny as she walked to the rear of the cabin and stood looking at the bed. "I see you have an extra bed."

"Ginny, you know you can't stay with me."

"What? Do you mean that after I rode all the way from The

263

Falls to see you, that you won't give me something to eat and a place to sleep?"

"You know I don't mean that, but you can't live here. What would my wife think if she found out I was living out here with a pretty woman?"

"Do you really think I'm pretty?" said Ginny, as she moved toward Alexander smiling.

"Yes, you're pretty, but you can't live with me."

"Did I say I wanted to live with you?"

"No, but you said you were going to live here."

"Yes, here in the wilderness, but not with you."

"Well who do you plan to live with?"

"Him," said Ginny pointing towards the door.

Spinning around, Alexander saw John Payne who had silently entered the cabin. He and Ginny broke into hysterical laughter.

"She had you going, didn't she mate?" laughed Payne.

"What is going on here?" asked Alexander as he walked back to face Payne.

"Just wanted you to be the first to meet my new wife."

"Your wife!"

"Thanks to you," said Ginny, throwing both arms around Alexander's neck and kissing him on the cheek. "You promised me you would remember me, and you did."

"I hope he didn't tell you that I sent him there to marry you!"

"He told me exactly what you said. Then he said that if you thought I'd make a good wife that was all he needed to know."

Obviously embarrassed, Alexander said, "Poor girl. I hope you know what you've gotten yourself into. You've got a big job ahead of you making a good husband out of this man."

"She has already started working on it," said Payne, smiling.

"I thought maybe you were dead or in jail when you didn't come back. I never thought you were off somewhere getting married."

"We had to go all the way to Williamsburg to find a minister."

"Well, congratulations and welcome back. I have plenty of work outside that I have to do, but I'll get you something to eat first."

"This time I'll furnish the coffee," said Payne. "Dixon paid me well for the hides so I bought some extra things from him, including coffee."

"Next time he'll get even with you for stealing Ginny."

"He wasn't too pleased about her leaving," laughed Payne.

"Does Elizabeth know about it?" asked Alexander.

"I don't think so," said Ginny.

"She's going to be surprised when I tell her you're here."

"When are you going home?" asked Payne.

"I've been waiting for you to get back. I'll probably leave tomorrow and go by the Hoopers on the way home to let them know I'm gone. Should I tell them about you getting married?"

"Why not? They'll have to learn about it sometimes."

"I'll tell them how your lovely wife has reformed you. Maybe they'll invite you over."

"You do believe in miracles, don't you?"

"I'm beginning to."

1731
Chapter 25

Homecoming

Alexander planned a brief stop at the Hoopers to tell them he was leaving and when he hoped to return. He had started early and was anxious to continue his trip, planning to arrive home before dark. They insisted he have a cup of tea before traveling on.

"We were hoping to see more of you while you were here," said Joseph Hooper.

"I had hoped so too. I didn't realize I would be so busy."

"Have you had a profitable trapping season?"

"Yes sir, better than I had hoped for. I've learned a lot in the short time I've been here."

"Good. Then I suppose Ben did a good job of teaching you, I'll tell him."

"Thank you sir. He was very patient with me."

"Have you had any encounters with John Payne?"

"Yes sir, I've seen him quite a few times."

"Has he caused you any trouble?"

"No sir. I don't think he's quite the trouble-maker he once was."

"Oh really? Why do you think that?"

"It may be because he has gotten married."

"Married! I can't believe anyone would marry that scoundrel."

Elizabeth Hooper almost dropped the teapot. Regaining her composure, she turned to Alexander and said, "Who on earth did he find to marry in this wilderness?"

"A young lady named Ginny who worked for Mr. Dixon at The Falls. My wife and I have known her for several years. She is really quite a nice person."

"I pray she can remain a nice person being married to that man."

The sky was overcast and there was a feeling of snow in the air as Alexander rode steadily towards home. He had stayed longer at the Hoopers than he intended so it would be late in the day before he arrived home. They were lovely people and very gracious hosts, but it was difficult to get away from them. He desperately wanted to make the trip home in one day. Fortunately, the ground was frozen hard so he didn't have to contend with being slowed down by a muddy road. The dogs trotted along ahead of the wagon as if they knew exactly where they were going. He was almost home when it began to snow. Snow always reminded him of his first Christmas with Elizabeth when they visited with the Carys and the Sclaters and walked home together in the snow. Soon he would be home to celebrate Christmas again with her and the children.

It was snowing harder and getting dark when he reached home. Elizabeth saw him coming and ran from the house to meet him. He jumped down from the wagon and gathered her in his arms and kissed her repeatedly. Four-year-old John had followed his mother into the yard where he stood with the snow swirling around him. Alexander swept him up into his arms and continued towards the house where two-year-old Joseph stood in the open doorway watching all the hubbub. As they reached the steps, the boy turned and scampered back into the house laughing loudly. Alexander ran after him, picking him up and tossing him into the air. His eyes grew large and he gasped as he reached out with both arms to his mother.

"You've scared him," said Elizabeth, reaching out to take the tot.

"Do me," said John, holding up both arms to his daddy who picked him up and tossed him in the air.

"Do it again," laughed John.

"You're heavy," said Alexander. "You've grown a lot since I've been gone."

"Both of them have," said Elizabeth. "They love to eat."

"So do I and I'm starved! I really look forward to eating

267

your good cooking again, I'm tired of eating mine."

"Go unload the wagon and take care of the horse and by then supper will be ready."

As Alexander turned to leave, someone knocked at the door. It was Henry Cary and Archibald.

"We saw you arrive. I just wanted to be sure all is well with you and tell you we're glad you're home safely."

"Everything is fine, sir, and it's good to be home."

"Good. We aren't coming in, I know you have things to do and want to spend time with your family so I'll wait until tomorrow to visit with you."

"I'll look forward to talking with you."

"Can I stay here and play with John?" asked Archibald.

"Another time would be better, son, maybe tomorrow. John needs to spend time with his mama and daddy right now."

The wet snow continued throughout the night, accumulating several inches on the ground and buildings. It looked beautiful clinging to the trees and bushes, unmoved by the cold breeze blowing from the west. It was a good day to stay close to the fire. Since Christmas was only two days away, Elizabeth was busy cooking some special treats and decorating the house with greenery.

"Aren't you glad you didn't wait until today to come home?" she asked.

"I don't even want to think about that. It would be miserable traveling today."

"I was expecting you home several days ago."

"That was my plan, but I had to change it. You remember that I told you last night about John Payne teaching me to trap?"

"Yes."

"There's a lot more that I haven't told you about him. He's married to Ginny."

"Ginny! When did they get married?"

"Earlier this week, that's why I couldn't leave sooner. He came down to the trading post at The Falls for supplies and I couldn't leave until he came back. He was gone several days longer than planned and when he came back he brought

Ginny with him and they were married. Do you remember what she told us about wanting a husband?"

"Yes."

"Payne was telling me one day about how he would like to have a wife and family and I told him about Ginny. He never commented on what I said but soon after that he left for The Falls and came back with Ginny."

"Is he a good man?"

"I think so but most people don't."

"Why?"

"They just don't know him."

"Are you sure you know him that well?"

"We've worked together trapping as partners for the past six weeks."

"Partners? Does Mr. Cary know that?"

"No. And don't say anything about it until I talk with him and explain it."

"Don't you think it would have been better to discuss it with him first?"

"How could I? I had to make the decision. I could have stayed three months and caught nothing or learn from someone who knew how to trap."

"When are you going to tell him?"

"As soon as I can talk with him. He said he would come visit today, but I don't know if he's still coming because of the snow. I've been thinking about going over to see him, but I would rather talk to him here."

Just then there was a knock on the door. It was Henry Cary.

Alexander took his coat while Elizabeth excused herself to make some tea.

"Well tell me about everything up the river. Did you get the buildings repaired?"

"I did, and also got enough firewood stored for several more months. I stayed very comfortable there, but I sure missed my family."

"I told George Payne you were there and asked him to stop by to see you. Did he ever come by for a visit?"

"He did. He came with one of his deputies shortly after he talked with you."

"What about the Hoopers, are they doing well?"

"They are. I visited with them yesterday before I left, that's why I was so late getting home."

Cary laughed, "They do love to talk don't they? I'm sure they must get lonesome there and when company comes they hate for them to leave. I know they are happy to have the Mayos living nearby. They are all fine people and very accommodating."

"They were very helpful to me. They allowed Ben to spend several days with me teaching me to build traps."

"He apparently taught you well from the looks of all those pelts on your wagon."

"I did catch a lot, but it wasn't because of Ben's teaching. He taught me how to make a trap, but not how to trap. He meant well, but he just didn't know. I never caught anything with his traps."

Cary looked puzzled. "Then how did you learn?"

"Do you remember the discussion at Hoopers that night about John Payne?"

"Indeed I do. The trespassing rogue who has no respect for anyone or anything. The Sheriff is anxious to catch him on my property."

"He taught me to trap."

Cary sat upright on the edge of his chair staring at Alexander. "I distinctly remember Joseph Hooper advising you to have nothing to do with that man. Apparently you did not value his opinion."

"Occasionally things happen that we have no control over."

"We can certainly control who we choose to associate with."

"Sometimes circumstances take away our choices."

"Young man, a life that is controlled by circumstances will amount to nothing. You had a choice about associating with a man like John Payne."

"The only choice I had was to do what you sent me to do or return home. I did what you sent me to do and I did no wrong. Let me tell you what happened."

Henry Cary and Elizabeth sat spellbound for the next thirty minutes as Alexander told about his encounter with Payne, the fight, Payne's illness, the Indians, the week of recovery, and how they had ended up being friends and working effectively together.

Cary sat back in his chair silently sipping his tea. Finally he spoke.

"That's an amazing story. If someone else told it to me, I wouldn't believe it. However, I am bothered that you took the liberty to allow that man to trap on my land without my permission."

"Didn't you give me the authority to trap your land and keep out trespassers?"

"I did, but you don't keep out trespassers by giving them permission to trespass!"

"I didn't. We became partners. He taught me to trap and we worked two trap lines together."

"On my land!"

"And his land."

"It seems that John Payne benefited the most from that arrangement."

"We all benefited. I benefited because he taught me to trap, otherwise I would have caught nothing. Now, I know how to trap and I have pelts to sell. He benefited from his catch, and you benefited because nobody trespassed on your land, you have less wolves than you had before, and the pelts will produce some income for you."

"I suppose he is still trapping on my land while you are here?"

"No sir. We agreed that he wouldn't do that."

"You seem very confident that he is a man who will keep his word," sneered Cary.

"I am."

"I must say that your confidence in him is greater than mine! I have never heard anyone speak one good word about that man."

"He is a much better man than most people realize."

"How can you be so supportive of a man who tried to kill

271

you?"

"Maybe I see something of myself in him. There have been times when I was so angry that I wanted to kill someone. I may have been like he was if nobody had believed in me and given me a chance in life, but you gave me a chance. Reverend Sclater did the same thing. You both have been good to me, far better than I deserve. I often wonder what I would be like if you two had not shown confidence in me and given me a chance."

Henry Cary finished his tea and sat staring in the empty cup.

"I suppose you plan to continue this partnership with Mr. Payne?"

"That depends on you. It's your land and I work for you. Because it's your land, a portion of what I sell my hides for belongs to you."

"What about Payne's pelts, do I get a portion of those too?"

"I'll pay you that also. He has paid me by teaching me to trap."

"I don't want any money from your pelts. Keep whatever they bring because you've earned it."

"Would you like more tea?" asked Elizabeth.

"No thank you, Elizabeth, I need to go home. I have a lot to think about."

After Henry Cary was gone, Elizabeth turned to Alexander and said, "I've never seen him that angry before. He's really upset with you."

"I know, but there's nothing I can do about it now. I had to tell him the truth."

"Maybe you shouldn't have had anything to do with John Payne."

"How could I have helped it?"

"You didn't have to ask him to be your partner."

"That's right! I could have spent the last three months up there alone running around in the woods, trying to keep him and others off of Mr. Cary's land. If I had survived, I could have looked at my empty traps every day and returned home with nothing!"

Elizabeth was shocked by his outburst. She stared at him for a moment and then began laughing. "Now you're getting upset."

"Yes I am. I did the very best I could and I think it turned out well. Apparently nobody else does."

"Ginny probably does," said Elizabeth smiling.

"So does John Payne," said Alexander with a grin. "But that doesn't change the way Mr. Cary feels about it."

"What do you think he'll do?"

"About what?"

"About his agreement with us. Do you think he'll still allow us to go there and live?"

"I don't know, but right now I'm going to enjoy Christmas and not worry about it. When he decides, he'll let us know."

Alexander and his family were invited to the Cary's home for their traditional meal on Christmas Day. Although Mr. Cary was cordial, he never mentioned their earlier conversation. The next day, he paid another visit to the Stinson's cottage.

"Alexander, I've been thinking about the discussion we had before Christmas. I'm afraid I may have been a bit abrupt with you, for that I apologize. As you know, I'm a reputable person and I was quite shocked when you said you had established a partnership with John Payne. After thinking about it, I'm sure your response to him was far more Christian than mine would have been, but I admit that I still have some reservations about him. How can you be sure this man is trustworthy?"

"Only by trusting him."

"How much do you know about him?"

"Not much because he doesn't talk a lot about himself. I think he's had a difficult life. I know he's a smart man. He knows a lot about the colony and it's people and has a wealth of knowledge about the wilderness. He has a good relationship with the Indians and has learned to speak their language. He is like one of them."

"Does he have a family?"

"He recently married Ginny from the Trading Post."

"The girl who works for Mr. Dixon?"

"Yes sir."

"Has she moved to the wilderness with him?"

"Yes sir."

"Amazing! She seemed like a nice girl."

"She is a nice person. Her and Elizabeth are good friends."

"Oh," said Cary, pausing thoughtfully for a few moments before turning and speaking to Elizabeth. "Well I suppose you are excited about having Ginny as a neighbor when you move up there?"

Caught off guard by the apparent change in the direction of the conversation, the surprised Elizabeth was slow to respond. Finally she spoke.

"Yes I am. I didn't see Ginny a lot when she was at the Trading Post. I hope I can see her more often now."

Turning to Alexander he asked, "Doesn't Payne live close to where you'll be living?"

"He does. Closer than the Hoopers, but in the other direction."

"I'm sure you'll be seeing a lot of each other if you are going to work together."

Now it was Alexander's turn to be surprised. "You mean that's agreeable with you?"

"I suppose. You spoke of trusting people. This is really going to be a matter of me trusting you to make the right decision about what is best for both of us. I certainly would not have made the decision you did about a partnership with John Payne, but it appears to have worked out well. If you decide to continue, that will be your choice."

"We were afraid you would change your mind about us going."

"That was my first thought," said Mr. Cary, smiling. "I needed to think about it for a few days before I decided. I'm willing to continue my original offer if you want to go back."

"We do."

"Do you still plan to wait until spring?"

"I had thought about going back sooner if you didn't object. There's still three months left in the trapping season."

"Would you take your family with you?"

"I haven't discussed it with Elizabeth. I wanted to know your feelings first."

"Let me think about this and discuss it with Mrs. Cary. That will also give you two an opportunity to talk about it," said Cary as he walked to the door. "It isn't going to be easy for any of us when it happens, but it does seem to me that a move like this may be easier on your family in warmer weather."

After Mr. Cary was gone, Elizabeth said, "I didn't know you were considering going back to trap."

"I hadn't considered it until Payne asked me about it."

"Is that what you want to do?"

"I don't know. I hate to move you and the children in the winter, but I don't want to leave you again either."

"Why can't we just wait until spring like we had planned?"

"We can, but I'll miss half of the trapping season if we do."

"You don't even know what those pelts will bring. They may not be worth the trouble."

"That's true, but I'll find out tomorrow when I sell them to Mr. Dixon."

Alexander was overjoyed when he returned from the Trading Post. The furs had brought more than double what he had hoped for.

"That's more than half a year's wages," exclaimed Elizabeth!

"I know. Mr. Dixon was excited about them too. He said they had been handled perfectly and were some of the best hides he had ever taken in. That's something else I have to thank John Payne for. Without his help they may have been worthless."

"I suppose you'll definitely want to go back now?"

"It sure is tempting. We could use the money to buy the rest of the things we need."

"Well, let's go!"

"Let's go? You mean you want to move now?"

"I'd rather move now than wait until spring."

"Why?"

"Because I'm going to have another baby."

"What! How long have you known?"

"Since last month."

"Why didn't you tell me?"

"I just did."

"No, I mean...why didn't you tell me earlier?"

"You had too many other things on your mind."

"Maybe it would be better to wait until later to move."

"It wouldn't. Let me tell you why," said Elizabeth. "Mrs. Cary will have to get someone else to help her when I leave. Even if I stayed, I will have three small children of my own to care for so I'd be very little help to her. The sooner they can find someone the better."

"I'm concerned about you having a baby out there."

"Why? All frontier families have their babies out there. If we're going to live there, we must have our babies there."

"But...who'll help you when you have the baby?"

"You," said Elizabeth, laughing.

"That's what I'm afraid of!"

"Don't forget, Ginny is there, she can help us. Don't you think that Indian Woman or someone at the Hoopers could help too if I needed them?"

"I suppose so."

"Quit worrying. With God's help, we'll do fine."

The next day Henry and Anne Cary came to visit. The two couples discussed the move in great detail, considering all the options. They all concluded that a quick move would be in everyone's best interest. They should choose a time when the weather was not too severe and Alexander and his family would make the move quickly with a lightly loaded wagon. Some of the men from the plantation would follow bringing the remainder of their things.

1732
Chapter 26

Moving To The Wilderness

Alexander was watching the expression on Elizabeth's face as they entered the clearing where the cabin was located. Joseph, tightly wrapped in a blanket, was asleep on his mother's lap. John, also bundled in a blanket sat wedged between his parents. As the cabin came into view, Elizabeth asked, "Is that it?"

"That's it."

"Why is smoke coming from the chimney?"

"Looks like we have company. That's Payne's horse and wagon out front."

"What would he be doing here?"

"We'll find out in a minute."

As soon as they pulled to the front of the cabin, the door flew open and a very excited Ginny came running down the steps, followed by John Payne.

"I can't believe you're here!" she said, reaching up to hug Elizabeth's neck and then take the sleeping little boy from her arms.

"We knew you were on the way," said Payne, "so we came over to get the house warmed up for you."

"How did you know that?" asked Alexander.

"Rabbit Man saw you fording Muddy Creek and came by to tell us you were on the way back."

"Rabbit Man?" asked Elizabeth with a puzzled look on her face. "Who is that?"

"One of the Indians," laughed Payne. "That's not his name, but that's what your husband calls him."

"I wish I had known earlier that you were coming," said Ginny, "I would have had supper ready for you."

"Don't fret about that, I'm thankful just to have a warm house," said Elizabeth, as she climbed down from the wagon. "It's so good to see you again," said Elizabeth, "how do you like living here?"

"I love it! I've never been this happy before. Now that your family is here, it will be even better. Are you here to stay?"

"We're here to stay."

Alexander lifted John down from the wagon to the ground. He stood there staring at John Payne.

"Are you the man that catches wolves?"

"I'm one of them," laughed Payne.

"When you catch another one, can I see it?"

"You sure can. I'll even let you touch it."

"I don't want to touch it, I just want to look at it."

"I'll remember to let you look at it."

"I want to see an Indian too."

"I'm sure you'll see one of those real soon."

Everybody was laughing as they walked to the house. John's wish to see an Indian and a wolf was quickly fulfilled when Rabbit Man appeared the next morning with a gift of two rabbits and Payne returned from the trap line that evening with another wolf. During the busy weeks following the move, the men's days were filled with working their trap lines, which continued to produce abundantly. Processing the hides was also time consuming. Sometimes, they would not be finished until after dark, especially when their travel was hindered by snow and ice. Ginny would usually spend her days with Elizabeth and the boys while the men were away. Her comforting presence and the communal time of the two family made the transition to wilderness living more bearable for all of them. It also produced a bond that would endure for life.

Ginny was ecstatic when she learned that Elizabeth was expecting another baby.

"This one has to be girl," she said, "we're being outnumbered by the men."

"The Lord is in control of that. Maybe He knows we need another man around here to help with all the work."

"My husband really wants a little one."

"I've noticed how much he enjoys being around our boys."

"He loves your boys and talks about them all the time, but do you know something? I think secretly, he would like to have a little girl."

"Why do you think that?"

"I just have a feeling about it. He's never really said so, but I think he would."

"Can you imagine how protective he would be of a little girl?" They were both laughing about the prospect when they heard a noise outside.

"Someone's coming," said Ginny, hurrying to the door. Elizabeth reached for the rifle sitting in the corner and stood waiting for a word from her friend.

"It's an older couple in a carriage," said Ginny. "I don't know them."

Sitting the rifle back down, Elizabeth hurried to the door.

"Good morning," said the man. "I'm Joseph Hooper and this is my wife Elizabeth, we're your neighbors. We just rode over to say hello."

"I'm so pleased to meet you. I'm Elizabeth Stinson, and this is my neighbor, Ginny Payne. Please come in."

"We hadn't planned to stay, we don't want to be a bother."

"You're no bother. I'm delighted to see you, please come in long enough for a cup of tea."

"I suppose we could do that, but we can't stay long," said the man, climbing down from the carriage and going around to help his wife.

"Oh what two precious little boys!" said Mrs. Hooper as she entered the cabin and saw the children for the first time.

Her husband, entering behind her, stepped around his wife and immediately struck up a conversation with John.

"How do you like living out here in the wilderness?"

"I like it. My daddy's going to take me trapping when I get bigger."

"Well, you're pretty big now! What do you plan to catch when you go?"

"A wolf. Have you ever caught one?"

"No, I've never caught one, but I've seen some."

"I touched one," said the boy, "did you ever touch one?"

279

"No, I never did. What did it feel like when you touched it?"

"It was cold and had thick hair."

"Did it have a long tale and big teeth?"

"Yes, but I didn't touch those."

Joseph Hooper was so caught up in his conversation with young John that they had to call him several times when the tea was ready. As the four adults sat around the table talking and drinking their tea, he repeatedly went back to conversing with the little boy. When the time came for them to leave, he made Elizabeth and Ginny promise to come visit them soon and bring the boys. "We would love for you to come and spend the day with us and bring the men with you. John and I have some more things to talk about."

The severe cold weather of winter finally gave way to a beautiful spring. With the trapping season behind them, the families began to concentrate on other tasks. There was land to clear, a vegetable garden to plant and fence, and the never-ending task of procuring firewood and food. One of the most important tasks at hand for Alexander was establishing a seedbed to raise tobacco plants and preparing the land to plant them. The Paynes were always there to help.

"I've never raised tobacco," said John Payne.

"That's something I can teach you. It's hard work, but it's a good money crop."

"I'll help you this year so I can learn, then I'll decide if it's something I want to do. I usually get by with selling my hides and collecting bounty, but up until now it's just been me to provide for."

"I'll soon have five to provide for. I also have to pay for my land so I need to do everything I can to make some money."

It was a hot July day when Elizabeth's baby decided to make its entry into the world. Even before the sun came up, it was hot. Elizabeth was miserable as she courageously went about her household duties. About mid-morning she told Alexander to go get Ginny. Quickly saddling the horse, he rode as fast as he could to the Payne's place, hoping they would be home. They were, and assured him they would be there without delay. Hurrying back home he found Elizabeth anxious over the increasing frequency of her labor pains and trying to decide what to do with the boys.

"We could let Payne take them back to his place and keep them," suggested Alexander.

"Suppose we need to send him for the Indian woman? I hate to put all this responsibility on Ginny, she's never done this before."

"I could take them over to Hoopers. They told us to let them know if they could help."

"Let John take them over there, I want you here with me."

"He's not going to like having to go over there by himself."

"He'll do it."

When John and Ginny arrived, Elizabeth told them the plan. John looked at Alexander apprehensively, but said nothing. He hurriedly took the boys to the wagon and left. When he returned an hour later, he brought one of the older slave women with him.

"This is Mandy, the Hoopers say she's a good midwife," said Payne proudly, "and she can stay as long as you need her. They sure are some nice people."

Shortly after the midwife's arrival, things progressed rapidly and without difficulty. Before long, baby Joanna made her long awaited debut.

"It's a girl!" shouted Ginny.

"Let me see her," said Elizabeth, with tears streaming down her cheeks.

Alexander and John both came rushing into the house.

"You men jest git out of here 'til we git this child all cleaned up," said Mandy. "I'll tell ya'll when ya'll can come in here."

The two men went sulking back outside to the porch.

"Bossy old thing," said Payne laughing.

"I noticed you didn't argue with her."

"I'm not going to argue with three women."

"Four. There's another one in there now and I'm anxious to meet her."

"She'll be your boss."

"Probably so."

"I'll trade you a hundred acres of good land for her without seeing her," teased Payne.

"No trade. You'll have to get your own."

"I'm trying."

Elizabeth was radiant as she held the tiny babe to her bosom. Ginny, standing beside the bed, was so excited she couldn't stay still. The two men stood awkwardly on the other side of the bed staring at the new baby.

"You want to hold her?" asked Elizabeth, as she looked at Alexander.

"Not now, she looks too comfortable to bother. How do you feel?"

"Wonderful. Things couldn't have gone better. Isn't she beautiful?"

Alexander was so emotional that all he could do was nod his head. After a few moments he said in a breaking voice, "Just like her mama."

"I offered to trade him a hundred acres for her, but he wouldn't trade," said Payne.

"Just wait," said Elizabeth, "you'll have so many of your own one day you'll be wanting to trade some of them off. It's my turn to play midwife to Ginny now."

"I'm ready," laughed Ginny.

It was late summer when Henry Cary and eleven-year-old Archibald made a surprise visit to the Stinson's farm. Alexander was outside with the two boys storing firewood when he saw them coming. He called Elizabeth who hurried out to greet them.

"What a wonderful surprise!" she said. "Where's the rest of the family?"

"They wanted to come, but this is just a quick trip for the two of us. I came up in the small carriage to examine the new road. It's much better than the old one so we can come back soon and bring everyone. We heard you have a new addition to the family and Mrs. Cary is anxious to see her."

"Would you like to see her?"

"Absolutely," said Henry Cary, as he climbed down from the carriage. Archibald hopped down from the other side and ran to give Elizabeth a hug before they all went inside to see the baby.

"She's a beautiful little girl," said Henry Cary, "what did you name her?"

"Joanna," said Alexander.

"That's a nice name. Was that your mother's name?"

"Yes sir."

"I know she would be pleased."

After an awkward silence, Elizabeth said, "I'm going to fix dinner for you."

"Please don't," said Cary. "We're in a bit of a hurry, but a cup of tea would be nice."

"You're not going back home today are you?"

"No, but William Mayo is expecting us to spend the night at his place. We are going across on the new ferry and down the river road on the other side tomorrow. I'm anxious to see how things are changing over on the north side."

As Elizabeth fixed the tea, the two older boys disappeared into the yard.

"I can't believe how much Archibald has grown," said Elizabeth.

"So have your boys. Wilderness living must be agreeing with them."

"They really like it here," said Alexander.

"You certainly have things looking nice. I saw your garden and fences when I came in. You've really done a lot of work on this place."

"Thank you. I never run out of things to do."

"Your tobacco is beautiful, it's a shame you don't have a larger crop."

"That was all the land I could get cleared before planting time."

"Maybe you can clear more next year."

"I plan to."

283

"You're also going to need some more space for your growing family. You need to cut a door right over there and put an addition on the back of this building."

"I'm afraid that might have to wait."

"Don't you think you could build it yourself?"

"Yes sir, but..."

"It wouldn't take that much material. You go ahead and put the foundation in this fall and I'll get the lumber for you. I've already started my new house at the plantation. I'm going to call it Ampthill. I'm getting the material cut for it now so I'll add enough to the list for you to build your addition and have it delivered in the spring."

"I'm not sure I'll have the money by then."

"You'll need the space by then. We can settle accounts later."

John and Ginny listened intently as Alexander told about Mr. Cary's visit and plans.

"John can help you build it," said Ginny.

"Be careful what you say woman! I've worked more since I met this man than I ever worked in my life," said Payne. "He always has something he needs help with."

"You need to learn how to build an addition so you can build one for us. He can help you and return the favor."

"I suppose so, since we're going to need the room for our growing family."

Elizabeth stared at him for a moment and said, "What do you mean?"

"Didn't Ginny tell you?"

"Tell me what?" she said, leaping to her feet and looking at Ginny. "Are you...?"

Ginny jumped up and grabbed Elizabeth in her arms and shouted, "Finally!"

"Looks like we're going to have to build two additions," said Alexander.

"Do you think Mr. Cary will get me some wood too?" laughed Payne.

"Sure. He'd probably like to settle accounts with you."

284

"I'll buy my own wood."

The two men were able to cut the timbers, gather the stones, and get both foundations built while the weather was still warm. Payne bought enough wood from a neighbor, John Phelps, to finish his smaller addition before the trapping season began.

The trap lines again produced a bountiful yield of quality furs that were delivered to the Trading Post before Christmas. Ginny had planned to go with John to carry his pelts so that she could see Mr. Dixon, but wasn't feeling well enough for the trip. She stayed with the Stinsons until he returned. Alexander took his furs when he and his family made their annual Christmas trip to the Carys.

One day while visiting with the Carys, John and Archibald went with Alexander to carry the furs to the Trading Post.

"I see you've had another good year," said Mr. Dixon. "Did these boys help you trap?"

"No, but I'm thinking about taking them after Christmas."

"Maybe you can teach them how to work the trap line and let them tromp through the snow while you sit by the fire."

"That's a great idea. Archibald has been wanting to come visit us so maybe I can persuade his Daddy to let him go home with me."

"Will you do it?" asked John, excitedly.

"I think I'll wait until summer," laughed Archibald.

"You boys get yourself a peppermint stick while I tally up Alexander's account. I may not have enough money to settle up with him."

"I always wanted to own a Trading Post."

Dixon laughed as he began counting up what Alexander had purchased. "Do you have a new rifle?"

"No sir, why?"

"This is a different size rifle ball mold than what you had."

"I'm doing a little trading with the Indians."

"You getting anything good from them?"

"I'm furnishing them rifle balls, powder, and deer skins and they're making me some buckskins and boots."

"Do they make good ones?"

"I'll let you know later, I don't have them yet."

"If you can get anymore, I'll buy them from you if they're any good. There's a good market for them."

"I want to get my boys some first. I'll see what I can do for you after that."

"Do you have three boys now?"

"Two. Our last baby was a girl."

"You need to get some of that pretty material over there to make her some little dresses."

"I've already heard about it. Elizabeth is real anxious to get over here and buy some. She doesn't trust me to pick it out so she'll be over to see you before we go home."

"Don't you dare put that little girl in buckskins!"

"You don't have to worry about that," laughed Alexander.

"John Payne was down the other day and said Ginny wasn't feeling well. Do you know if she's doing any better?"

"She's not sick, but feels bad because she's expecting a baby."

"Oh, he didn't tell me that. I hope everything goes well for her, give them my regards."

"I will. Come on boys, we need to get across the river."

1733
Chapter 27

The Funeral

Alexander worked diligently all day on the new addition and was exhausted when night came. He was sleeping soundly until Elizabeth sat upright in the bed.

"What's wrong?" he asked in a startled voice.

"I thought I heard somebody calling 'Hallo'. There it is again."

"That sounds like Payne," said Alexander, jumping out of bed and rushing to the door.

John Payne was riding furiously across the clearing and was almost to the porch.

"I need both of you to come fast, Ginny's having trouble."

"We'll be there as quick as we can."

Payne spun the horse around and disappeared into the dark.

"Get the children ready while I bring the wagon," said Alexander.

By the time Elizabeth woke the children and got them dressed, he was back.

"Alexander, you're going too fast, slow down! I can't even see the road."

"I can see it."

"I wonder what's wrong with Ginny? I hope she's not having the baby, she still has two months to go."

When they arrived at Paynes, Elizabeth handed Joanna to Alexander and said, "Stay here with the children until I find out what's going on."

In a few minutes she returned. "It's what I feared, the baby's coming and I'm going to need some help."

"Should I go to the Hoopers for Mandy?"

"John says go to the Indian village for the Doctor Woman. Give me the baby and take the boys with you. Please be careful."

Alexander drove as fast as he dared toward the Indian village wondering what kind of reception he would receive when he arrived. His two little boys were huddled close together on the seat beside him. Although they said nothing, he knew they must be afraid. As they approached the village, a dozen dogs announced their coming. Remembering what Payne had done earlier; he began to cry out repeatedly, "Payne needs help. Payne needs help."

He knew they would understand the word Payne and hoped they would recognize his voice. Suddenly, several torches appeared in the dark, illuminating small groups of Indians surrounding them.

"Doctor Woman," said Alexander, pointing towards the village. He then pointed towards Payne's house and said, "Payne's woman sick." A murmur swept through the group and in just a minute, the Doctor Woman appeared with her buckskin bag.

"Climb into the back, boys" said Alexander. They quickly clambered over the seat to provide room for the woman. As he turned the wagon around, two of the men hopped into the rear. Alexander wished he could see his boy's faces. He knew they must be sitting there in wide-eyed amazement as they shared their space with the Indians.

It seemed to take forever to get back to the house. Jumping down from the wagon, the Indian woman hurried inside. John and Joseph quickly scrambled back onto the wagon seat, where they sat watching the two men who had climbed down from the wagon. In a few minutes, a badly shaken Payne exited the house and walked towards Alexander.

"How are things going?"

"Bad," whispered Payne, as he lowered his head, trying to conceal his tears.

"Do you want me to go get Mandy?"

"No. Don't you go anywhere."

"Is there anything I can do?"

"Pray," said Payne, as he turned back towards the house.

After what seemed like hours, Elizabeth slipped outside,

gently closing the door behind her. She never made eye contact with Alexander until she was close enough to touch him. Throwing herself into his arms she began to weep bitterly. Finally, she gasped and said, "She's dead."

"Ginny or the baby?" whispered Alexander.

"Both. She had a little girl."

"What happened?"

"Bleeding. We couldn't stop the bleeding. I've never felt so helpless in my life. All I could do was stand there and watch her die."

"Where's John?"

"Inside. You need to go in there with him."

"Where's Joanna?"

"Asleep."

Alexander quietly opened the door and stepped inside. The Indian woman, who was moving softly about the room, glanced at him when he entered and then returned to the tasks at hand. John Payne sat on a stool beside the bed holding his wife's lifeless hand. His large shoulders sagged as he leaned forward staring at the floor. Ginny's body, once beautiful and full of life, rested motionless on the bed. A tiny baby, partially wrapped in a cloth, lay dead upon her bosom. Alexander wanted to turn and run. Quietly walking over to the side of his friend, he reached out and placed his hand on his shoulder. Payne never moved. Scanning the house, Alexander saw Joanna sleeping soundly on the far side of the dimly lit room. He wished he could move her from Payne's view, but there was nowhere else to put her.

"This is all my fault," said Payne, never looking up.

"It's not your fault."

"It is. I'm the one to blame for her being dead. It was me that wanted children."

"Ginny wanted children as much as you did. She would be upset to hear you blame yourself."

Payne began to cry, sobbing uncontrollably for several minutes before speaking again.

"I need you to help me."

"What do you want me to do?"

"Build a coffin. I want it big enough for both of them, I have plenty wood."

"I'm going to take my boys over to stay with the Hoopers when it gets daylight. I'll start on it as soon as I get back. Elizabeth will take care of things here."

"I want to bury her on your place. On top of the little hill beyond your house."

"Why?"

"Your family is the closest thing to a family we have. I don't think I can keep living here without her. I don't know where I'll end up and I don't want her grave to be lost in this wilderness. Can I bury her there?"

"If that's what you want."

"It is."

Elizabeth had come back inside and overheard most of their conversation.

"Ask Mr. Hooper if he will contact a minister for us and send word to Mr. Dixon. You also need to go by our house and get a change of clothes for the boys."

When Alexander returned from the Hoopers, he brought two of the slave women with him and lots of food that they insisted he bring. Elizabeth and the Indian woman had finished preparing Ginny's body for burial. She was laid out in the dress she was married in. It was the same one she was wearing the day she showed up at the cabin after her wedding. Alexander thought about how happy she was that day and he broke down and began crying. Not wanting to be seen by the others, he walked over and picked up his little daughter, hugging her tightly to his chest. After regaining his composure, he turned to Elizabeth and asked, "Where is John?"

"He went out to get the lumber for the coffin. He stacked it in the yard for you and then went for a walk while we were getting Ginny ready."

"I'm going home and get started, do you need anything before I go?"

"I need to go with you and change my soiled clothes. I'm going to make the baby a little dress and you can bring me back when I finish. These women can take care of things here until I come back."

About that time John Payne walked in the door. He glanced at the women in the kitchen and then walked to the bed where his wife's body lay and stood gazing at her face. He stood there crying for several minutes and then left the house. Alexander followed him into the yard and watched in silence as Payne leaned against the side of the wagon and stared into the woods. Sensing Alexander's presence, he spoke without looking at him.

"Did you see Mr. Hooper?"

"I did, and left the boys there. He's going to notify the other neighbors and Mr. Dixon. He's also going to contact the minister."

"Suppose he's not available?"

"He'll let us know later today. He sent two of his people to help us."

"I saw them."

"He'll probably take them home when he comes over this evening."

"Ginny looks pretty."

"Yes she does."

"Elizabeth did a good job."

"She wants to make a little dress for the baby so I'm taking her home for a while."

"Oh God!" cried Payne. "How am I going to stand this?"

Alexander said nothing.

After a few minutes, Payne walked over to the stack of wood and began to load it on the wagon. "I know you both have a lot to do. You need to get going."

Alexander was busy at work on the coffin when Joseph Hooper drove up in his carriage.

"I'm on the way over to see John Payne, but I wanted to talk with you first. The Parish Minister is in Williamsburg and won't be back for several days."

"We can't wait that long. We'll have to bury her without him."

"I understand. I have no other suggestion for a speaker, do you?"

"Are you planning to attend?"

Hooper stared at him with a questioning look on his face. "Of course. My wife and I will attend, but surely you aren't thinking about me..."

"I was wondering if you might read something from your Bible."

"I suppose I could do that. Maybe some of you might share a personal remembrance of her also."

"Maybe, but I don't think I could."

"We sent word to Mr. Dixon and the neighbors, some of them may be here also."

"Thank you for all you've done."

When Mr. Hooper glanced toward the house, Alexander turned to see Elizabeth walking in their direction with Joanna in her arms.

"Good morning Elizabeth."

"Good morning Mr. Hooper. How are the boys doing?"

"They are doing fine, absolutely no trouble at all. We're enjoying having them."

"We really appreciate your help, we didn't know what else to do with them."

"You did the right thing. If you would like us to, we will keep them overnight and bring them back for the funeral tomorrow."

"That would help us tremendously if you would do that, I'm anxious to get them back home. I would invite you in for tea, but I must go back to the Paynes."

"I'm going there now, would you like to ride over with me?"

"That would help us too if you don't mind, Alexander has a lot to do today."

"Alexander, I wondered if you might need some more nails so I brought these along."

"Good, I was worried that I wouldn't have enough. Now I

don't have to be so stingy with what I have."

"It takes a lot of nails for one of those."

Alexander rolled one of the nails between his fingers and looked at it. "Do you have a forge?"

"I do, but I don't have anyone who knows how to use it. Those weren't made here, I bought them at The Falls."

"Don't buy anymore, I can make you some."

"Do you know how to do blacksmith work?"

"Nothing fancy, but I can make nails."

"Wonderful! We'll talk some more about this later."

It was the middle of the afternoon when John Payne showed up with several of the Indian men.

"We're going to dig the grave," he said.

"I was going to do that."

"You have enough to do."

"But you shouldn't have to do it."

"You ever build one of these before," asked Payne, as he measured the coffin with a stick, scratching a mark on it for the length and width and bringing an end to the conversation about the grave.

"No."

"It looks fine."

"I'm doing my best."

"Only one of the women went back with Mr. Hooper, the other one will stay until tomorrow to help Elizabeth. The Mayos stopped by for a visit and brought some more food."

"What about the Doctor Woman?"

"She's going to stay until you bring the coffin."

"I'll be a few hours yet."

"We'll be finished by the time you are and we can help you load it."

The two men rode slowly towards Paynes with the coffin in the rear of the wagon.

"I don't have anything to set the coffin on," said Payne.

"I made something."

Payne looked back at the two rectangular boxes in the

wagon, studied them for a minute and turned again to the front.

"I dread thinking about tomorrow."

"Did Mr. Hooper tell you the Minister wouldn't be here?"

"He did. He said you asked him to read something from the Bible."

"Is that alright with you?"

"Yes. He also said he thought it would be nice if someone else would say something. I think it would too and was hoping you or Elizabeth would do it."

"Like what?"

"Something personal about Ginny. You knew her better than anyone else."

"John, I can hardly think about her without getting choked up. I don't know if I could say anything without losing my voice."

"Maybe Elizabeth can. She's a strong woman."

When they arrived at the house, Elizabeth had already cleared an area for the coffin to sit. It was a simple matter for the two men to place it in position.

"Alexander, you will have to help us get her situated," said Elizabeth. "John, you can wait outside if you would rather."

"No. I want to help too."

The two men gently picked up Ginny's lifeless body and placed it in the coffin. John stared at her longingly for several minutes and then abruptly left the room.

Alexander started to follow him and Elizabeth said, "Let him go, he needs to be alone."

When John returned, the baby, dressed in her pretty little dress, was cradled in her mother's arms. He stood by the coffin and wept unashamedly, refusing to be comforted. An hour passed before he turned away and seated himself at the table. Looking at Elizabeth, he asked, "Will you make me some coffee?"

"I already have some for you," she said, placing it on the table. "Both of you need to eat something, you haven't had anything all day."

294

"I don't want anything," said Payne.

"I don't think I can eat," said Alexander.

"I want both of you to try. We have a long night ahead of us and a hard day tomorrow. We have plenty of food that needs to be eaten."

As the two men sat picking at their food, Alexander remembered a day long ago in his grandparent's home when he felt the same way he did now. That morning, his grandmother was encouraging him to eat when he couldn't. This time, it was Elizabeth.

"Did Alexander talk to you about tomorrow?" asked Payne, as he sat sipping on his coffee.

"About speaking?" asked Elizabeth.

"Yes."

"I would like to, but I don't know if I can. Let me think about it tonight."

"Both of you think about it."

The closed coffin was loaded onto Alexander's wagon for the trip to the graveyard. Elizabeth, holding little Joanna in her arms, sat beside her husband as they rode slowly towards home. John Payne followed behind them on his horse.

"Did you decide whether you are going to say anything?" asked Alexander.

Elizabeth began to cry. "I want to, but I can't," she said weakly.

Alexander looked at his wife and realized she was exhausted. He thought about her phenomenal accomplishments during the last two days, and now they were asking her to attempt another difficult task, one nobody wanted to do. He knew how important it was to John, but he must not allow her to endure any more.

"I'll do it," he said.

Elizabeth stared at him doubtfully. "What are you going to say?"

"I've been thinking about some things," he lied.

When they reached the cabin, they were surprised by the

number of people that had gathered on the hill beyond the house. Joseph and Elizabeth Hooper were there as they had promised. They were accompanied by one of their slaves who was taking care of John and Joseph. Mr. and Mrs. Joseph Mayo, William Mayo, his daughter Anne, and her new husband George Carrington stood beside the Hoopers. Alexander Trent, John Childress, Henry Cary, Archibald Cary, and Mr. Dixon were also there. A small group of Indians stood off to one side of the group. Several of the men stepped forward to help Alexander remove the coffin and gently set it on two small logs that had been placed across the grave for that purpose. The decision was made to wait a short time before beginning the service to ensure that no others were coming. Alexander approached Mr. Cary and spoke with him.

"Did you know that we don't have a minister?"

"I heard."

"Would you be willing to help us?"

"How?"

"Mr. Hooper is going to read from the Bible and John wants me to make some personal remarks about Ginny. Since you are a Vestryman, could you have a prayer when I finish?"

"Like 'The Benediction', that ends a service?"

"Yes sir. That would be fine."

"I will do that."

"Thank you."

When they were convinced that no others were coming, Joseph Hooper approached the head of the coffin and began to speak.

"On behalf of Mr. Payne, I want to thank each of you for being here today. I know that some of you have traveled a great distance to be present. As most of you know, our Parish Minister could not be here so others of us will do our best to conduct this service. I have been asked to read some passages from The Bible."

Alexander tried to concentrate on the words as Mr. Hooper

began reading from the Psalms, but his mind was running ahead trying to think of what he would say when his time came to speak. His hands were shaking and his legs felt as if they may fold up at any moment. Elizabeth, aware of his dilemma, reached out and took him by the hand, giving it a reassuring squeeze. Alexander looked at her face and then refocused his attention on the speaker who was now reading from the Gospel of John. Alexander, who had not been aware of the transition, now began listening intently to the words being read. *"Jesus said unto her, I am the resurrection, and the life: he that believeth in me, though he were dead, yet shall he live: And whosoever liveth and believeth in me shall never die, Believeth thou this? She saith unto him, Yea Lord: I believe that thou art the Christ, the Son of God, which should come into the world."*

"May God bless the reading of His Word and use it to bring comfort to our hearts," said Joseph Hooper as he looked at Alexander and walked away from the grave.

Alexander nervously stepped forward and took his place near the coffin. He scanned the group of people assembled there. Everyone's eyes were fixed on him. They were all people that he knew and had conversed with before, but he now wondered if any sound would come forth when he opened his mouth. It was time to try.

"I also want to thank each of you for coming here today. I've been thinking about a sermon I once heard about God's people living in the wilderness. The minister said that God used the wilderness to teach them. God is still using the wilderness to teach us today. Growing up in Williamsburg, I heard many stories about this place beyond The Falls. People said it was a place of beauty, but also one of danger. For some, it was a place that could help them grow rich. For me, it was a place that offered freedom and opportunity. It was a place that I dreamed of making my home some day. My wife, Elizabeth, shared that dream with me during some years when neither of us had freedom. Thanks to some of you, Mr. Cary in particular, we were given the opportunity to make our dream come true. We became wilderness people and that is how we met most of you. God continues to use you, and the wilderness, to teach us about life.

Ginny Payne also had a dream. She dreamed of having a new life with a husband, a home, and a family. She came here to find that new life. She knew that life here was dangerous. The dangers aren't always from wild animals or evil people. They can come from something as normal as giving birth to a child. She understood that and was willing to face that danger to make her dream come true. Ginny Payne brought something with her to the wilderness that many people did not bring. She brought love. She loved her husband, she loved my family, she loved people, she loved life, and she loved God. Jesus said that people would know that we belonged to Him by the way we showed love to others. Ginny showed that kind of love. It would be easy for us to become bitter and discouraged because of the death of this wonderful young woman. That is not what she would want and it is not what God wants. He wants to use her life and death to teach us to have the kind of faith she had. A faith that will help us love Him and to love others the way she did. If we learn from this wilderness experience, Ginny Payne will not have died in vain."

Alexander walked back to his wife's side and stood with his head bowed. Elizabeth reached out and gripped his trembling arm firmly. Henry Cary had stepped to the coffin. Lifting his hand towards heaven he began to speak.
"Now may the grace of the Lord Jesus Christ, and the love of God, and the communion of the Holy Ghost, be with you all. Amen."

Landowner and Slave Owner

Alexander and Elizabeth stood on the porch of their home and watched Henry Cary's carriage disappear from view. He had come to deliver the deed to the 400 acres they had agreed to purchase from him seven years earlier when they moved to Goochland County. Benjamin Harrison, Arthur Hopkins and David Bell came with Mr. Cary to witness his signature on the document. All that remained to be done was to have the document recorded at the Court House.

Looking at her husband, Elizabeth smiled and said, "Sometimes I wondered if this day would ever come."
"It's been a long time, but it was worth the wait. We are finally landowners."
"Now we have land, but no money," laughed Elizabeth. "We've worked so hard to earn the fifty pounds to pay him. I often thought we would never make it."
"Time to catch some more wolves before the price drops again!" laughed Alexander.
"I think raising more tobacco would be the best solution. It's easier to get it to market now with the improved roads."
"That's something else I'll have to be doing, now that I'm a landowner."
"What?"
"Become a surveyor of a section of road."
"Surveyor? You don't know anything about surveying do you?"
Alexander laughed. "Not that kind of surveying. The county appoints all landowners to oversee a certain section of road and keep it in good repair. They call them road surveyors."
Instead of responding to her husband, Elizabeth motioned with her hand and said, "Look over there."

John Payne was riding along the edge of the woods, almost concealed by the trees. They watched in silence as he disappeared from sight, riding towards Ginny's grave.

"He never misses a day of going there," she said. "Some days he goes more than once."

"I know. It's been five years since she died and he still grieves like it was yesterday."

Two-year-old Anna awoke from her nap and began crying for her mama. Joanna and little Alexander ran to her bed and began consoling her.

"Let me hold her," said Joanna.

"You can hold her later sweetie, I think she wants to eat right now."

Alexander followed his wife into the house and sat down beside her at the table while she fed the baby. "Do you know what I want to start saving for now?"

"What?"

"A woman slave. With five children and another due soon, you need someone to help you."

"You need help as much as I do. John has been so distraught since Ginny's death that you can't depend on him anymore."

"I want to get you some help first, the boys are doing a lot to help me now."

"Here comes Uncle John," said young Joseph, as he came hurrying in from the porch. In just a minute, John Payne appeared at the door.

"You folks had some important visitors today," he said, as he entered the room.

"Important people for important business," smiled Alexander.

"What important business?"

"They brought the deed to our land."

"Good. You've worked long enough for it," said Payne, as he took baby Anna from her mother's arms and sat down at the table. Joanna, jealous for his attention, sidled over to him and placed her little hand on his arm.

"Have you been helping your Mum with baby Anna?"

"I play with her and sometimes I hold her for Mama."

"Good for you. Your Mama needs a big girl like you to help her."

"Will you stay for dinner, John?" asked Elizabeth.

"Not today. I'm going to ride over to the village when I leave here and see what's happening there. Probably nothing."

"I'm going over to Hoopers tomorrow and do some blacksmith work," said Alexander, "would you like to ride along?"

"Not tomorrow. Maybe next time."

Alexander and Elizabeth watched him ride away, with his old yellow dog trotting along behind him.

"I feel so sorry for him," said Elizabeth.

"I do too, but I don't know what to do about it. At least he played with the children a little today, he rarely does that anymore."

"You were talking about buying slaves, I thought you wanted to get more land?"

"I do, but I'm not going to buy any. I'm going to request a Patent on some."

"Do you know where?"

"It will have to be west of here because there's none left in this area."

"How far west?"

"Not too far, but there's nothing left along the James River, it will have to be inland. Colonel Mayo says there's some available further up the Willis River, but they are smaller tracts."

"How small?"

"There are still tracts with several hundred acres in them, but none with thousands. You have to go a lot further south or west for those. I may request one of those too."

Another baby girl was born the next year, and following their custom, they named her after her mother. Alexander became more determined than ever to find someone to help Elizabeth. Following her suggestion, he increased his planting of tobacco and the new land produced a bountiful crop requiring several trips to the warehouse at The Falls to sell it. On his first trip, he stayed overnight with the Carys.

"How does Elizabeth manage with six children?" asked Anne Cary.

"Amazingly well," said Alexander. "Joanna is seven and is a big help to her mother. The boys are also good about helping, but she needs a woman to help her full time. I'm trying to find one now, so if you hear of a good one I wish you would let me know."

"A slave or a servant?" asked Henry Cary.

"Probably a slave since we are going to need them a long time."

"I think that's a wise choice. When are you coming back with the next load of tobacco?"

"I plan to come a week from today if the weather is good."

"I may be able to find one by then. From what I was told about her, she's very good with children and household work, but I'll be sure that's true."

"I wonder if she can cook like Dinah?"

Mr. Cary laughed. "That's too much to hope for. Dinah is still in Williamsburg and seems to be doing well for her age."

"I would love to see her."

"She still cooks at Jean Marot's ordinary."

"Do you remember Miss Allen's man, Cooper?"

"Vaguely."

"I've often wondered what happened to him."

"I don't know where he is."

The following week, Alexander returned to the Carys and learned that he was the owner of his first slave. She was a middle-aged woman named Molly who had been born in the colony and had served one Tidewater family her entire life. Now that her services were no longer needed, the heirs wanted to find her a home so they could settle the estate. Because of the family's devotion to her, they were unwilling to sell her at auction, but sought to relocate her through their network of friends. Henry Cary was one of those friends.

Alexander could sense Molly's anxiety as she left Falling Creek the next morning for her new home in Goochland County.

"How many children did you take care of Molly?"

"Dey had two little boys and two little girls. All of dem grown now an moved 'way. Don't none of dem have chillun. How many you have?"

"Six. Three boys and three girls."

"How old they are?"

"The oldest boy is 14, the next one is 11. The two older girls are 8 and 3, Alexander, who is named after me, is 5, and baby Elizabeth, who is named after her mother, will be 1 in a few months."

"Do yo wife take care of all dem chillun by herself?"

"Yes. That's why she needs some help."

"I reckon she do! Do she do all da cooking to?"

"The children help her some, but she does most of it. I help her too when I can, but I work outside most of the time. I raise tobacco, a vegetable garden, cut all the wood, and work a trap line in the winter."

"You don't hav no help neither?"

"Sometimes a neighbor helps me."

"Dat's all?"

"That's all except for my two boys."

"What you catch in dem traps?"

"Beaver, muskrat, mink, otter, rabbits, wolves..."

"Woofs! Lawd hav mercy on my soul! I dent know I was goin to live in no sech place that was full of woofs! Nobody told me 'bout dat!"

Alexander exploded in sidesplitting laughter. Molly stared at him in wide-eyed bewilderment. The more she glared, the more he laughed. Finally gaining control of himself, he said, "You don't have to worry about them. You'll probably never see one except a dead one."

"I don't wanna see none of dem neither," she said quickly. "No suh, no dead ones and no live ones! Why you wanna fool with dem things?"

"I trap them in the forest and collect bounty money for them."

"What they do wif a dead woof?"

"They just want to get rid of them. They pay people to kill them."

"Dats a good thing to do. Yes sir, get rid of all dem things."

Alexander knew Elizabeth and the children were going to love Molly. Her endless questions and hilarious responses to his answers helped the time pass quickly.

"Where I'm gonna sleep?" she asked.

"In the children's room. The two older boys sleep in the loft and the baby sleeps with us. The others sleep in a big room we built for them on the back of the house. You can sleep with them until I build you a little house in the woods," teased Alexander.

"No suh! Don't want no house in da woods with dem woofs and things. I'll jest sleep with dem babies in dat big room. You don't have to go outside to get dere do you?"

"No, there's an inside door. You're not scared of the dark are you?"

"Never hav been, but I never lived 'round no woofs before."

"They don't come around the house, they're afraid of my dogs."

"Dem dogs bite?"

"Not unless I tell them to. They'll like you if you feed them."

Molly cut her eyes towards him again, but didn't respond. After a brief pause she continued asking questions.

"Folks say Injuns still live 'round here, you evah see any?"

"Only when they come to visit us."

"You don't let dem in da house do you?"

"Sometimes."

"You ain't skeered of 'em?"

"They're our friends."

She sat there shaking her head from side to side and mumbling to herself about wolves and Indians as they rode toward home. Just as he had hoped for, Molly quickly became a much-loved member of the family.

Two years passed before The Council took action on Alexander's request to patent twelve thousand acres of land in western Goochland County. They were going to meet in the spring to consider a total of forty patent requests. Alexander was anxious to learn the outcome of the meeting so he traveled to Williamsburg to see what he could find out. Several days later, he returned home. When Elizabeth saw the sullen look on his face, she could tell things had not gone well.

"What happened?" she asked.

"My request was rejected."

"Why?"

"You don't really want to know."

"Tell me."

"They said that since I was not known to any of the Board they thought it was too much land for so obscure a person."

"Obscure! Did they reject any of the other requests?"

"Only one more. Peter Jefferson and some of his friends."

"He's certainly not an obscure person. What reason did they give for him?"

"They thought his request was also too great, but for a different reason," snorted Alexander. "They had already granted him 15,000 acres earlier in the meeting and he had a second request for 40,000 more!"

Elizabeth could tell he was crushed.

"I guess I'll have to start sitting in the church balcony again since I'm such a nobody."

"Please don't feel like that. I know you are upset, but we are still blessed people. We'll just have to believe that God didn't want us to have that land now."

"I've been brooding about it all the way home. So much is determined in the colony by what family you were born into or who you marry. Everybody on that Council is kin either by blood or marriage!"

"I wouldn't trade you or my family for all the land in

Goochland County."

"You know I wouldn't either, but it still annoys me. I'm sorry I acted so childish."

"You'll feel better after you get something to eat. I have supper ready for you."

"I have some more news."

"What?"

"I saw Dinah."

"Where?"

"At Marot's Ordinary. She's still cooking there."

"Is she well?"

"She seemed to be, she hugged me so tight she almost broke my ribs! She couldn't believe we had seven children. Guess what she asked me when I told her we had a new baby boy named David?"

"What?"

"She wanted to know if we named him after Mr. Cunningham," laughed Alexander.

"I told her 'no, that it was a family name'. She begged me to bring you to see her."

"I don't suppose I'll ever get back to Williamsburg. Have things changed much?"

"Just more fops and dandies. I'm glad to be back home."

"Are you going to try another Patent request?"

"Absolutely, but the next time it will be for less acres or with someone else who is better known. Every time they meet, they'll be looking at a request from me. Sooner or later those bigwigs will have to deal with this 'obscure person' in buckskins whether they like it or not."

"Good for you," said Elizabeth, as she gave her husband a hug and a welcome home kiss.

After another outstanding tobacco crop, Alexander decided that he would not work the trap line that year as he had in the past. The bounty on wolves was decreasing while tobacco prices were on the rise. He was going to use his time in the fall to build some slave quarters and vigorously pursue acquiring some field hands before summer. Payne, who had opted not to raise tobacco, was still totally dependent on trapping for his income. It was more than adequate for his needs and he also liked the solitude. Alexander was busy working on the foundation for the new building when he saw John Payne approaching.

"We have a new family that moved in over my way," said Payne, as he swung down from the horse.

"I didn't know there were any vacant houses over there."

"There were none. They've built a little pole hut over near the creek just beyond my line."

"Do you know who they are?"

"Trent sold them the land. He said the man's name is John Wright and that he has a wife and little girl. He plans on being a trapper," smiled Payne. "I haven't met him yet, but thought I might ride over and see him tomorrow. You want to go with me?"

"Sure, I'll go with you. What time do you want to go?"

"Come by mid-morning and we'll ride over."

Elizabeth was excited when Alexander told her there was another young mother and little girl in the community. "I wish I could go with you and meet them. My girls would love a new playmate. Be sure to invite them to come by and visit us."

"I will. She could become a new friend for you too."

"That would be wonderful. I'm so glad that John initiated the visit, that's the first time he's done anything like that for years."

John and Alexander were talking as they rode along the trail that led to the new house. When they were about fifty paces away, a man stepped from behind a large tree with a cocked rifled pointed at them.

"Stop right there!" he yelled.

The two men reined in their horses.

"What are you doing on my land?"

"We're your neighbors and just dropped by meet you," said Alexander.

"Well now you've met me. Turn around and get off my land before I shoot you."

"We didn't mean any harm, we just..."

"Get off my land now!"

The two men turned around and rode slowly back down the trail, never speaking until they crossed onto Payne's property.

"Friendly chap, wasn't he," said Payne, grinning.

"Glad you think it's funny. I was afraid the idiot was going to shoot one of us."

"I met a man like that in the woods once," teased Payne.

"You lied to that man and tricked him into putting his gun down," said Alexander. "Why didn't you do the same thing today?"

"Why didn't you bust his nose like you did mine?"

"That rifle barrel was too long."

It felt good to banter with Payne and see him laughing again.

"Did you see the woman and little girl standing inside the door of that hut?" asked Payne.

"No. I was too busy looking at the big hole in the end of that rifle barrel."

"They were standing back in the shadows watching us. The little girl was about as big as Anna, maybe four or five years old."

Elizabeth could hardly believe the story that Alexander and John told her. "I wonder what's wrong with him?"

"Sound like he crazy," said Molly. "Hope he don't come 'round here."

Chapter 29

Frontier Justice

Alexander was back at work on the slave quarters as soon as it was light enough to see. He was almost finished with the foundation and was anxious to get started with the framing.

Rabbit Man had collected the nightly catch from his snares and was walking back towards the village when John Wright suddenly appeared in the path before him with rifle in hand. The unarmed Indian knew he should have nothing to fear from the man, but he stopped to see what he wanted. Suddenly, Wright raised his rifle and fired at the Indian. The rifle ball struck him in the center of the chest, sending him tumbling backwards onto the path dead.

A short time later, Wright appeared at the home of William Mayo demanding the Indian be certified for a bounty.

"You had no right to kill that man!" said Mayo.

"That's not a man, that's an Indian," said Wright. "Is there a bounty on Indians or not?"

"Only on bad Indians. That old law was passed for marauding Iroquois, not our Indians."

"An Indian is an Indian. Will you certify him or not?"

"I'll record that you killed him, but I'll also report it to the Sheriff. I'm sure you'll be receiving a visit from him."

"Let him visit, I didn't break the law. The law says the county will pay me a bounty for killing an Indian so give me a certificate."

"Here's the certificate, but I would advise you not to do that again. You may cause another uprising to the harm of all of us."

"Then change the law," sneered Wright. "Do you want the dead Indian?"

"Absolutely not! Take him back to his people so they may bury him."

"Let them come get him and I'll collect some more bounty

on them," said Wright, with an evil laugh.

When Alexander saw John Payne riding hard towards his place, he knew something was wrong. He stopped working on the building and went to meet him.

"John Wright killed Rabbit Man," said Payne.

"Why?"

"Shot him for bounty."

"Who told you?"

"Colonel Mayo. I carried a wolf by to have it certified. He's upset about it too and wants one of us to go tell the Sheriff."

"Are you going?"

"No, I want you to go. I'm going to the village. I'm sure they already know, but I'm going to help them get Rabbit Man back so they can bury him."

"Where is he now?"

"Wright still has him. Mayo thinks he is going to use him to bait the Indians so he can kill some more of them."

"What are you going to do?"

"Whatever I have to."

"I'll go tell the Sheriff if you promise me that you'll let the law handle it."

"The law is on his side!" shouted Payne.

"Don't you kill him! They'll hang you for murder."

Elizabeth heard the raised voices of the two men and came out to see what was wrong. When they told her, she began to cry.

"I'm going across the river to tell the Sheriff what happened," said Alexander. "I don't know how long it'll take me to find him so I may not be back until tomorrow."

"I'll get your stuff ready," said Elizabeth, disappearing into the house.

"John, you stay out of trouble, you hear?"

As Payne suspected, the Indians already knew that one of their own had been murdered. They knew where Wright was and what he was planning to do. He had placed the dead Indian in a clearing not far from where he had shot him and concealed himself nearby hoping that some of the others would come to retrieve the body. John Payne had another plan. Several of the Indians silently made their way unseen into positions near the clearing where they could move quickly to recover their brother when the opportunity came.

John Payne left his horse a long distance away and quietly circled the small ridge above Wright until he could see him plainly. Situating himself behind the crest of the hill, he took careful aim and fired. The ball plowed through the brush about a foot from Wright's head, showering his face with twigs and leaves. He screamed and jumped to his feet, trying to clear his eyes and search for the location of the shooter. The smoke from the black powder was drifting lazily down the ridge, but Wright could find nobody. Following the shot, Payne had ducked below the ridge and reloaded. Moving silently through the woods, he concealed himself behind some thick brush and peeked over the summit again to locate Wright. He was still in the same spot, diligently searching for whoever had shot at him. Payne took aim again and fired. The ball spun off the side of a nearby tree throwing bark in the air. Quickly rebounding, Wright could see the smoke from the rifle and took aim. Instantly, Payne lifted his hat into view with a stick and Wright fired. The hat was untouched, but Payne dropped it from sight. Picking it up quickly, he continued down the back side of the ridge out of sight. When he knew Wright couldn't hear him, he ran as hard as he could to his horse, not even stopping to reload.

Confident that he had killed or crippled his foe, Wright reloaded and crept to the top of the hill to find nothing. Suddenly, he remembered the dead Indian and rushed back to the clearing. The Indian's body was gone.

Alexander crossed the ferry and rode directly to Goochland Courthouse hoping to find the Sheriff, but he was not there. After getting directions to his house, he rode there and found him home. George Payne listened intently to the story.

311

"This is a serious thing," he said. "It could cause a lot of problems for all of us. Come in for something to drink and let me think about this for a few minutes."

"Mr. Mayo thinks he is using the dead Indian to bait the others, hoping to kill more of them if they try to recover the body."

"The other thing to consider is that they may kill him. You know what would happen if a group of Indians killed a white man."

"Can't you arrest him?"

"I can, but I don't know if a court would convict him because there is a bounty law. Killing our Indians was not the intent of the law, but it's an unclear law."

"Can't we get it changed?"

The Sheriff was silent for a moment and then said, "It needs to be changed, but that'll take time. We need to do something now to stop this. Will you do me a favor?"

"Sure."

"I'm going to take one of my men tomorrow morning and go arrest Wright. I may have to charge him with trespassing or something. I don't know how long I can hold him so we need to have something more permanent. Since you know Henry Cary so well, I want you to go tell him what has happened and what I am going to do. He'll know who to contact to begin the process of getting the law changed. Ask him to write me a letter telling me of his intent to get the law changed and bring the letter back to me. Is that asking too much of you?"

"No sir. I'll leave for Ampthill now so I'll probably get back here tomorrow before you return. Do you want me to wait here for you?"

"No. Just leave the letter with my wife and you can go home. You'll probably meet me somewhere along the way."

John Payne sat concealed in the brush near one of John Wright's deadfall traps watching the trail. The trap had been thrown and a trail of blood led over the hill where a dead wolf lay in sight of the trap. Payne grew tense when he saw

312

the trapper coming up the trail. When Wright saw the trap had been thrown, he jumped from his horse to examine it. Seeing the blood trail and the dead wolf, he leaned his rifle against a tree and ran eagerly down the hill. Moving quickly, Payne grabbed the rifle and rammed the barrel into the damp clay bank as hard as he could. Wiping the mud from the outside of the barrel, he placed it back against the tree and disappeared into the woods. Several minutes later, Wright returned, lugging the dead wolf back to his horse.

Payne waited until Wright reset the trap and walked over for his rifle. "Ginny, if this doesn't work," he whispered to himself, "I'm going to be seeing you soon." He had located himself about forty paces away when he called out to Wright.
"I thought you murdered Indians for a living. When did you start killing wolves?"
The startled man looked up to see Payne aiming his rifle at him. Payne fired. The ball went tearing through the brush beside Wright. As Payne pretended to be reloading, Wright grabbed his rifle, took aim at Payne, and fired. A muffled explosion came from the weapon as Wright tumbled backwards on the ground with blood gushing from his face and throat. He tried to get up, but fell again, mortally wounded on the trail. Payne leisurely reloaded his rifle before walking to where the still figure lay. The shattered rifle lay close by, it's barrel split and curled with several sections of steel missing.
"I don't suppose you'll be needing my wolf," said Payne, as he picked up the dead animal and returned to his horse.

Arriving back in Goochland, Alexander left the letter with the Sheriff's wife and rode to the ferry. He was within a few miles of his house when he met Sheriff Payne and his deputy returning home.
"Where's Wright?" asked Alexander, "I thought you were going to arrest him."
"I didn't have to, he's dead."

Fear gripped Alexander thinking that John Payne might have killed his neighbor. He was afraid to ask the next question.

"What happened to him?"

"His gun blew up in his face. A piece of metal cut his throat and he bled to death. I went to his house and he wasn't there. His wife said he never returned from checking his traps so we went looking for him. We found him by one of his traps dead. Looked like he was firing at something when the gun exploded. He must have had a ball stuck in the barrel or too much charge in it."

"Where are his wife and little girl?"

"At John Payne's house."

"What's she doing there?"

"She's scared to death of the Indians. Because her husband killed one, she thinks they are going to kill her and the little girl. She wouldn't stay alone at her place and wouldn't let us leave her. I took her over to stay with Payne while we buried her husband."

"Where did you bury him?"

"In the woods where he fell. That's what she wanted us to do."

"I asked Payne to watch after her and the girl until I come back and we can decide what to do with her. I don't know what she'll do; she doesn't have any family or money. You ever been inside that house?"

"No. We went over to see them once but he threatened to shoot us and chased us away."

"It's nothing but a hut. They don't have anything."

"I'll go by and check on them. We'll make sure they are taken care of."

"Did you talk to Henry?"

"I did, and left the letter with your wife."

"Hopefully, this takes care of the problem for now, but we need to get that law changed."

"Did you tell Colonel Mayo about Wright?"

"I didn't have time to go by. I need to get to the ferry before they close for the day."

"I'll go by and tell him tomorrow," said Alexander.

314

Alexander stopped briefly at home to tell Elizabeth what had happened and let her know that he was going over to Payne's house. "Go hook up the wagon, I want to go with you," she said. "John may want us to bring Mrs. Wright and the girl home with us."

"Where would we put them?"

"We'll find room."

John Payne saw them coming and met them at the door. A petite woman stood across the room with a wide-eyed little girl clinging tightly to her. Payne introduced Alexander and Elizabeth to the woman and said, "These are my friends that I was telling you about." Turning back to his neighbors, he said, "This is Rebekah Wright, and her little girl Ruth."

"We're pleased to meet you," said Elizabeth. "We were very sorry to hear about your husband's accident."

"Thank you."

"What can we do to help you?"

"I don't know of anything right now. The Sheriff wants us to stay here until he returns."

"You are welcome to come home with us if you would like."

"We'll stay here."

John Payne looked very uncomfortable with the predicament he found himself in.

"Mrs. Wright doesn't want to offend the Sheriff after he found her somewhere to stay and I do have more room than you folks. You have a full house already," laughed Payne.

"Do you have a large family?" asked the woman.

"We have six children," said Elizabeth, "three boys and three girls."

"I'd love to meet them."

"John would probably be glad to bring you over tomorrow," said Alexander.

"That's a good idea," said Elizabeth, "why don't you bring Mrs. Wright and Ruth over to our place tomorrow morning for a visit and plan to stay for dinner?"

"I would like for all of you to call me Rebekah. I'm not accustomed to anyone calling me Mrs. Wright. It makes me feel old."

For the first time, everyone laughed.

There were a few awkward minutes with the children when little Ruth arrived because she would not leave her mother's side. Soon she was deeply involved in playing with the other children and Rebekah was helping Elizabeth with the cooking. Molly seemed to be everywhere at once, tending the fire, overseeing the children, and joking with the two men. A pleasant atmosphere filled the house.

"Let's go outside and take a look at your new building," said Payne.

"I don't have much done on it," said Alexander as he started for the door.

Once outside, Payne said, "I just wanted to come out here and talk to you about Rebekah. After you and Elizabeth left yesterday, we ate supper. After supper, little Ruth asked me if I was going to be her new daddy."

Alexander laughed. "What did you tell her?"

"I don't know. I stammered and sputtered and said nothing that made sense. Finally, her mama told her that they were just staying with me until they could find a new home."

"Did that satisfy her?"

"No! She said she didn't want another home that she liked me and my home and wanted me to be her daddy. Then, the little tyke looked at me and said I was a good man, but her daddy was a mean man because he beat her and her mama."

"What did her mama say?"

"It embarrassed her. She told little Ruth not to talk about it anymore."

"Has Rebekah mentioned it again?"

"Oh yes! After Ruth went to sleep, we sat up all night talking. I feel so sorry for that woman. She's had a hard life. I'm so confused this morning I don't know what to do."

"What are you confused about?"

"My feelings. I think I must be losing my mind. I've only known the woman one day and already I don't want her to go away. I can't stand the thought of her and that little girl going off somewhere to try to find another place to live.

What can she do, work in a tavern? Indenture herself and that little girl? I don't know what to do about it."

"John, you sound like you're in love."

Payne stared at him inquisitively. "Now isn't that a thought! The woman has only been a widow one day and I've only known her one day and you think I'm in love with her!"

"Are you?"

Payne grew silent as he stared into the distance. "I don't know," he finally said. "I told you I was confused. When I think about loving another woman and then think about Ginny, I feel so guilty it nearly kills me. The love we had for each other was so different. I've never felt like that about anyone before and don't want to feel like that about anyone again. Maybe I'm afraid to feel that way again. If I ever loved another woman like I did Ginny, and something happened to her, I know I couldn't stand it."

"So you would rather keep on living alone and being miserable the rest of your life?"

"I didn't say that!"

"You said you were afraid to love another woman."

"You know, you're not being fair to me. I told you I didn't have any sleep last night!"

"If you don't get your mind straightened out, you won't sleep tonight either."

"I know. And I keep thinking about the Sheriff showing up tomorrow or the next day."

"She doesn't have to leave with him."

"She doesn't, does she? But what would I tell him, that she's going to be living with me?"

"Maybe you'll have an answer by the time he shows up."

"Maybe I will."

Welcoming An Old Friend

Alexander had spent his spare time during the winter months building the slave quarters that he hoped to have occupied before spring. The building would be ready to live in as soon as the roof was finished. He was teaching his boys how to split shingles with a froe and a mallet when his lessons were interrupted by the dogs charging across the clearing barking at two men approaching on horseback. He recognized one of them as Archibald Cary. Elizabeth, who had come to the door to investigate the uproar, also recognized young Cary and came rushing out to greet him.

"Archibald, what a pleasant surprise to see you! What brings you out here?"

"I've been waiting for you to come to see me at Falling Creek and you never did so I decided I would have to come here to see you."

"I know that's not the reason," she laughed, "but we're happy to see you anyway."

The big man riding the other horse had quietly dismounted and stood smiling as he listened to the exchanges between the old friends.

Motioning to the man with him, Archibald asked, "Have either of you had the pleasure of meeting Major Peter Jefferson?"

"We have not," said Alexander, extending his hand and introducing himself. "This is my wife Elizabeth and these are our two oldest sons, John and Joseph."

"It's my pleasure to meet you," said the man, bowing to Elizabeth as she curtsied to him. "Archibald has been telling me about your long friendship with his family."

"I was there the day he was born," said Elizabeth.

"That was twenty one years ago," said Archibald, proudly.

"You couldn't be that old!" gasped Elizabeth.

"This year," he said, smiling. "That's the real reason we're out here. Father is giving me the plantation, Buckingham, on the Willis River. Major Jefferson and Colonel Mayo are doing the survey work for us."

"Congratulations," said Alexander.

"You gentlemen please excuse me while I go in and fix us some tea," said Elizabeth. "We can talk some more inside."

"I understand from Colonel Mayo that there is still land available to be patented along the Willis," said Alexander.

"Quite a bit," said Jefferson, "but in small tracts."

"I plan to request a patent this year for some land in that area."

"Have you chosen the place?"

"Not exactly, but I'd like to have it border the Willis River. Some people think that one day, small boats will navigate the Willis transporting goods."

Jefferson chuckled, "That's an interesting possibility that some are discussing, but I don't know if it will ever happen in our lifetime."

"Even if it never happens, I would still prefer land bordering the river because the bottom land is much better for crops and pasture."

"There was four hundred acres available in the Cattail Creek area on the north side of the Willis that joined Henry Cary. I will check to make sure it has not been taken. If it is still available, I will be glad to record it in the entry book for you and submit it to the office in Williamsburg if you would like for me to."

"I would greatly appreciate that."

"I'll let you know something soon."

Several days later, Colonel William Mayo came to visit Alexander. "I'm honored that one of the busiest men in the county has time to come for a visit," quipped Alexander.

"If I'm one of the busiest, you must be the other one," retorted Mayo. "I really didn't come by to visit, but to repay the act of kindness that you showed me during our recent

Indian crisis. Not only did you spend two days on the road trying to resolve it, but you also made a special trip to tell me the news about its resolution. Now, I've come to tell you some good news. My assistant, Major Jefferson, told me about his recent conversation with you concerning the Cattail Creek property on the Willis. He wanted you to know that it was still available and your request for a patent for the four hundred acres has been placed in the entry book."

"That is good news."

"As you know, the land patent process is a slow one, but hopefully it will not be too long before you learn something. If you see where I can help you please let me know."

"That's very kind of you and I sincerely thank you for taking the time to come by and tell me about it."

"You're welcome. Before I leave, tell me how John Payne and his new wife are doing?"

"They are doing well and both seem to be very happy."

"Good, they deserve it. He has endured a lot of unhappiness for many years and I understand that she did too. Please tell them I asked, and that I wish them the very best. Give your family my best wishes also."

When the new slave quarters were complete, Alexander turned his attention to getting some workers before planting time. He had asked his neighbors to notify him if they learned of any slaves for sale. He received word from one of them that the latest issue of the *Virginia Gazette* had advertised an upcoming auction in the recently incorporated city of Richmond. The area around The Falls had experienced rapid growth in the last decade. William Byrd, who owned most of the land and businesses at The Falls, had successfully resisted the development of a city at that site for many years. Several years earlier, he had given in to the inevitable and employed Colonel Mayo to survey for a city there which Byrd had named Richmond. Now there were over two hundred and fifty inhabitants in the growing city. Although slave auctions were something Alexander normally shunned because of the highly emotional displays that often accompanied them, he decided he would attend the one in Richmond. He had some vivid memories of slave auctions in Williamsburg and none of them were good.

On the day of the auction, Alexander stood at the edge of the crowd waiting for the sale to begin. The slaves had been assembled in a central location to provide an opportunity for the buyers to view them. As the auction began, the slaves were presented individually and a brief, biased description was given before the bidding started. The exception was that a family was normally presented as a group, but there was no guarantee they would not be sold separately. Purchasing a slave was a great risk unless you could get a reputable recommendation like Mr. Cary had secured for Molly. Every issue of the *Virginia Gazette* carried ads for runaway slaves, many of whom were never found. Although Alexander's experiences with slaves had generally been good, he knew that some of the slaves were sullen and rebellious and a perpetual problem for their owners.

Alexander studied the bloated planters who had gathered for the auction and listened to their indolent voices. He wished that he had not come and was considering leaving. As he looked at the group of slaves to be sold, his attention was drawn to one of the men. He was a tall, muscular man who appeared to be healthy, but his snow-white hair gave testimony to his advanced age. Unless he had special skills, there would be little interest in him as a field hand. He had been standing emotionless the entire time with his head lowered staring at the floor. As Alexander studied him, the man lifted his head and methodically scanned the crowd. Alexander wondered what he was thinking. He probably was wondering where he would spend the rest of his days. When he made eye contact with Alexander, the man paused for a moment like there was a glimmer of recognition. He then dropped his gaze back to the floor.

"Cooper!" thought Alexander. "Is that Cooper?" If it were, he would have to be well over sixty years old. In a moment, the man lifted his eyes again. Instead of scanning the crowd, he looked directly at Alexander. It was Cooper!

It was time for the auction to begin. The bidding was lively for those considered to be the best of the bunch and they sold rapidly. Only ten of the old and imperfect were left for sale and Cooper was among the group. Alexander's heart sank when someone called out, "I'll give fifty pounds for the ten that remain."

"No sale sir! We'll sell them one at a time until there are no bids left. Give me a bid on this man Cooper. He's strong and a good worker. There are still some good years left in this man, what am I bid?"

"Five pounds a head is still my offer," said the same man. "I'll give you five pounds!"

"A good start sir, who'll give me ten?"

"I'll give you six," said another.

"Six pounds, who'll give me eight?"

"Seven said the first man."

"Eight," said Alexander.

The first man turned around and stared contemptuously at him. "Nine!" he said.

"Ten," said Alexander.

"Ten, who'll make it twelve?" asked the auctioneer.

After a lengthy pause he shouted, "Sold to the man in buckskin for ten pounds!"

Alexander made his way through the crowd to pay and receive his bill of sale. He did not look at Cooper because he was afraid he could not control his emotions. When he received the paper work, he said to Cooper, "Come with me."

Cooper followed him to the street where the wagon was parked. When he arrived at the wagon, Alexander said, "You drive."

Cooper stared at him a moment and climbed in the wagon. Pausing to look at Alexander again, he asked, "How you know I can drive?"

"You haven't forgotten already have you?"

"How you know me?"

"I'll tell you on the way home."

"Which way you want to go?"

"Take the River Road towards Goochland Court House."

As soon as they were out of town, Cooper asked him, "When you gonna tell me how you know me?"

"You kept me from getting killed one time."

"How?"

"I was going after the Sheriff one day with an axe. You caught me and squeezed me so hard you nearly killed me."

Cooper stared at him. "Mistuh Alexander?" he asked.

"Alexander. Miss Allen's servant boy."

The big man began to laugh and cry at the same time. "Lawd, I don't bleeve dis," he kept saying over and over as tears streamed down his face.

"Da last time I saw you, Mistuh Cary done bought yo papuhs and you were gone wit him."

"I worked for him fifteen years after I was free. He has been very good to me."

"Mistuh Cary, he was always a good man."

"Where did you go?"

"Sent me to Mistuh Cunningham's plantation 'til it was sold to pay Miz Allen's debts. Been a field hand ever since. New owners have too many slaves so dey gettin rid of de ole ones. I'm one of dem, in case you ain't notice!" laughed Cooper.

"How old are you Cooper?"

"I don't know. Not too ole to do a good day's work. I can still do mo work den some of dem young bucks can. I reckon I'm wurf what you paid fuh me," he laughed.

"You ever been back to Williamsburg?"

"Nevah have."

"Dinah is still down there."

"She still livin?"

"Still living and still cooking."

" Um...Um...Now dat woman can cook."

"I still remember the first time I ate her cooking. I was living over the barbershop with John Timberlake."

"Where you liv now?"

323

"I have a home on the other side of the river."

"Dat sounds like a song," laughed Cooper. "How we get over dare?"

"On a ferry."

"I've seen dem things, but nevah rode on one." He laughed again and said, "I'll let you driv dis wagun when we get dare."

"I was scared the first time I ever rode on one."

"I might be too, but I reckon you gotta get cross dat river some how. How many folks live at yo house?"

"I have a wife and seven children and we'll have another one soon."

"Seven chillun! Dat's a lot of babies. All of dem hav da same mama?"

"Same mama."

"Yo wife must be a strong woman."

"She is. She got strong from eating Dinah's cooking."

Cooper stared at him while he processed that statement. "You didn't marry Miz Lizabeth did you?"

"I sure did. Just as soon as I was free and able."

Cooper laughed loudly, "You dun a good thing alright. Miz Elizabeth, she's a fine person."

Alexander and Cooper arrived back home before dark. Elizabeth and the children had been watching for him and John was the first to see him. "Here comes Daddy," he said. "Does he have anyone with him," asked Elizabeth.

"One old man."

"Oh no! I hope he hasn't spent our money on somebody that's too old to work."

Alexander pulled up close to the porch where all the family had gathered. "I want you to meet our new man, Cooper," he said.

"Cooper!" Shouted Elizabeth, rushing down the steps and grabbing the old man in her arms. "I can't believe it's really you."

The children stared at their mother in silence, trying to comprehend what was going on. "Mistuh Cooper," said

Molly, "I don't know who you are, but you sho mus be somebody real impotant. She sho dent treat me like dat when I got here!"

With the three boys and Cooper to help him share the work, Alexander was finally beginning to be rewarded for his years of labor on the land. Except for some unforeseen event, his tobacco crop would be outstanding. The five tired workers had just returned home from the tobacco field when the Paynes drove into the yard.

"Your timing is perfect as always, John!" shouted Alexander.

"And your insults are unwarranted!" responded Payne. "I think I'll just go back home without telling you why I came."

"Don't do that. I would miss getting a hug from your pretty wife."

"We really can't stay long," said Rebekah, "it's too close to supper time."

"We're going to feed eleven anyway, I'm sure that three more won't bother Elizabeth. Besides, I don't think you're going to get Ruth to leave until she has time to play with the children."

Elizabeth, who had overheard the conversation, stepped outside and said, "Don't even think about going anywhere, get down and come on in. Rebekah can help me finish supper."

After they were all inside, Alexander asked Payne, "So what is this great news you came to tell me?"

"Well I just thought you might be interested in knowing that your Goochland County property holdings have doubled."

"What! Who told you that?"

"Colonel Mayo asked me to tell you that the council approved your patent request for the four hundred acres on the Willis River at Cattail Creek."

Alexander was ecstatic. "Finally! Can you believe those Tidewater aristocrats honored a common man's request for land? They are usually so greedy; they gobble up all the land for themselves and their families leaving no place for the likes of us. I can't believe they will grant me land in the name of good King George. I will have to name my next son after him because of their great benevolence! George Stinson, that's what I'll name him!"

Everyone was laughing hilariously at his raving.

"Are you going to move up the river to your new land?" asked Rebekah.

A hush filled the room as everyone looked at Alexander and waited for an answer.

"Why's everyone looking so worried?" laughed Alexander. "It will be at least another year before the patent will be granted, the land hasn't even been surveyed yet. We can't move until we build a house to live in and that takes a long time."

"I don't want to move," said Joanna.

"Me either," said Anna, tearfully.

"Now wait a minute," said Elizabeth, "if we move, it will probably be years from now. Rebekah just asked a question and it was a good question. The answer is that we don't know what we will do with the land. One day soon, we'll all get in the wagon and ride up to see what it looks like. Right now, it's time to eat."

Rebekah walked over to Alexander and whispered, "I'm sorry I caused a stir."

He laughed again. "It had to happen sooner or later. We were all caught off guard because we've never talked about moving. We never had a reason to discuss it before."

"Well I had a reason for asking. If your family is going to move, I want to move there too. You are the only close friends we have." Looking at her husband, she asked, "Why don't you try to patent some land near them?"

Payne had a devious look on his face. "I did," he said.

"What do you mean you did?"

"When I found out that Alexander had requested a patent, I also asked for one. They approved mine too."

"Well aren't you the sly one," said Rebekah. "Why didn't

you tell anyone?"

"I didn't think they would ever approve one for me. If I told everybody and then it was rejected I'd be angry and embarrassed." Looking at Alexander, he said, "I remember how you felt two years ago when they rejected your request."

"How do you feel about moving?" asked Alexander.

"Unsettled. If it wasn't for your family and Ginny's grave, I would have been gone. This place is getting too crowded for me. I'm glad now that I didn't leave. If I had, I wouldn't have Rebekah and Ruth. I always thought that you would stay here because you've worked so hard on the land. It's going to be a lot harder for you to leave than me. I'm a trapper, not a planter. Moving further west would be good for me."

"It wouldn't be good for us to move and leave them here," said Rebekah. "Friends are more important than furs."

"You don't have to tell me," laughed Payne.

"I have something to tell all three of you," said Elizabeth. "We're waiting for you to come and eat. You can continue your discussion later."

The Paynes had gone home and all the children were in bed except seventeen-year-old John, who was outside visiting with Cooper. Alexander was sitting by the fire enjoying a cup of coffee while Elizabeth tidied up the house. John came in and sat down at the table across from his daddy. He was a handsome young man of medium build whose size belied his strength. His dark, wavy hair was the envy of his siblings and others. His observant brown eyes, like his lithe young body, were quick to respond to any changes in his surroundings. Alexander loved all of his children, but this young man held a special place in his heart because he reminded him so much of his deceased father, John's namesake. Alexander wasn't the only one who held an unusual fondness for his firstborn. Joseph and Elizabeth Hooper loved the Stinson children and treated them like they were their own flesh and blood, but John was clearly their favorite. They used every opportunity to have him visit with them or to do work for them. When

Elizabeth finished her household tasks, she came over and sat beside her son at the table.

"If we move to the new land, how long do you think it will be?" asked the young man.

"Here we go again," laughed Alexander.

"That's all the girls talked about before bedtime," explained Elizabeth to her son, who seemed perplexed by his father's remark.

"Like your mama explained at supper, we really don't know, but if we do move, it will be several years. We'd have to clear land, build a house and outbuildings. All of that takes a lot of time."

"What would you do with this place?"

"We don't know that either. Why are you asking?"

"In a few years, I'll be of age. I thought maybe I could stay here and work this place," said the young man shifting uncomfortably on his seat, "and look after Mr. and Mrs. Hooper. If we move, they won't have anybody here to take care of them."

"They have their slaves," said Elizabeth, "and the Mayos check on them regularly."

"Most of them live so far away and Colonel Mayo stays gone for weeks at a time."

"I appreciate your concern for them, but your daddy is going to need you to help him. You are his main helper."

"I plan to help daddy with everything. But while we are working out there, we're still going to need a place to live and raise crops until everything is ready to move. I was wondering if we could keep both places and I live here after you move?"

"If we keep both places, somebody will have to live here to oversee it," said Alexander. "It's twenty-five miles out there and the roads are bad. It may not be practical to raise tobacco there and try to get it back to market at The Falls. I may have to go back to trapping. We have a lot to think about."

Alexander and John Payne were both anxious to see their new land on Cattail Creek. Elizabeth, who was expecting her eighth child soon, knew how badly the men wanted to go and did not want to hinder them.

"Why don't you and John take the older boys with you and go for a few days? Rebekah and Ruth can stay with us. Cooper and Molly will be here to help, so we'll be fine until you get back."

The two men decided to take John and Joseph with them. Nine-year-old Alexander stood on the porch watching the group prepare to leave. He never said a word about going, but his daddy knew how badly he wanted to go. "Go get your coat," he said to the boy. "You can go with us."

As the boy ran into the house for his coat Elizabeth asked, "Is that wise? He doesn't have a horse to ride like the rest of you."

"He can ride with me."

"We can all take turns riding double," said Payne. "I'm glad you're letting him go, it was breaking my heart watching him. He had tears in his eyes as big as a shilling!"

The other children were disappointed they couldn't go too, but were reassured by their father's promise that he would take all of them soon.

When they reached the Indian village they were astonished to find it deserted.

"John, did you know they had moved?" asked Alexander.

"No. They were here two days ago, but they move whenever they feel the need."

"I'm surprised they didn't tell you they were leaving."

"I'm not."

"Wonder where they went?" asked Joseph.

"Further up the Willis or over on the James, I reckon," said Payne.

The men were happy to find that the trail to Cattail Creek was well traveled and would be easy to negotiate in a wagon. Payne was excited by the signs of wild game he saw on the property and Alexander was equally pleased with the rich soil along the river.

When the group returned home two days later, it was impossible to tell who was the most excited, the boys or the men.

"We climbed this big mountain near our land," said Joseph, "called Williss's Mountain, and we saw a bear!"

"There was a cave on the mountain, and we went in it," said little Alexander. "Daddy found where somebody had been writing on the wall a long time ago."

"Do you think it was Indians?" asked Anna.

"No, but we found the Indians," said John. "They've moved from here and are living up near that mountain. They told Uncle John about the cave!"

"When can we go see it?" asked little Elizabeth.

"We'll all go as soon as your mama's able to travel," said Alexander.

"That'll be a long time," said Joanna.

"Not as long as you think," said her mother, with a discerning smile.

"You've told us about the mountain and the Indians," laughed Rebekah, "but what about the land?"

"It's beautiful land," said Alexander, and some of it will be easy to clear. There's lots of big timber, plenty of streams, and several good places to build a home."

"Is that on your property or ours?"

"Both," said Payne. "And lots of good trapping too."

"What about the roads?" asked Elizabeth.

"Much better than I had hoped," said Alexander. "Wagon travel will be no problem. When you are able to travel, we'll take the wagons and all of us will go up to see it."

"Lawd hav mercy!" said Molly. "Here I go movin agin. I can jest see it comin right now. We gonna be leavin dis place and goin to dat mountain with all 'em Indians and woofs and bears. It ain't no tellin what else might be livin in dat cave! Why in de world ya'll wanta leave a good place like dis and go takin dem babies out somewhere like dat, I don't know! Lawd help us all if we go movin to dat Cattail Creek place!"

A New Home On Cattail Creek

Alexander sat on the porch of his new home watching the small group of people walking across the field towards the house. Little George held Joanna by one hand and Anna with the other. Their younger sister, Elizabeth, walked closely behind them chatting with Molly. Young Alexander and David were the last in the procession. The children had busied themselves for the past hour playing in Cattail Creek, and picking wild strawberries in the adjoining field. The father smiled as he recalled the children's apprehension about moving and how those feelings had gradually faded as they made regular visits to the new homestead while their house was being built. They soon developed a love for their new home that helped them overcome the loss they felt from leaving their old one.

"I wondered what you were doing," said a voice from behind him.
"I'm looking and thinking," said Alexander as he turned towards his wife who had slipped quietly out the door and stood watching him.
"I see what you are looking at. What are you thinking about?"
"How quickly time has gone by. A few years ago, you were my pretty little girlfriend in Williamsburg. Now you are my pretty wife in the wilderness and the mother of my nine children."
Elizabeth smiled as she walked to her husband's side and took his hand. "Do you really think I'm still pretty?"
"You're beautiful."
"Thank you," she said as she leaned down and kissed him.
"What else were you thinking about? I know all of your thoughts weren't about me!"

Alexander laughed. "I can never fool you can I?" After a moment, he became serious. "Do you realize that with the last two land patents I received, we now own over two thousand acres of land?"

"Suppose you're granted the one in Brunswick County that you filed with Archibald, and David Bell?"

"I don't expect we'll get that one, it's for fifteen thousand acres."

"But suppose you do get it?"

He smiled and said flippantly, "Then I'll own five thousand more acres."

"If you do get it, don't even think about moving again."

"You love it here, don't you?" said Alexander, growing serious again.

"We all do. I want to live here the rest of my life and be buried on top of the hill behind the house."

"Whoa! Don't go talking about dying. You've got a lot of living to do yet, and a house full of chaps to raise."

"Just don't get any thoughts about moving me or those chaps away from Cattail Creek."

"Yes ma'am Miz Lizabeth, I hear you."

"I'm serious!"

"Oh, I can tell you're serious. I wouldn't dare think about moving you and your chaps."

"You'd better not, if you know what's good for you."

"I know what's good for me," said Alexander as he stood and took his wife in his arms, "you're good for me."

"You have a way of changing the subject when you don't want to talk about something."

"I didn't change the subject," laughed Alexander. "We were talking about what's good for me."

"We were talking about never moving again."

"I have no intentions of ever moving again."

"Promise?"

"I promise."

"Good. Now we can talk about something else."

"Like what?"

"Like how it's going to feel being grandparents?"

"That's scary. I'm too young to be a grandpa, I still have a three-year-old son!"

"Cary will be four by the time John's baby is born."

"How do you feel being married to a grandpa?"

"That is scary!"

John, according to his wishes, had stayed behind to operate the old plantation near the mouth of the Willis. He had married a neighbor, Martha Childress, the previous year and they were expecting their first child. Young Alexander had assumed some of the workload from his father and Cooper on the Cattail Creek plantation, which allowed Joseph to divide his time between the two places. Depending on the season, he would sometimes spend weeks helping John before returning home. When he rode into the yard after being gone only one day, the family knew something was wrong.

The slender young man dismounted at the house and tied his horse to the hitch. The entire family waited on the porch in anticipation of the news he was carrying.

"What's wrong?" asked his mother.

"Mr. Cary is dead. Archibald came by this morning on his way to Ampthill and told us. He asked me to come tell you."

Elizabeth began weeping as she looked at her husband. "I don't suppose there is any way I can go to his funeral. Are you going to try to make it?"

"They'll probably bury him tomorrow. If I leave soon, I can spend the night with John and Martha and leave at daylight tomorrow. That should give me enough time."

"Take one of the boys with you."

"Joseph can go with me and stop at John's on the way home. Alexander and Cooper can take care of things here until I get back. We need to leave as soon as possible."

"I wish I could go," said Elizabeth, "but I know I can't. Please give Archibald and the girls my regrets."

"I will."

"The last time I saw Mr. Cary was at Archibald's wedding

five years ago," said Elizabeth. "He seemed fine and enjoyed himself so much."

"That's a good memory to have of him."

"We have many good things to remember him by. He did so much for us."

Alexander and Joseph arrived at Ampthill a few hours before the funeral service. A large crowd had already gathered and others continued to arrive by boat, carriage, and horseback. Archibald, ever the gracious host, tried to greet each new guest as they arrived. His wife, the former Mary Randolph, was continually at his side. Their four-year-old daughter, Anne, anxious from all the activity, clung tenaciously to her mother's hand. Judith Cary Bell and her husband David were good friends and neighbors of Alexander, living at nearby Belmont. They also circulated freely among the crowd trying to insure that everyone's needs were being met. When Sarah, the other daughter, saw Alexander and Joseph in the crowd, she came immediately to them and introduced her new husband, Alexander Spiers, a merchant from Scotland.

"I'm happy to finally meet you, sir," said Spiers. "The family speaks of you frequently."

"I'm glad to know they still remember me," said Alexander, "since I seldom see them."

"I can assure you they have many fond memories of you and your wife. Is she well?"

"She is, thank you, and sends her regrets that she could not be here today."

"I really appreciate your coming," said Sarah. "It was a long trip for you and Joseph."

"It was the least I could do for your father and the family. I've always regretted not being here when your mother died, but I didn't learn about it until after she was buried."

"We understood. Dad always felt bad that he didn't send someone to tell you. I think he was concerned that you would have felt obligated to come and he knew how difficult it would have been for you."

"I would've been here if I had known it."

"We knew that."

"You need to tell him our news," said Spiers.

"We're going to be moving to Scotland in a few months," said Sarah.

"For how long?"

"Indefinitely. Alexander wants to go home and work from Glasgow. They are still shipping large amounts of tobacco there from Virginia."

"How do you feel about moving?"

"I'm looking forward to seeing his country and meeting his family, but I'll miss my family and friends here."

"We'll miss you too Sarah. I hope Elizabeth will be able to see you before you leave. May God grant you both a safe voyage and bring you back to see us some day."

"Thank you Alexander, I'll miss Virginia."

After the funeral, a meal was served and some of the people left, but a large group would be spending the night. Archibald took Alexander aside from the crowd and said, "I want you and Joseph to spend the night here. It's too far for you to return home today."

Alexander smiled. "That's considerate of you, but I'm afraid you may not have a place to sleep yourself. I think you're going to have more people tonight than you have beds."

"We'll find room for you. You don't have enough time to get home before dark."

"I'm not going to try. We'll spend the night at the Trading Post. They still rent beds don't they?"

"Yes, if they're not already full."

"If they are, we'll sleep in the stable. That'll be a good experience for Joseph; he's heard me talk about the Trading Post, but has never been there. Who's operating it now?"

"Mr. Dixon is still there."

"Good. I look forward to seeing him again."

"I hate for you to leave so soon. I was hoping to spend more time with you."

"You spend your time with the other guests tonight and when things settle down, you and Mary bring Anne up to

Cattail Creek to visit with us for a few days. It's hard for us to get away and Elizabeth would love to spoil you a little bit. She's so tied down with the children that she never goes anywhere. The last social function she attended was your wedding and we had to rush back home as soon as it was over. Your visit would mean a lot to her."

"Father wanted me to move here to Ampthill after his death because his wife will be going back to live in her home at Williamsburg. Judith and David aren't interested in leaving Belmont, and Sarah is moving to Scotland. I promise you we'll come for a visit before I move if you promise me you'll bring your family here for a visit after I move."

Alexander laughed loudly. "You should wait until you visit us before you ask me to make that promise. With a clan like we have, Ampthill may never be the same if we visit here."

"We'll talk about that some more when we visit you. Isn't your youngest child about the same age as my Anne?"

"I think so, he's almost four."

"What's his name?"

"Cary."

Archibald stared at him. "Are you serious?"

"I'm serious. His name is Cary."

Tears formed in his eyes as he looked at Alexander. "Did you name him after my father?"

"Your father, and you, and your family. With everything your family has meant to me and Elizabeth, we felt it was a worthwhile tribute to them."

"We'll be up to visit you soon."

As they rode towards the ferry, Alexander stopped his horse and said to Joseph, "I'm going to tell you something I've never told anybody before. I shot two men right here one day."

Joseph stared at his daddy in amazement. "Did you kill them?"

"No. I didn't try to kill them. I just wanted to stick some shot in their backsides and I did."

"Why?"

Alexander told his son the story as they continued riding towards the ferry.

"How come you never told anyone?"

"Didn't want to worry your mama and was afraid Mr. Cary might get upset with me."

"Can I tell John about it? He'd love to hear that story."

"I suppose so. It's been long enough now that I guess it doesn't matter. Your mama knows I've done some crazy things before. She won't be surprised that I did it, but she might get upset because I never told her."

"Wait until I get home before you tell her," laughed Joseph, "I want to hear what she says."

****

The following year, Joseph Hooper died. A few days before his death, he sent for Alexander to come visit him. When the old fellow saw his former neighbor, he rallied and propped himself up in the bed.

"Thank you for coming," he said weakly. "I have several things I want to talk with you about. First, I wanted to thank you and your family for being so kind to me and my wife all these years."

"You've also been kind..."

"Please let me finish," interrupted Hooper, "I don't have much time or strength. I've made my will and I wanted to discuss it with you before I die. I left a few things to your older children because they are like my own flesh and blood. John has been like a son to me. We were so happy when you decided to let him stay here after you moved. I don't know what we would have done without his help. He and Martha brought the baby to see me yesterday. I'm happy they named him after you. I like to see families keep traditions. Unfortunately, we hardly know your younger children, but we don't want them to be offended because they weren't named in my will. I want you to explain that to them."

"I will. They'll understand."

"Good. Obviously, I'm concerned about my wife; I left most

of my things to her and some other family members. I've tried to make provisions for her to remain here if she wants to. Do you think John and his family will continue to live here?"

"John's not going anywhere. He and Martha love it here."

"Good. Now that I know that, I can die in peace."

When Alexander arrived home from the Hoopers, he found that John Payne, Rebekah, and their three children were visiting. The two families had remained close friends and visited each other frequently. Ruth, who was almost as big as her mother, was a tremendous help in caring for her two younger brothers. After exchanging greetings with everyone, they all listened attentively as Alexander told about his visit with Joseph Hooper.

"I don't know how you can talk to somebody like that about dying," said John Payne. "I don't think I could do it."

"Dying is something we all have to do," said Alexander. "Sometimes we need to talk about it."

"When my time comes, I don't want to talk about it, I just want to go," said Payne.

"Like the Indians did?" asked Ruth.

"What do you mean?" responded Anna.

"They're gone."

"Gone where?"

"Nobody knows. They're just gone."

Alexander gave Payne a questioning look.

"That's right," said Payne. "They're all gone. Some folks think they've gone west into the mountains, but nobody knows for sure."

1781-1790
Chapter 32

The Hill Behind The House

Alexander climbed slowly up the hill behind his house and sat down on a rock near his wife's grave. It had been over five years since Elizabeth died and he missed her more as each day passed. He longed for the day when they could be together again. He went there every day, regardless of the weather, where he sat to think and pray. Some people said he went there to talk to Elizabeth. He smiled when he heard that. He knew Elizabeth wasn't there--she was with her Lord. She had always been the one with the strong faith. She was the one who taught it to their children and the one who kept him on course when he could have easily drifted away. Now, his faith was his greatest possession.

When he thought about the long life that he and Elizabeth had shared, it gave him great joy and he thanked God for it. They had been married more than half a century and she had been his childhood friend before that. During those indentured years when neither of them had anyone else, they had each other to depend on. They had moved to the wilderness when it was all Goochland County. It continued to be divided into other counties. Now their farm was in Buckingham County and John's was in Cumberland. He had seen many other changes in his life. Few people from his generation were still alive. Judith and Archibald were the only two Cary children still living. Sarah never returned from Scotland and had died there. From where he sat, he could look down the hill to the slave cemetery and see the graves of Cooper, Molly, and several others. He could watch his fine stock of cattle grazing along the creek and see the fields of tobacco, recalling the backbreaking work required to clear those fields.

The solitude he enjoyed on the hill behind his house was

sorely missing most places in his beloved land. For five years war had raged between the colonies and their mother country. At this very moment, British troops controlled the northern colonies and were marching through the south inflicting death and destruction. The ill-equipped, under-funded, and poorly trained Continental Army seemed helpless to stop the superior forces they faced. Alexander and his sons were too old to be soldiers, but responded as patriots by sending the army beef and other supplies.

Alexander's thoughts were interrupted by two horsemen riding up the road towards his house. Rising to his feet, he stared at the approaching figures trying to identify them. He recognized one immediately as his neighbor, Peter Francisco. Peter was a giant of a man though he was hardly old enough to be considered one. A huge sword swung from his belt as he galloped along the road. Alexander was halfway down the hill before he recognized the other rider as his young grandson, Alexander Junior. They all arrived at the house at the same time.

"Hi Grandpa."
"Morning Alex. What brings you up this way so early?"
"I'm on the way to North Carolina to join the Virginia Militia and stopped by to tell you."
Alexander stared at the young man, trying to comprehend what was taking place.
"Good morning Mr. Stinson," said Peter.
"Good morning Peter," said Alexander, never taking his eyes off his grandson. "How about telling me what this is all about, Alex."
The two men had dismounted and were tying their horses. "Cornwallis is moving the British Army north through the Carolinas towards Virginia. Our militia is recruiting men to try to stop them. I'm going with them."
"Son, you haven't had any military training. You don't know how to fight in a war. Peter has served several years in the Army, he's had training and experience, and you haven't.

Peter, is this your idea?"

"No sir, Mr. Stinson. It's Alex's idea. When he heard that I was reenlisting he asked if he could ride along with me."

"I have a horse and a gun Grandpa, and that's what they need, men with horses and guns."

"Alex, you've got a young wife and daughter at home. What's going to happen to them?"

"I hope they'll be safe until I get back. If we don't stop the British in North Carolina, they'll soon be here and nobody will be safe. I'm doing this for all of us Grandpa. Sarah, Nancy, you, mama, daddy, our entire family. We need to stop them before they get here."

The old man grew silent as he saw the determined look in his grandson's eyes. Alexander knew that if he were younger, he'd be going with him.

"What kind of gun are you taking, son?"

"The only one I have, an old fowler."

"Leave it here and take one of mine."

"I can't take your gun Grandpa, I know how you feel about your guns. Something might happen to it."

"I'd rather something happen to the gun than to you. You need one that's accurate and doesn't weigh a ton. I have enough rounds for my gun to kill half the redcoats down there. Give me that thing and come inside and get a good gun."

News of the war traveled slowly and wasn't always accurate. Days turned into weeks and anxiety mounted as the Stinson family awaited news concerning their young soldier. The *Virginia Gazette* reported the bloody battle at Guilford Courthouse and the retreat of Cornwallis to the coast. Alexander arose early one morning and rode to Hunting Tower, the home of Judge Anthony Winston, to see if he had heard any news from his adopted son, Peter Francisco.

"Good morning Alexander, what brings you out so early?"

"Morning Judge. I was wondering if you had heard from Peter. My grandson left with him and the militia and we haven't heard anything from him since."

"It's interesting that you came this morning. Peter returned home last night. He was wounded again at Guilford Courthouse and it has taken him this long to recover sufficiently to walk home. He is very poorly and is resting in bed."

"I hate to bother him, but I would like to see if he has any news about Alex."

"I'm sure he won't mind. Actually, he mentioned he needed to talk with you."

Rapping on the door, the Judge called out, "Peter, there's somebody here to see you." He opened the door slowly to reveal the Virginia giant, awake, but lying in bed.

"Hello Mr. Stinson, come in."

"Thank you Peter, I'm sorry to bother you, but I was looking for news about Alex."

"I have some news for you, but it's not good. Alex was wounded in the same battle that I was, but he's not recovering well from his wounds. Things don't look too good for him. I was going to come over today and tell you about it."

"What kinds of wounds does he have?"

"From grape shot. Our troops were getting the upper hand when Cornwallis ordered his men to fire canisters of grape shot into the midst of the battle, killing and wounding their own men along with us. Some of the shot hit Alex in his legs and back. His wounds aren't healing well."

"Where is he?"

"Same place I was, in a Quaker community on the New Garden Road."

"Is he in a hospital?"

"There's no hospital there, but he's getting excellent care from those Quaker people."

"Is he well enough to travel in a wagon."

"I don't think so, he wasn't when I left."

"Where can I find him?"

"I was with the Robinson family. They live near the battlefield. Find John Robinson and he'll take you to Alex."

"Thank you Peter. Take care of yourself and I hope you get well soon."

"Thank you sir."

As Alexander turned to leave, Peter called out to him, "Mr. Stinson?"

"Yes Peter?"

"I'm real sorry about Alex and I want you to know it really wasn't my idea for him to go."

"I know that Peter. Thank you."

Alexander's legs were weak as he walked to the door. The Judge was talking to him about the war, but he paid little attention to what he was saying, his mind was racing, trying to decide what he needed to do. When he arrived home he shared the news with the family and said, "Cary, go tell John what I found out and tell him to get here as soon as he can so we can go get Alex. You stay with Martha and the children until we get back. Tell him we'll take my wagon."

"Daddy, that's a long trip for you. Why don't you stay here and let me go with John?"

"I'm going, now hurry up and go tell John. Be sure to take your gun. There are reports of British raiding parties in Virginia."

"Yes sir."

There were signs of the battle everywhere as the two men approached Guilford Courthouse. They found the New Garden Road and soon located the home of John Robinson where they inquired about Alex. Stepping outside and closing the door behind him the man said in a hushed voice, "I'm John Robinson and Alexander Stinson Junior is inside. Please tell me thy name."

"I'm Alexander Stinson and this is my son John. He is Alexander Stinson Junior's father."

"I see. Your son is gravely ill. He is growing weaker by the hour and has scarcely been awake today."

"Has a doctor seen him?"

"Yes, almost every day since he was brought here from the battlefield. He has advised against moving him because of his serious back injuries. We have given him the best care we could provide."

"We will pay you for your care."

"I thank thee, but I will accept no pay for doing what our Lord told us to do. Come inside to see thy son."

They entered the house and followed John Robinson to a rear bedroom. Young Alex lay deathly still on the bed with his eyes closed. Two women stood beside the bed, but left as the men entered the room. John walked to the bedside and spoke to his son.

"Alex."

The young soldier struggled to open his eyes and focus them on his father. "Dad?"

"Hi son."

"How'd you get here?"

"I hired this old man to drive me," said John, as Alexander stepped to the bedside.

"Hi Grandpa," said Alex, as he closed his eyes and smiled. "I knew you would find me."

"We came down to see if you needed a ride home."

"I do. I'm almost ready to go. It's a good thing you got here when you did. I was afraid I was going to get buried in North Carolina and I didn't want that. I want to be buried in Buckingham, on the hill behind your house near Grandma."

"You don't need to talk about that now, you'll probably feel better tomorrow."

"I won't be here tomorrow. Daddy, I've already made my will. Mr. Robinson has it. You'll probably have to come back here later to file it with the court. I want you to help Sarah so I made both of you executors. I left everything to her and little Nancy. I really miss them. Tell them I love them. I love all of you."

"We love you too, son and are very proud of you. You did what you came to do. You stopped the British."

The young man smiled and closed his eyes. "Good. Let's go home."

With tears streaming down their cheeks, the three men stood silently by the bed while they watched the young soldier take his last breath.

John Robinson, aware of the inevitable, had already made arrangements for a coffin. When daylight came, the Virginians were ready to begin their long ride home.

"Will thy journey be longer than a day?" asked Robinson.

"We will have to finish it in the dark," said Alexander, "but those roads will be familiar to us."

"I shall pray for thy safety and peace."

"Thank you. We deeply appreciate all you've done."

"Thou art welcome."

News spread quickly through the countryside about the death of Alex Stinson. Expecting only family members to be present at the hastily arranged funeral, Alexander was surprised by the large crowd that gathered on the hill behind the house. The Baptist minister spoke long and loud, giving thanks to God, and extolling the virtues of this one who had sacrificed his life that those present could have freedom from tyranny and freedom to worship their God in the place and manner of their choosing.

As the months passed, war news became more encouraging. Cornwallis eventually entered Virginia in May with 7,500 troops and established a base at Yorktown, only to be trapped by the French from the sea and General George Washington and his French allies from land. After months of bombardment, Cornwallis surrendered on October 19, 1781. Yorktown was the beginning of the end. Although there were other skirmishes and battles before the final treaties were signed two years later, America had won her independence. The damage inflicted upon Cornwallis's army at Guilford Courthouse turned them back towards the coast and eventual defeat. It was the turning point of the Revolutionary War. Following generations would be forever indebted to those who stood in the path of the advancing enemy and gave their lives to stop them.

****

A burst of cold wind greeted Alexander when he stepped out on the porch. After pausing to button the top button on his coat, he picked up his walking stick that was leaning against the wall and started walking slowly up the hill behind his house. It was becoming increasingly more difficult for him to make the walk each day and he would stop frequently to rest. The children begged him not to go when the weather was bad and the boys even offered to take him up the hill in the wagon. He would laugh and say, "I'll be alright. I'll take my time." He was almost at the top when a pain started in his chest. He stopped for a minute and it got better. By the time he reached the rock, it had started again. He decided to sit down and rest briefly and then return to the house. It would be easier walking downhill.

When Cary Stinson came home for dinner, his wife met him at the door. "Your daddy has been at the cemetery for a long time, I think you should check on him."
Cary hurried up the hill. When he neared the top, he could see Alexander lying on the ground beside Elizabeth's grave. He called out to him and received no response. Rushing to his side, he knelt beside his aged father and took him by the hand. When he looked into his face, he knew he was dead. Alexander's life had ended just the way he would have chosen. He died beside his beloved Elizabeth, on the hill behind the house. There he would be buried, and a fieldstone would mark his grave. Having fulfilled his dream, he now rested from his labors.

****

As the eighteenth century drew to a close, so did an era of New World exploration. The American colonies had become a new nation that was rapidly expanding its frontiers. The Indians, the bison, and the wolves were gone from Buckingham County. The pioneers who risked their lives to conquer the backwoods area of Virginia above The Falls were also gone. Some of those frontiersmen rested in unmarked graves in the wilderness. Others, like Alexander and Elizabeth, would leave behind a home, a family, and a rich heritage to guide those who followed after them. Some of them would seek new frontiers as the unspoiled lands of the south and west became available and beckoned to them. Others would choose to remain on their ancestral lands at Cattail Creek. One day, they too would be buried on the hill behind the house, and a fieldstone would mark their grave.

APPENDIX

I have chosen to include a bibliography and some informative pictures for the benefit of those who desire to do more research on the life of Alexander Stinson and the times in which he lived. It is my hope that future researchers will benefit from this information. Enjoy.

YORKTOWN'S WATERFRONT

"Eighteenth century commerce moved by water whenever possible. Yorktown's waterfront reflected this. Tobacco warehouses, ships chandleries, grogshops, and wharves lined the waterfront...among them passed the diverse array of merchants and sailors, planters, and inspectors, travelers and laborers and slaves who kept business moving briskly."

- National Park Service, Harpers Ferry Commissioned Art Collection

SUSAN CONSTANT

This recreation of the *Susan Constant* may be seen at Jamestown, Virginia. It was the flagship and largest of the three ships that brought the first permanent English settlers to America in 1607. Once the colony had been established, she returned to England continuing her career as an ordinary trading vessel. She was typical of the merchant ships of the Colonial era that made voyages from the British Isles to Virginia. These sailing ships remained basically unchanged from 1600 to 1800 and would have been similar to the *Bristol Merchant*.

CHARLES CHURCH MARKER

CHARLES CHURCH
OF CHARLES PARISH YORKE COUNTY

FIRST NAMED NEW POQUOSON PARISH 1642-3
CHANGED TO NEW TOWNSON PARISH ABOUT 1680
NAMED CHARLES PARISH BEFORE JULY 8, 1702
AND SO REMAINED UNTIL THE CLOSE OF THE
CHARLES PARISH REGISTERS 1789.
MINISTERS WHO SERVED CHARLES PARISH
REV. JAMES SCLATER
REV. JAMES FALCONER
REV. THOMAS WARRINGTON
REV. JOSEPH DAVENPORT
REV. SAMUEL SHIELD
ERECTED BY THE YORKTOWN BRANCH OF THE ASSOCIATION
FOR THE PRESERVATION OF VIRGINIA ANTIQUITIES
1940

COLONIAL GRACE CHURCH

YORK-HAMPTON PARISH

"A National Shrine At The Cradle of the Republic"

Grace Church has survived over 300 years of war, political calamity, and fire. These are the original walls, built of marl in 1697.

By 1700, York County encompassed three parishes along the York River: Charles Parish; York Parish; and Hampton Parish. In 1706, the vestries of York and Hampton parishes merged and in 1789, Charles Parish closed. Rev. James Sclater served in all three of these parishes beginning in 1701.

The York-Hampton Parish continues an active ministry today as Colonial Grace Church in Yorktown, Virginia.

ALEXANDER CRAIG HOUSE

COLONIAL WILLIAMSBURG, VIRGINIA

The Alexander Craig House is located on the north side of Duke of Gloucester Street just four lots west of the Capitol on Colonial Lot 55, next door to historic Raleigh Tavern. The lot was sold in 1712 to Susanna Allen who operated an ordinary there each year until her death in 1719. In her will she mentions her servant boy, Alexander Stinson.

The house was sold in 1775 to Alexander Craig, a saddler and harness maker. Today it is owned by Colonial Williamsburg and is used as a private residence. It is not open to the public.

ALEXANDER CRAIG HOUSE KITCHEN

BARBER SHOP

Duke of Gloucester Street, Colonial Williamsburg, Virginia.

STEPS IN THE BARBER SHOP

Colonial Williamsburg, Virginia

THE WELL BEHIND THE BARBER SHOP

THE MAGAZINE AND GUARDHOUSE

COLONIAL WILLIAMSBURG, VIRGINIA

Erected in 1715, the magazine was colonial Virginia's storehouse for guns, ammunition, and military supplies. The action of British Governor Dunmore on the night of April 20-21, 1775, in removing gunpowder belonging to the Colony, touched off the Revolution in Virginia before news of the Battle of Lexington reached Williamsburg. The reconstructed Guardhouse was originally built during the French and Indian War. A comprehensive collection of military equipment includes antique Brown Bess muskets.

Henry Cary was "keeper of the Magazine" in 1726.
- *The Virginia Carys, an Essay in Genealogy p.88*

BRUTON PARISH CHURCH

COLONIAL WILLIAMSBURG, VIRGINIA

Services on Sunday & Special Days

One of the oldest Episcopal Churches in America, this
historic building has been in service to God and Man
continuously since 1715.

OPEN TO VISITORS EVERY DAY

Record of the Deed for 400 acres that Alexander Stinson purchased from Henry Cary in 1738. Witnesses were Benjamin Harrison (of Berkeley Plantation), Arthur Hopkins, and David Bell, (son-in-law of Henry Cary). - *Goochland County, Virginia Wills and Deeds 1736 - 1742, p 175.*

(17)

		Tobacco.	rafk
Goochland County - - - - - - - Dr			
To the Proportion of the Publick Levy.			
To Thomas Atkinson . . . . .200.			
To the Clerk - - - - - - - - 20.			
To Thomas Christian . . . . . 360.		1732.	
To Benjamin Bradshaw . . . . 768.			
To Thomas Murrell for his wife . . 384.			
To William Tabor for one Wolf's head certified by George Hains . . .		200.	
To William Croafy for one Do certified by Daniel Stouer		200.	
To Richard Ward for two Do certified by William Cabbell		400.	
To Richard Wilson for one Do certified by Daniel Stouer		200.	
To Thomas Christian Junr for three Do certified by George Hains . . .		600.	
To Alexander Stinson for four Do certified by William Mayo . . .		800.	
To Alexander Stinson for one Do certified by Daniel Stouer . . .		200.	
To Alexander Stinson for one Do certified by Daniel Stouer . . .		200.	
To Thomas Christian Junr for one certified by Daniel Stouer . . .		200.	
To Thomas Christian Junr for six Do certified by William Cabbell . .		1200.	
To Edmond Wood for five Do certified by William Cabbell . . .		1000.	
To Edmond Wood for three Do certified by Daniel Stouer		600.	
To William Halliday for seven Do certified by William Cabbell . .		1400.	
To Benjamin Woodson Junr for three Do certified by John Woodson . .		600.	
To James Corke for one Do certified by John Woodson . . .		200.	
To William Owen for one Do certified by William Cabbell . . .		200.	
To William Atkinson for one Do certified by Allen Howard . . .		200.	
To Thomas Hall for two Do certified by George Payne . . .		400.	
To John Ripley for one Do certified by James Skelton . . .		200.	
To John Atkins for one Do certified by John Woodson . . .		200.	
To Benjamin Stingo for one Do certified by William Mayo . . .		200.	
To Joseph Hooper for one Do certified by William Cabbell . . .		200.	
To James Whaley for one Do certified by William Cabbell . . .		200.	
To Allen Howard for one Do certified by James Holman . . .		200.	
To Allen Howard for one Do certified by George Hains . . .		200.	
To forrost Green for one Do certified by Allen Howard . . .		200.	
To Thomas Tindall for two Do certified by Allen Howard . . .		400.	
To Richard Powell for one Do certified by Allen Howard . . .		200.	
Carried over		12732.	

This is a copy of page 17 of the Goochland County Levy
Court records for 1731 showing that Alexander Stinson
received 1200 pounds of tobacco as bounty for six wolves.
Certified by William Mayo and Daniel Stouer.

RED WOLVES

The red wolf is one of the most endangered animals in the world. This shy species once roamed the Southeast as a top predator and were the wolves that Alexander Stinson and other Virginia trappers received bounty for in the eighteenth century. Aggressive predator control programs and clearing of forested habitat combined to bring the red wolf to the brink of extinction. The U.S. Fish and Wildlife Service have been successful in reintroducing the species into the wild in northeastern North Carolina where it now roams over more than 560,000 acres. More information may be received from the Red Wolf Project, Alligator River National Wildlife Refuge, PO Box 1969, Manteo NC 27954.

-Picture used by permission of the artist, Janet Allen (Walker) Myrick.

MONUMENT

This monument was erected in memory of Alexander Stinson, Sr. on the Cattail Creek Farm he once owned in Buckingham County, Virginia. It reads as follows:

IN MEMORY OF

ALEXANDER STINSON, SR.

PIONEER SETTLER OF BUCKINGHAM COUNTY
AND AMERICAN REVOLUTIONARY WAR
PATRIOT WHO RECEIVED A LAND PATENT
FROM KING GEORGE THE SECOND OF
GREAT BRITIAN, FRANCE, AND IRELAND
IN 1743 AND LIVED HERE UNTIL HIS DEATH;
AND TO HIS FAMILY MEMBERS WHO LIVED
HERE UNTIL 1970, MANY OF WHOM LIE
BURIED IN THE AREA BEHIND THIS MARKER.

ERECTED 2000 A.D. BY HIS DESCENDANTS

GRAVE MARKERS

Fieldstone grave markers in the Stinson cemetery. These are located on top of the hill behind the house at the Cattail Creek Farm in Buckingham County.

CATTAIL CREEK

Cattle still graze on both sides of Cattail Creek at the old Stinson Farm in Buckingham County, Virginia. The *Virginia Public Claims Records* lists Alexander Stinson, Sr., John Stinson, David Stinson, and Joseph Stinson as patriots for supplying beef and services to the militia of the Continental Army during the American Revolution.

Alexander Stinson, Sr. is listed on the *Albemarle Public Service Claims Records* for his contributions.

State of Virginia Historical Marker located on US Route 60 at the county line of Buckingham and Appomattox counties.

PETER FRANCISCO'S SWORD

Charles Stinson holding a sword that once belonged to Peter Francisco. This sword is located at The Housewright House Museum and Library in Buckingham Courthouse, Virginia.

MOORE HOUSE

YORKTOWN, VIRGINIA
REVOLUTIONARY WAR BATTLEFIELD AREA

A nearby sign reads:

"The Battlefield was quiet October 18, 1781 under temporary truce. That day two Allied commissioners met with two British and drafted the terms of surrender. They met in this house, now restored and refurbished. It was then the home of Augustine Moore, merchant of Yorktown."

BIBLIOGRAPHY

Aaron, Larry G. *The Race to the Dan: The Retreat That Rescued the American Revolution.* Lynchburg, Virginia: Warwick House, 2007

Andrews, Peter. *Christmas In Colonial and Early America.* Chicago, Illinois: World Book Encyclopedia, 1975.

Bailey, Ron. "A Surveyor for the King". *Colonial Williamsburg Journal* Summer 2001. (The story of Peter Jefferson and William Mayo).

Ballagh, James Curtis. *White Servitude in the Colony of Virginia: A study of the system of indentured labor in the American Colonies 1619-1788.* Baltimore, Maryland: The Johns Hopkins Press, 1895

Bell, Landon C. *Charles Parish, York County, Virginia History and Register.* Richmond, Virginia: The Virginia State Library Board, 1932.

Bigham, Barbara. "Colonists in Bondage: Indentured Servants in America." Reprinted by permission from *Early American Life:* October 1979.

Billings, Warren M. *The Old Dominion in the Seventeenth Century, A Documentary History of Virginia, 1606-1689.* Chapel Hill, NC: The University of North Carolina Press, 1975. Published for the Institute of Early American History and Culture at Williamsburg, Virginia.

Brock, Robert K. *Archibald Cary of Ampthill: Wheelhorse of the Revolution.* Richmond, Virginia: Garrett and Massie, 1937.

Byrd, William. *Histories of the Dividing Line betwixt Virginia and North Carolina.* New York, NY: Dover Publications, Inc., 1967.

Caswell County North Carolina Court Records. *The Will of Alexander Stinson, Jr.* Deeds, Book A, 1781-1782, p.182. March 1782.

Dabney, Virginius. *RICHMOND The Story of a City.* Charlottesville, Virginia: The University Press of Virginia,1990

Daniels, Roger. *Coming to America, A History of Immigration and Ethnicity in American Life.* New York, NY: Harper Collins, 1990

Farrar, Emmie Ferguson. *Old Virginia Houses Along the James.* New York, NY: Bonanza Books, 1957

Fischer, David Hackett. *Albion's Seed, Four British Folkways in America.* New York, NY: Oxford University Press, 1989

Gibbs, Patricia Ann. "Taverns in Tidewater Virginia, 1700-1774". *A Thesis presented to the faculty of the Department of History, The College of William and Mary in Virginia.* Williamsburg, Virginia: Colonial Williamsburg Foundation Library, 1968.

Gill, Harold B., Jr. *The Gunsmith in Colonial Virginia.* Williamsburg, Virginia: The Colonial Williamsburg Foundation, and The University Press of Virginia, 1974.

Goodwin, William A.R. *The Record of Bruton Parish Church.* Edited, with revisions and additions, by Mary Frances Goodwin. Richmond, Virginia: The Dietz Press, 1941

Harrison, Fairfax. *The Virginia Carys: An Essay in Genealogy.* New York: Privately printed, De Vinne Press, 1919.

Harding, A.R. *Deadfalls & Snares.* Columbus, Ohio: A.R. Harding, Publisher, 1935.

Hawke, David Freeman. *Everyday Life in Early America.* New York, NY: Harper & Row, 1989

Houck, Peter W., M.D. *Indian Island in Amherst County.* Lynchburg, Virginia: Progress Printing Co., Inc.1984.

Kirkham, Jean and Boyce, Deborah. *In Every Generation. A Celebratory History of Grace Episcopal Church, Yorktown, Virginia 1697-1997.* Newport News, Virginia: Minuteman Press, 1997.

McGraw, Marie Tyler. *At The Falls Richmond, Virginia, & Its People.* Chapel Hill & London: The University Of North Carolina Press, 1994.

Mittelberger, Gottlieb. "The Passage of Indentured Servants, (1750)". From Gottlieb Mittleberger, *Journey to Pennsylvania in the Year 1750 and Return to Germany in the Year 1754.* American History Online.

Moon, William Arthur. *Peter Francisco, The Portuguese Patriot.* Pfafftown, North Carolina: Colonial Publishers, 1980.

Nelson, John K. *A Blessed Company, Parishes, Parsons, and Parishioners in Anglican Virginia, 1690-1776.* Chapel Hill, North Carolina: The University of North Carolina Press, 2001.

Pawlett, Nathaniel Mason. *Historic Roads of Virginia: Goochland County Road Orders 1728-1744.* Charlottesville, Virginia: Faculty Research Historian, Virginia Highway & Transportation Research Council and the University of Virginia, VHTRC 75-R71, 1975.

Stephenson, Mary A. *Alexander Craig House, 1956.* Williamsburg, Virginia: Alexander Craig House Historical Report, Block 17 Building 5 Lot 55, Colonial Williamsburg Foundation Library Research Report Series - 1341, 1990.

Stinson, Frances Louise. *Alexander Stinson Sr. of Buckingham County Virginia*, (With Some Descendants), Researched and Complied, April 1993, Revised, May 1999. Dallas Texas: Privately printed. Revised copy on file at Virginia State Library, Richmond, Virginia. 1999.

Trudell, Clyde F. *Colonial Yorktown.* Richmond, Virginia: Dietz Press, 1938.

Tunis, Edwin. *Colonial Craftsmen and the Beginning of American Industry.* New York, New York: Thomas Y. Crowell, Co. 1965.

Weisiger, Benjamin B. *Chesterfield County, Virginia Wills 1749-1774.*

Woodfin, Maude H. and Tinling, Marion. *Another Secret Diary of William Byrd of Westover for the years 1739-1741.* Richmond, Virginia: The Dietz Press, Inc. 1942

Wright, Louis B. and Tinling, Marion. *The Secret Diary of William Byrd of Westover 1709-1712.* Richmond, Virginia: The Dietz Press, 1941.

York County Court House, Yorktown, Virginia, *York County Deeds, Orders, Wills, Book 15, 1716-1720.*

GENEALOGICAL RECORD

From **ALEXANDER STINSON, SR.**, to **CHARLES L. STINSON**
Line of descent is <u>underlined</u>, **bold**, and marked with an *
Some dates are approximate

1-*<u>**Alexander Stinson, Sr**</u>. 1702-1790
+Unknown
    2-John Stinson b. 1727
    2-Joseph Stinson b. 1729
    2-Joanna Stinson b. 1732
    2-Alexander Stinson 1734-1831
    2-Anna Stinson b. 1737
    2-Elizabeth Stinson b. 1739
    2-David Stinson 1741-1823
    2-George Stinson 1743-1798
    2-*<u>**Cary Stinson**</u> 1746-1822
    +Unknown
        3-James Stinson b. 1776
        3-Susanna Stinson 1778-1868
        3-Alexander W. Stinson 1780-1840
        3-Cary Stinson, Jr. b. 1785
        3-Stephen Stinson 1787-1832
        3-George Stinson 1794-1874
        3-*<u>**Thomas B. Stinson**</u> b. 1797
        +Martha Eagle +Susan Price
            4-*<u>**Robert Jackson Stinson**</u> 1830-1917
            +Martha A. Bryant 1830-1885
            4-Louisa Stinson 1831-1916
            4-William C. Stinson 1832-1900
            4-Elizabeth Stinson b. 1836
            4-George David Stinson 1837-1934
            4-James Wesley Stinson b. 1840
            4-John David (Drury) Stinson b. 1844
            4-Charles Thomas Stinson 1846-1911
            4-Susan Stinson 1848 (m.Benjamin C. Tyree)
                5-Martha Sue Stinson 1855-1924
                5-Thomas Stinson 1858-1935
                5-Mary Elizabeth Stinson 1860-1934
                5-Rebecca Stinson b. 1862
                5-John Stinson 1869-1915
                5-George Stinson 1873-1940
                5-*<u>**Robert Lee Stinson**</u> 1865-1938
                +Minnie E. Bryant 1873-1958

6-***Herman D. Stinson** 1892-1987
+Lelia Viola Marks 1903-1984
6-Nettie Stinson 1895-1975 (Clyde Adcock)
6-Massie Clarence Stinson 1896-1992
6-Alvin R. Stinson 1898-1960
6-Ruth E. Stinson 1900-1938 (Paul Scott)
6-Rolfe Stinson 1903-1989
6-Ethel Stinson 1906-1982 (m. Albert Kidd, 2-Tom Amos)
6-Elliott L Stinson 1906-1970
6-Minnie Stinson 1909-1946 (m. Luke Kidd)
6-Admire C. Stinson b. 1912
      7-Frank Owen Stinson 1921-1952
      7-Dorothy Lee Stinson 1923-2000 (m. Tommy Riner)
      7-Richard Earl Stinson 1926-
      7-Ralph Kenneth Stinson 1928-
      7-Margaret Louise Stinson 1930-2000 (m. Harold Compton)
      7-Robert Preston Stinson 1933-2004
      7-***Charles Linwood Stinson** 1935-